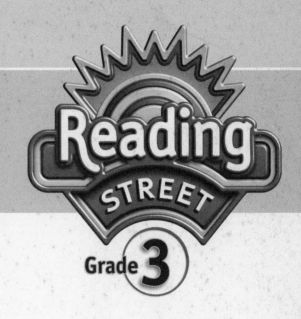

Reading STREET

Grade **3**

Scott Foresman

Texas

Reader's and Writer's Notebook

D1279404

PEARSON

Glenview, Illinois • Boston, Massachusetts • Chandler, Arizona •
Upper Saddle River, New Jersey

The *Texas Essential Knowledge and Skills for English Language Arts and Reading* reproduced by permission, Texas Education Agency, 1701 N. Congress Avenue, Austin, TX 78701

ISBN-13: 978-0-328-49580-1
ISBN-10: 0-328-49580-8
8 9 10   V039   18 17 16 15

Unit 1: Living and Learning

Unit 2: Smart Solutions

Unit 3: People and Nature

Unit 4: One of a Kind

Unit 5: Cultures

Unit 6: Freedom

Name _____

Unit 1 Independent Reading Log

Reading Time	Title and Author	What is it about?	How would you rate it?	Explain your rating.
From ____ to ____			**Great** 5 4 3 2 1 **Awful**	
From ____ to ____			**Great** 5 4 3 2 1 **Awful**	
From ____ to ____			**Great** 5 4 3 2 1 **Awful**	
From ____ to ____			**Great** 5 4 3 2 1 **Awful**	
From ____ to ____			**Great** 5 4 3 2 1 **Awful**	

3.11.A Read independently for sustained periods of time and paraphrase what the reading was about, maintaining meaning and logical order.

Unit 2 Independent Reading Log

Reading Time	Title and Author	What is it about?	How would you rate it?	Explain your rating.
From ___ to ___			**Great** 5 4 3 2 1 **Awful**	
From ___ to ___			**Great** 5 4 3 2 1 **Awful**	
From ___ to ___			**Great** 5 4 3 2 1 **Awful**	
From ___ to ___			**Great** 5 4 3 2 1 **Awful**	
From ___ to ___			**Great** 5 4 3 2 1 **Awful**	

3.11.A Read independently for sustained periods of time and paraphrase what the reading was about, maintaining meaning and logical order.

Name _____

Unit 3 Independent Reading Log

Reading Time	Title and Author	What is it about?	How would you rate it?	Explain your rating.
From ___ to ___			Great 5 4 3 2 1 Awful	
From ___ to ___			Great 5 4 3 2 1 Awful	
From ___ to ___			Great 5 4 3 2 1 Awful	
From ___ to ___			Great 5 4 3 2 1 Awful	
From ___ to ___			Great 5 4 3 2 1 Awful	

3.11.A Read independently for sustained periods of time and paraphrase what the reading was about, maintaining meaning and logical order.

Independent Reading 3

Unit 4 Independent Reading Log

Reading Time	Title and Author	What is it about?	How would you rate it?	Explain your rating.
From ___ to ___			**Great** 5 4 3 2 1 **Awful**	
From ___ to ___			**Great** 5 4 3 2 1 **Awful**	
From ___ to ___			**Great** 5 4 3 2 1 **Awful**	
From ___ to ___			**Great** 5 4 3 2 1 **Awful**	
From ___ to ___			**Great** 5 4 3 2 1 **Awful**	

3.11.A Read independently for sustained periods of time and paraphrase what the reading was about, maintaining meaning and logical order.

Name _____

Unit 5 Independent Reading Log

Reading Time	Title and Author	What is it about?	How would you rate it?	Explain your rating.
From _____ to _____			**Great** 5 4 3 2 1 **Awful**	
From _____ to _____			**Great** 5 4 3 2 1 **Awful**	
From _____ to _____			**Great** 5 4 3 2 1 **Awful**	
From _____ to _____			**Great** 5 4 3 2 1 **Awful**	
From _____ to _____			**Great** 5 4 3 2 1 **Awful**	

3.11.A Read independently for sustained periods of time and paraphrase what the reading was about, maintaining meaning and logical order.

Independent Reading 5

Unit 6 Independent Reading Log

Reading Time	Title and Author	What is it about?	How would you rate it?	Explain your rating.
From ___ to ___			**Great** 5 4 3 2 1 **Awful**	
From ___ to ___			**Great** 5 4 3 2 1 **Awful**	
From ___ to ___			**Great** 5 4 3 2 1 **Awful**	
From ___ to ___			**Great** 5 4 3 2 1 **Awful**	
From ___ to ___			**Great** 5 4 3 2 1 **Awful**	

🌟 **3.11.A** Read independently for sustained periods of time and paraphrase what the reading was about, maintaining meaning and logical order.

Selection Title _____ **Author** _____

Narrative poems tell a story. Like stories, narrative poems have plots, settings, characters, and a theme. Characteristics of narrative poems include the following.

• As with most poems, words are specially arranged in lines.

• The author chooses words and phrases carefully to create a particular rhyme and rhythm.

• The author often expresses his or her thoughts and feelings.

Directions As you read *When Charlie McButton Lost Power*, look for examples of how words are specially arranged in lines, the rhyme and rhythm of the words and phrases, and how the author expresses her thoughts and feelings. Write those examples below.

Arrangement of Lines _____

_____

_____

Rhythm and Rhyme _____

_____

_____

Author's Thoughts and Feelings _____

_____

_____

Explore the Genre

Think about the special arrangement of lines, rhythm and rhyme, and the thoughts and feelings of the author in another narrative poem that you've read. What similarities and differences do you find between that poem and *When Charlie McButton Lost Power*? Write about it. Use a separate sheet of paper if you need more space.

_____

_____

3.20.C.1 Write responses to literary texts that demonstrate understanding.

Name _____

Selection Title _____ **Author** _____

A **fable** is a very short story whose theme is a moral or a lesson. Characteristics of fables include the following.

- Characters in fables are very simple.
- Instead of names, characters are often named for the role they play in the story.
- Characters usually have one identifiable trait.

Directions As you read *What About Me?*, look for examples of character names and character traits and identify the theme or moral of the fable. Write the examples and moral below.

Character Names _____

_____

_____

Each Character's Trait _____

_____

_____

Theme or Moral _____

_____

_____

Explore the Genre

Think about the characters, character traits, and moral of another story you've read that is a fable. What similarities and differences do you find between that story and *What About Me?* Write about it. Use a separate sheet of paper if you need more space.

_____

_____

_____

3.20.C.1 Write responses to literary texts that demonstrate understanding.

Selection Title _____ Author _____

A **tall tale** is a humorous story that uses realistic details to tell a story about characters and events that are impossible. Characteristics of a tall tale include the following.

- Many details are from everyday life.
- Characters are greatly exaggerated.
- The events described could not really happen.

Directions As you read *Kumak's Fish,* look for examples of realistic details, exaggerated characters, and impossible events that make the story a tall tale. Write those examples below.

Realistic Details _____

_____

_____

Exaggerated Characters _____

_____

_____

Impossible Events _____

_____

_____

Explore the Genre

Think about the realistic details, exaggerated characters, and impossible events in another story you've read that's a tall tale. What similarities and differences do you find between that story and *Kumak's Fish*? Write about it. Use a separate sheet of paper if you need more space.

_____

_____

3.20.C.1 Write responses to literary texts that demonstrate understanding.

Comprehension 9

Selection Title _____ **Author** _____

Background knowledge is what we already know about a topic. Using background knowledge can help us better understand what we're reading. Activate your background knowledge by doing the following.

• Preview the selection to find out what it's about.

• Think about what you already know about the topic.

• Connect the selection to your own world—to people, places, and events you already know.

Directions Use the KWL chart below to chart your background knowledge about the selection. List what you already know in the K column. Then list what you want to learn in the W column. After reading, list what you learned in the L column. Write a brief summary of the selection on a separate sheet of paper.

What We **K** now	What We **W** ant to Know	What We **L** earned

3.2.C.2 Monitor comprehension, making corrections and adjustments when that understanding breaks down.

Name _____

Selection Title _____ Author _____

Story structure refers to the important parts of the story that happen at the beginning, middle, and end of a story. To identify story structure, strategic readers do the following.

- Look for the conflict, or problem, at the beginning of the story.
- Track the action as conflict builds.
- Recognize the climax when the characters face conflict.
- Identify how the conflict gets resolved.

Directions As you read the story, chart the story structure using the plot map below. When you are finished, briefly retell the story on a separate sheet of paper.

Characters

Setting

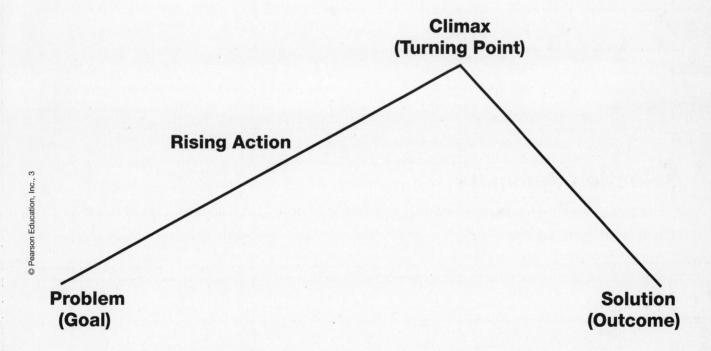

Climax (Turning Point)

Rising Action

Problem (Goal)

Solution (Outcome)

3.8.A.2 Summarize the plot's main events.

Name _____

Selection Title _____ Author _____

Strategic readers **monitor** their understanding of what they've read and use fix-up strategies to **clarify** understanding. Ways to monitor and clarify include the following.

- Ask questions during and after reading and summarize to check your understanding.
- Adjust your reading rate, read on, or reread the section that caused confusion.
- Visualize what you are reading.
- Use text features and illustrations to help clarify the text.

Directions As you read, write down the page numbers of places that you had trouble understanding. Then describe the fix-up strategy you used to clarify the meaning.

Where in the text I had trouble: _____ _____ _____

_____ _____ _____ _____ _____

Fix-Up Strategies I Used

_____

_____

_____

_____

_____

Selection Summary

Write a two- or three-sentence summary of the selection. Use a separate sheet of paper if you need more space.

_____

_____

_____

_____

3.2.B.2, 4 Ask relevant questions and seek clarification about other texts. **3.2.C.3** Monitor comprehension, making adjustments when that understanding breaks down.

Selection Title _____ **Author** _____

We **visualize** to create pictures in our minds as we read. Creating pictures can help us better understand what we're reading. To visualize, try the following.

- Combine what you already know with details from the text to make a mental image.
- Think about the events of the story or selection. Use your five senses to create pictures and to try to put yourself in the story or selection.

Directions As you read the selection, use your senses to help you visualize what's happening or the information the author provides. Write down what you can see, hear, taste, smell, and touch.

See _____

_____

_____

Hear _____

_____

_____

Taste _____

_____

_____

Smell _____

_____

_____

Touch _____

_____

_____

3.10.A.1 Identify language that creates a graphic visual experience.

Name _____

Selection Title _____ Author _____

A **fantasy** tells a make-believe story and often includes illustrations. Characteristics of fantasies include the following.

- Characters and settings may not be real.
- Animals may do things that only people could do.
- Events happen that are not real.

Directions As you read *Prudy's Problem*, look for examples of characters and settings that are not real, animals that do things that only people do, and events that cannot really happen. Write those examples below.

Characters and Settings _____

_____

_____

Animals _____

_____

_____

Events _____

_____

_____

Explore the Genre

Think about characters and settings that are not real, animals that do things that only people do, and events that cannot really happen in another fantasy that you've read. What similarities and differences do you find between that story and *Prudy's Problem*? Write about it. Use a separate sheet of paper if you need more space.

_____

_____

3.20.C.1 Write responses to literary texts that demonstrate understanding.

Selection Title _____ **Author** _____

When we **predict,** we tell what we think might happen in a selection. Predictions are based on our preview or what we've already read. We **set a purpose** to guide our reading. We can do the following to predict and set a purpose.

- Read the title and the author's name. Look at the illustrations and other text features.
- Think about why you're reading and set a purpose.
- Use your prior knowledge—what you already know—to make a prediction.
- As you read, check and change your prediction based on new information.

Directions Preview the selection. Make a prediction and set a purpose for reading the selection. As you read, check your predictions and set a new purpose as necessary. When you finish reading, write a summary of the selection.

Before Reading
Make a Prediction _____

_____

Purpose for Reading _____

_____

During Reading
Check and Change Prediction _____

_____

Set a New Purpose _____

_____

After Reading
Write a Summary _____

_____

_____

_____

3.2.A Use ideas to make and confirm predictions.
RC-3.A Establish purposes for reading based upon own and others' desired outcome to enhance comprehension.

Selection Title _____ Author _____

Expository nonfiction tells about real people and events. Expository text is a type of expository nonfiction. Characteristics of expository text include the following.

- The topic provides information about the real world and people.
- The information in the text is factual.
- Selections often include text features such as diagrams, maps, charts, and graphs.

Directions As you read *Amazing Bird Nests,* look for examples of expository text. Write those examples below.

Selection Topic _____

_____

_____

Facts _____

_____

_____

Text Features _____

_____

_____

Explore the Genre

Think about another selection you've read that is expository text. What similarities and differences do you find between that selection and *Amazing Bird Nests*? Write about it. Use a separate sheet of paper if you need more space.

_____

_____

_____

© Pearson Education, Inc., 3

3.20.C.2 Write responses to expository texts that demonstrate understanding.

Selection Title _____ **Author** _____

Important ideas in nonfiction texts are the main ideas and details about a topic that the author wants the reader to understand. You can do the following to help identify important ideas and details as you read.

- Preview the selection and read the title, headings, and captions.
- Look for words in special type such as italics, boldface, and bulleted lists.
- Watch for signal words and phrases such as *for example* and *most important.*
- Use text features including photographs and illustrations, diagrams, charts, and maps.

Directions As you read the selection, use the chart below to write down any important ideas and details that you find. List any text features or signal words you used to locate these ideas. Use the important ideas and details to write a short summary of the selection.

Important Ideas	Details

Write a Summary _____

_____

_____

_____

_____

Selection Title _____ Author _____

Dramas, or plays, are stories that are written to be acted out for an audience. Dramas have the same story elements as other types of fiction. Story elements of dramas include the following.
- Character and setting
- Plot
- Theme

Directions As you read *Pushing Up the Sky,* look for examples of the story elements of drama. Write those examples below.

Character and Setting _____

_____

_____

Plot _____

_____

_____

Theme _____

_____

_____

Explore the Genre

Think about character, setting, plot, and theme in another drama that you've read. What similarities and differences do you find between that drama and *Pushing Up the Sky*? Write about it. Use a separate sheet of paper if you need more space.

_____

_____

_____

⊛ **3.20.C.1** Write responses to literary texts that demonstrate understanding.

Selection Title _____ **Author** _____

Text structure refers to the way an author organizes a text. Cause and effect and compare and contrast are two types of text structure. Knowing how a text is structured can improve our comprehension. Here are ways to identify text structure.

- Before you read, preview the text. Make predictions, ask questions, and use titles, headings, and illustrations to try to identify the structure.
- As you read, look for language that gives clues to the organization.
- After reading, recall the organization and summarize the text.

Directions As you preview and read the selection, write down features of the text that help you identify the text structure. Remember to ask questions, use text features, and look for language clues to identify the text structure. After reading, write the name of the text structure and a brief summary of the selection.

Before Reading _____

_____

_____

_____

During Reading _____

_____

_____

_____

Text Structure/Summary _____

_____

_____

_____

_____

★ Identify the text structure of expository text.

Selection Title _____ **Author** _____

Fiction is a made-up story, either serious or humorous, of imaginary people who generally behave as we expect people to behave. Fiction might include real places and events, but the story is created from the author's imagination. Characteristics of fiction include the following.

- Characters generally behave like real people.
- Settings may or may not be real.
- The plot, or events that happen in the story, may or may not seem real.

Directions As you read *A Symphony of Whales,* look for examples of character, setting, and plot that make this story fiction. Write those examples below.

Character _____

_____

_____

Setting _____

_____

_____

Plot _____

_____

_____

Explore the Genre

Think about another story you've read that is fiction. What similarities and differences do you find between that story and *A Symphony of Whales*? Write about it. Use a separate sheet of paper if you need more space.

_____

_____

🌐 **3.20.C.1** Write responses to literary texts that demonstrate understanding.

Selection Title _____ Author _____

The content of **narrative nonfiction** consists of real people, things, or events. It can be told in different forms such as a story, a letter, a field guide, or a poem. Characteristics of narrative nonfiction include the following.

- The content is about real people or things.
- The setting is a real place.
- Events are based on fact.

Directions As you read *Around One Cactus: Owls, Bats and Leaping Rats,* look for examples of people and things, settings, and events that make this selection narrative nonfiction. Write those examples below.

People and Things _____

_____

_____

Settings _____

_____

_____

Events _____

_____

_____

Explore the Genre

Think about another selection you've read that is narrative nonfiction. What similarities and differences do you find between that selection and *Around One Cactus: Owls, Bats and Leaping Rats*? Write about it. Use a separate sheet of paper if you need more space.

_____

_____

3.20.C.2 Write responses to expository texts that demonstrate understanding.

Name _____

Selection Title _____ Author _____

When we **summarize** and **paraphrase,** we capture the important ideas or events of a selection in a few sentences. Paraphrasing is putting what we've read into our own words. Good readers summarize and paraphrase what they've read to check understanding and improve comprehension. Keeping important ideas and events in a logical order also improves comprehension. To summarize or paraphrase, do the following.

- In fiction, look for the important events of the plot, including the climax.
- In nonfiction, look for the important ideas that the author presents.
- Jot notes as you read to help you summarize or paraphrase, keeping events in a logical order.
- Restate important pieces of information in your own words.

Directions As you read the selection, use the chart below to write down any important ideas or plot events. Remember to record events in a logical order. When you're finished reading, use your notes to summarize or paraphrase the selection.

Important Ideas or Events

_____

_____

_____

_____

_____

Summary

_____

_____

_____

_____

_____

3.11.A.2 Paraphrase what the reading was about, maintaining meaning. **RC-3.E** Summarize information in text, maintaining meaning and logical order.

Selection Title _____ **Author** _____

Important ideas in nonfiction texts are the main ideas and details about a topic that the author wants the reader to understand. You can do the following to help identify important ideas and details as you read.

- Preview the selection and read the title, headings, and captions.
- Look for words in special type such as italics, boldface, and bulleted lists.
- Watch for signal words and phrases such as *for example* and *most important.*
- Use text features including photographs and illustrations, diagrams, charts, and maps.

Directions As you read the selection, use the chart below to write down any important ideas and details that you find. List any text features or signal words you used to locate these ideas. Use the important ideas and details to write a short summary of the selection.

Important Ideas	Details

Write a Summary _____

_____

_____

_____

_____

🔖 **3.2.B.8** Locate details about other texts.

Selection Title _____ Author _____

One type of literary nonfiction is a **biography**. Biographies tell the story of all or part of a real person's life. Events in the person's life are generally told in the order that they happen. Characteristics of a biography include the following.

- The subject is part or all of the life of a real person.
- The events in the person's life are told in the order that they happen.
- Events are told in a third-person narration using *he, she, him,* or *her* when referring to the person.

Directions As you read *Rocks in His Head*, look for examples of who the subject is, events in order, and third-person narration that make this selection a biography. Write those examples below.

Subject _____

_____

_____

Events _____

_____

_____

Third-person Narration _____

_____

_____

Explore the Genre

Think about another selection you've read that is a biography. What similarities and differences do you find between that biography and *Rocks in His Head*? Write about it. Use a separate sheet of paper if you need more space.

_____

_____

3.20.C.2 Write responses to expository texts that demonstrate understanding.

Selection Title _____ **Author** _____

Good readers ask questions as they read. **Questioning** helps us monitor our comprehension and clarify anything that's confusing. Questioning also helps to make inferences, interpret the texts we read, and promote discussion. As you read, use the following questioning strategy.

- Preview the selection and think about any questions you have about the topic.

- Read with a question in mind and make notes when you find information that addresses the question.

- Write down other questions that come up as you read and look for answers in the text.

- Remember that not all questions are answered in the text. Sometimes we have to make inferences or interpretations based on the information the author provides.

Directions As you read the selection, use the chart below to write down any questions that you have about the text in the column on the left. Write down any answers you find or inferences you make in the right hand column.

Questions	Answers, Inferences, Interpretations

3.2.B.2 Ask relevant questions about other texts. **3.2.C.3** Monitor comprehension, making adjustments when that understanding breaks down. **RC-3.B.2** Ask interpretive questions of text.

Selection Title _____ Author _____

Folk tales are stories that were created by an unknown storyteller and handed down orally from generation to generation until someone wrote them down. Characteristics of folk tales include the following.

- The subject matter often shows the customs or beliefs of a particular culture.
- Human and animal characters usually represent some human trait or aspect of human nature.
- Themes about human nature are expressed.

Directions As you read *Fly, Eagle, Fly!*, look for examples of subject matter, characters, and theme that make this story a folk tale. Write those examples below.

Subject Matter _____

_____

_____

Characters _____

_____

_____

Theme _____

_____

_____

Explore the Genre

Think about another story you've read that is a folk tale. What similarities and differences do you find between that story and *Fly, Eagle, Fly*!? Write about it. Use a separate sheet of paper if you need more space.

_____

_____

3.20.C.1 Write responses to literary texts that demonstrate understanding.

Selection Title _____ **Author** _____

Realistic fiction tells the story of imaginary people and events. Characteristics of realistic fiction include the following.

• The characters seem like real people that you might know.

• The setting is realistic, such as a city or town, a school, or other places you might know.

• The plot is possible and could happen in real life.

Directions As you read *Suki's Kimono,* look for examples of character, setting, and plot that make this story realistic fiction. Write those examples below.

Character _____

_____

_____

Setting _____

_____

_____

Plot _____

_____

_____

Explore the Genre

Think about the characters, setting, and plot in another story you've read that's realistic fiction. What similarities and differences do you find between that story and *Suki's Kimono*? Write about it. Use a separate sheet of paper if you need more space.

_____

_____

_____

© Pearson Education, Inc., 3

3.20.C.1 Write responses to literary texts that demonstrate understanding.

Selection Title _____ **Author** _____

When we **infer,** we use our background knowledge with information from the text to come up with our own ideas about what we're reading. To infer, or make inferences, try the following steps.

- Think about what you already know about the topics.
- Combine what you know with information from the text to make inferences.
- Based on your inferences, think about ideas, morals, lessons, or themes in the text.

Directions As you read the selection, use your background knowledge and clues from the text to make inferences. Use the chart below to show how you made your inferences. Then write a statement that summarizes the theme, moral, or lesson from the selection.

What I Know	Information from the Text	What I Infer

Statement that summarizes the theme, moral, or lesson _____

_____

_____

_____

RC-3.D.1 Make inferences about text.

Selection Title _____ **Author** _____

Strategic readers **monitor** their understanding of what they've read and use fix-up strategies to **clarify** understanding. Ways to monitor and clarify include the following.

- Ask questions during and after reading and summarize to check your understanding.
- Adjust your reading rate, read on, or reread the section that caused confusion.
- Visualize what you are reading.
- Use text features and illustrations to help clarify the text.

Directions As you read, write down the page numbers of places where you had trouble understanding. Then describe the fix-up strategy you used to clarify the meaning.

Where in the text I had trouble: _____ _____ _____

_____ _____ _____ _____ _____

Fix-Up Strategies I Used

_____

_____

_____

_____

_____

Selection Summary

Write a two- or three-sentence summary of the selection. Use a separate sheet of paper if you need more space.

_____

_____

_____

_____

© Pearson Education, Inc., 3

3.2.B.1 Ask relevant questions and seek clarification about stories.
3.2.C.3 Monitor comprehension, making adjustments when that understanding
breaks down. **RC-3.C** Monitor and adjust comprehension.

Comprehension 29

Selection Title _____ **Author** _____

When we **summarize** and **paraphrase,** we capture the important ideas or events of a selection in a few sentences. Paraphrasing is putting what we've read into our own words. Good readers summarize and paraphrase what they've read to check understanding and improve comprehension. Keeping important ideas and events in a logical order also improves comprehension. To summarize or paraphrase, do the following.

- In fiction, look for the important events of the plot, including the climax.
- In nonfiction, look for the important ideas that the author presents.
- Jot notes as you read to help you summarize or paraphrase, keeping events in a logical order.
- Restate important pieces of information in your own words.

Directions As you read the selection, use the chart below to write down any important ideas or plot events. Remember to record events in a logical order. When you're finished reading, use your notes to summarize or paraphrase the selection.

Important Ideas or Events

_____

_____

_____

_____

_____

Summary

_____

_____

_____

_____

_____

⊛ **3.5.A.1** Paraphrase themes of fables, legends, myths, or stories.
3.8.A.2 Summarize the plot's main events. **RC-3.E** Summarize information in text, maintaining meaning and logical order.

Selection Title _____ **Author** _____

Historical fiction, like realistic fiction, is a made-up story which may include both real and imaginary characters and events. Characteristics of historical fiction include the following.

- The story takes place in the past.
- The setting is a place that still exists or existed in the past.
- Authentic details about the characters and setting help the reader understand what it was like to live in that place at that time.

Directions As you read *Me and Uncle Romie,* look for examples of the time and place in which the story is set and the authentic details that make this story historical fiction. Write those examples below.

Time _____

_____

_____

Place _____

_____

_____

Authentic Details _____

_____

_____

Explore the Genre

Think about the time, place, and authentic details in another story you've read that's historical fiction. What similarities and differences do you find between that story and *Me and Uncle Romie*? Write about it. Use a separate sheet of paper if you need more space.

_____

_____

3.20.C.1 Write responses to literary texts that demonstrate understanding.

Selection Title _____ **Author** _____

Good readers ask questions as they read. **Questioning** helps us monitor our comprehension and clarify anything that's confusing. Questioning also helps to make inferences, interpret the texts we read, and promote discussion. As you read, use the following questioning strategy.

- Preview the selection and think about any questions you have about the topic.

- Read with a question in mind and make notes when you find information that addresses the question.

- Write down other questions that come up as you read and look for answers in the text.

- Remember that not all questions are answered in the text. Sometimes we have to make inferences or interpretations based on the information the author provides.

Directions As you read the selection, use the chart below to write down any questions that you have about the text in the column on the left. Write down any answers you find or inferences you make in the right hand column.

Questions	Answers, Inferences, Interpretations

3.2.B.2 Ask relevant questions about other texts. **3.2.C.3** Monitor comprehension, making adjustments when that understanding breaks down. **RC-3.B.2** Ask interpretive questions of text.

Name _____

Selection Title _____ Author _____

When we **infer,** we use our background knowledge with information from the text to come up with our own ideas about what we're reading. To infer, or make inferences, try the following steps.

- Think about what you already know about the topics.
- Combine what you know with information from the text to make inferences.
- Based on your inferences, think about ideas, morals, lessons, or themes in the text.

Directions As you read the selection, use your background knowledge and clues from the text to make inferences. Use the chart below to show how you made your inferences. Then write a statement that summarizes the theme, moral, or lesson from the selection.

What I Know	Information from the Text	What I Infer

Statement that summarizes the theme, moral, or lesson _____

_____

_____

_____

Selection Title _____ **Author** _____

A **photo essay** is a collection of photographs that share a common topic or theme. Characteristics of a photo essay include the following.

- An introduction often explains the topic of the essay.
- Text is included that explains the people, animals, or events in the photographs.
- Each photograph usually has a caption that gives specific information about it.

Directions As you read *Talking Walls: Art for the People,* look for examples in the introduction, text, and captions that make this selection a photo essay. Write those examples below.

Introduction _____

_____

_____

Text _____

_____

_____

Captions _____

_____

_____

Explore the Genre

Think about another selection you've read that is a photo essay. What similarities and differences do you find between that selection and *Talking Walls: Art for the People*? Write about it. Use a separate sheet of paper if you need more space.

_____

_____

_____

3.20.C.2 Write responses to expository texts that demonstrate understanding.

Name _____

Selection Title _____ Author _____

An **animal fantasy** is a made-up story that uses animal characters instead of people. Characteristics of an animal fantasy include the following.

- The animal characters talk and live as humans do.
- The animal characters show human feelings.
- Illustrations help the reader understand the story and identify with the characters.

Directions As you read *Two Bad Ants,* look for examples of animals behaving like humans, showing feelings like humans, and illustrations of animals that make this story an animal fantasy. Write those examples below.

Animals with Human Behavior _____

_____

_____

Animals with Human Feelings _____

_____

_____

Illustrations _____

_____

_____

Explore the Genre

Think about another story you've read that is an animal fantasy. What similarities and differences do you find between that story and *Two Bad Ants*? Write about it. Use a separate sheet of paper if you need more space.

_____

_____

3.20.C.1 Write responses to literary texts that demonstrate understanding.

Selection Title _____ **Author** _____

Like a folk tale, a **legend** is an old story passed down by word of mouth. Characteristics of a legend include the following.

- The story is usually about the great deeds of a hero.
- The events in many legends are impossible.
- Legends are often based on some historical facts.

Directions As you read *Atlantis,* look for examples of a hero's great deeds, impossible events, and historical facts that make this story a legend. Write those examples below.

Great Deeds _____

_____

_____

Impossible Events _____

_____

_____

Historical Facts _____

_____

_____

Explore the Genre

Think about another story you've read that is a legend. What similarities and differences do you find between that story and *Atlantis*? Write about it. Use a separate sheet of paper if you need more space.

_____

_____

_____

© Pearson Education, Inc., 3

3.20.C.1 Write responses to literary texts that demonstrate understanding.

Name _____

Book Talk Tips

Book Talk Tips
- Speak clearly.
- Make eye contact.
- Talk about a book YOU liked reading.
- Don't give away the ending.
- Talk for 2–4 minutes, sharing amusing or important information from the book.

Directions Use the talking points below to help organize your book talk.

1. What is the title of the book?

2. Who is the author?

3. What is the genre?

4. What other book has the author written?

If your book is fiction…

5. What is the most exciting part of this book? The plot, characters, theme? Explain why.

6. Briefly describe a setting, scene, or character from this book.

If your book is nonfiction…

7. What important information did you learn from this book?

8. Briefly describe an interesting part of the book.

9. Do you have a personal connection with the story or topic? Explain.

10. Explain why your listeners should read this book.

© Pearson Education, Inc., 3

3.11.A.2 Paraphrase what the reading was about, maintaining meaning.

Peer Conferencing Tips

Before writing

- Help your partner brainstorm ideas for writing.
- Discuss the writing topic with your partner. Does he or she need to narrow the topic or expand it?

After the first draft

- Before you exchange papers, tell your partner what you would like him or her to look for when reading your writing.
- Using sticky notes or a piece of notebook paper, note any questions or comments you have about your partner's writing.
- Point out the information or ideas that are well written.
- Discuss any information that seems unneeded or confusing, but make sure your comments are helpful and considerate.

Revision

- Read your partner's paper out loud to listen for strengths as well as places for improvement.
- Always tell your partner what you think works well in his or her paper.
- Start with a compliment, or strength, and then offer suggestions for improvement. For example, "I liked how you _____. What if you also _____?"
- Remember also to look for correct spelling and grammar.

Other areas you might comment on:

- Title
- Introduction
- Conclusion
- Descriptions
- Examples
- Use of verbs, nouns, adjectives or adverbs

3.17.A.2 Plan a first draft by generating ideas through a range of strategies.

Writing Self-Evaluation Guide

Name of Writing Product _____

Directions Review your final draft. Then rate yourself on a scale from 4 to 1 (4 is the highest) on each writing trait. After you fill out the chart, answer the questions.

Writing Traits	4	3	2	1
Focus/Ideas				
Organization/Paragraphs				
Voice				
Word Choice				
Sentences				
Conventions				

1. What is the best part of this piece of writing? Why do you think so?

   _____

   _____

   _____

   _____

2. Write one thing you would change about this piece of writing if you had the chance to write it again.

   _____

   _____

   _____

   _____

Short Vowels: Syllables VC/CV

Directions Choose the word with the **short vowel** sound in the **first syllable** to complete each sentence. Write the word on the line.

_____ **1.** My mom works in a big (hotel/hospital).

_____ **2.** She got the job last (April/winter).

_____ **3.** She works for a (doctor/painter).

_____ **4.** Mom writes (poems/messages).

_____ **5.** She uses a (pencil/notepad).

Directions Circle the word with the **short vowel** sound in the **first syllable**. Then underline the letter that stands for that short vowel sound.

6. happen	higher	hoses
7. miner	problem	music
8. paper	private	puppet
9. lately	lettuce	likely
10. trial	toaster	tunnel
11. napkin	native	notebook
12. spoken	spider	signal
13. baby	basket	biker
14. sister	safety	season
15. tasteful	timer	tennis

Home Activity Your child identified words with a short vowel sound in the first syllable, such as *happen*, *lettuce*, and *tennis*. Have your child make a collage of magazine pictures showing items that have a short vowel sound in the first syllable of each item's name. Help your child label each picture.

3.1.B.1.i Use common syllabication patterns to decode words including closed syllable (CVC).

Name _____

Literary Elements: Character, Setting, and Theme

- A **character** is a person or an animal in a story.
- The **setting** is when and where a story takes place.
- The **theme** is the lesson or meaning of a story.

Directions Read the story. Then fill in the chart to describe in your own words details about the characters, setting, and theme.

Annie rushed into the family room. Her older sister Marsha was using the computer.

Annie held up her yellow pad. "May I use the computer now?" she asked. "I need to type the final draft of my story. It's due tomorrow."

"No," said Marsha. "I'm busy chatting with Paula and Roy. So get lost!"

"That's not fair!" said Annie. "You've been using the computer for more than an hour."

Just then Dad poked his head in the door. "What's all this noise about?" he growled.

The girls looked at each other. They knew Dad would make them turn off the computer if they could not find a way to share it.

"We're sorry," Annie said. "We'll work together to make a fair schedule for using the computer."

"Good for you," Dad smiled. "Solving problems on your own shows that you're grown up enough to use a computer."

Characters	Setting	Theme
Annie seems more responsible because she does her homework and suggests a way to share the computer.		

© Pearson Education, Inc., 3

Home Activity Your child restated the characters, setting, and theme, or lesson, of a story. Read a story together. Discuss the characters, setting, and theme with your child and ask which story details helped with his or her ideas.

3.5.A.1 Paraphrase themes of fables, legends, myths, or stories. **3.5.A.2** Paraphrase supporting details of fables, legends, myths, or stories.

Comprehension 41

Writing • Narrative Poem

Key Features of a Narrative Poem

- tells a story
- has rhythm or a repeated accent
- often has lines that rhyme and use meter
- has a setting, characters, plot, and theme
- may be humorous or dramatic

Supper in the Storm

One afternoon last week at the park,
Blue sky quite suddenly grew very dark.
I raced home, and as I reached the door
heavy rain started falling, more and more.

Flickering lights killed my hope of a meal.
Thunderstorms make my mother feel
the kitchen is not the best place to be,
so good-bye to dinner for Dad and me.

Suddenly there stood Dad at the door,
and I could hope for some food once more!
"I knew that we could use some supper,"
and he handed me a sack—things looked up and upper!

After we ate, all the lights came back on,
Now Mom's fears of the kitchen were gone.
"I think," she said, "this is the night to make
our very favorite chocolate cake!"

1. Read the poem. Who are the characters in this poem?

_____

2. What problem does the narrator have? How is the problem solved?

_____

_____

_____

Short Vowels; Syllables VC/CV

Classifying Write the list word that belongs in each group.

Spelling Words

happen
lettuce
basket
winter
sister
problem
supper
subject

lesson
spelling
napkin
collar
traffic
suggest
puppet

1. lunch, breakfast, _____

2. toy, animal, _____

3. cabbage, spinach, _____

4. box, container, _____

5. reading, math, _____

6. placemat, tablecloth, _____

Rhymes Finish each sentence. Use a list word that rhymes with the underlined word.

7. Franco got a <u>splinter</u> when he built the shelves last _____.

8. My _____ uses a <u>mister</u> to spray the plants.

9. I _____ that you get some <u>rest</u>.

10. She will charge a <u>dollar</u> to sew your _____.

Making Connections Draw a line to connect the first syllable with the second syllable to make a list word. Write each word you make.

First Syllable	Second Syllable	
hap-	-son	**11.** _____
sub-	-lem	**12.** _____
les-	-fic	**13.** _____
traf-	-ject	**14.** _____
prob-	-pen	**15.** _____

Home Activity Your child wrote words with short vowel sounds. Have your child circle the VC/CV (vowel-consonant-consonant-vowel) pattern in each list word.

3.24.A.1 Use knowledge of letter sounds to spell. **3.24.A.4** Use knowledge of syllabication to spell. **3.24.D.1** Spell words with common syllable constructions.

Spelling Short Vowels; Syllables VC/CV **45**

Web A

Vocabulary • Context Clues

- **Homonyms** are words that are spelled and pronounced the same way but have different meanings.
- **Homographs** are words that are spelled the same way but have different pronunciations and meanings.
- Use **context clues,** or the words around a homonym or homograph, to figure out what the word means.

Directions Read the following passage. Then answer the questions below. Look for context clues that show the meanings of homonyms and homographs as you read.

> When the power went out, I was bored. Then my friends and I decided to play baseball. My team had a great game. We couldn't do anything wrong. Every fly ball came right down into our mitts. When we dove for the ball, we got it. As I walked home, I saw a bat flying around a lamppost. It was too dark to play baseball, so I went inside to read a good sports book.

1. In this passage, does *down* mean "a bird's soft feathers" or "from above"?

   _____

2. The word *dove* has two pronunciations and two meanings. What clues tell readers the word's pronunciation and meaning in this passage?

   _____

   _____

3. What does *bat* mean in this passage? How does the context help you?

   _____

   _____

4. How do you pronounce the word *read* in the last line?

   _____

Home Activity Your child used context clues to understand homonyms and homographs. Provide sentences with homonyms such as *ball* (a round object/a dance) or *row* (to move a boat with oars/a line of people or objects) and homographs such as *bow* (to bend down) and *bow* (a loop made with ribbon). Ask your child to use context clues to determine the meaning of each word.

3.4.B.1 Use context to determine the relevant meaning of unfamiliar words. **3.4.B.3** Use context to distinguish among homographs.

Reference Texts

Books have different features that help you find the information you need. At the front, a **table of contents** lists chapters, articles, or stories and their page numbers. An **index** lists subjects that the book covers and tells the page on which the information can be found. An index is usually in the back of the book.

Directions Use the table of contents and the index to answer the questions.

1. In which chapter will you look to read about the invention of the light bulb?

_____

2. On which page will you look to find information about Thomas Edison?

_____

3. Which chapter has information about Ben Franklin?

_____

4. On what page does Chapter 2 start?

_____

5. On what page would you find information about atoms?

_____

© Pearson Education, Inc., 3

Home Activity Your child used a table of contents and an index to answer questions about reference texts. Ask your child to locate information using a table of contents and an index in a favorite book.

3.13.D.1 Use text features to locate information.

Short Vowels; Syllables VC/CV

Proofread a Sign The Rodriguez family stopped at a farmers market. Circle four spelling mistakes on the sign. Write the words correctly. Then find the punctuation error. Write the sentence correctly.

Spelling Words

happen
lettuce
basket
winter
sister
problem
supper
subject

lesson
spelling
napkin
collar
traffic
suggest
puppet

FRESH CORN
We suggest grilled corn for supper?

berries	$3 a baskit	letuce	$1 a head
sweet peas	$2 a bunch	summer an wintar	
melon	$4 each	squash 2 for $3	

1. _____   2. _____

3. _____   4. _____

5. _____

Frequently Misspelled Words

then
and
with
was

Proofread Words Circle the word that is spelled correctly. Write it.

6. happen   hapen   6. _____

7. prablem   problem   7. _____

8. spulling   spelling   8. _____

9. subject   subjeck   9. _____

10. traffick   traffic   10. _____

11. supper   super   11. _____

12. seggest   suggest   12. _____

Home Activity Your child identified and corrected misspelled words with short vowel sounds. Have your child sketch a sign that contains several spelling words and frequently misspelled words.

⭐ **3.24.A.1** Use knowledge of letter sounds to spell. **3.24.A.4** Use knowledge of syllabication to spell. **3.24.C.1** Spell high-frequency words from a commonly used list. **3.24.D.1** Spell words with common syllable constructions.

Spelling Short Vowels; Syllables VC/CV   **49**

Sentences

Directions Read the selection. Then read each question that follows the selection. Decide which is the best answer to each question. Mark the space for the answer you have chosen.

Using Computers

  (1) Computer games can be a lot of fun (2) You can use a computer for other things, too. (3) Keep track of your money. (4) A computer can help you with your math work. (5) A computer to talk to your friends. (6) You can use it to learn about almost anything in the world. (7) What do you use computers for.

1 What change, if any, should be made to sentence 1?

- ⬭ Change *Computer* to **computer**
- ⬭ Change *fun* to **fun?**
- ⬭ Change *fun* to **fun.**
- ⬭ Make no change

2 What change, if any, should be made to sentence 3?

- ⬭ Change *money.* to **money?**
- ⬭ Change *Keep track* to **You can keep track**
- ⬭ Change *Keep* to **keep**
- ⬭ Make no change

3 What change, if any, should be made to sentence 4?

- ⬭ Change *A computer* to **A Computer**
- ⬭ Change *work.* to **work,**
- ⬭ Change *math work.* to **math work and sometimes.**
- ⬭ Make no change

4 What change, if any, should be made to sentence 5?

- ⬭ Change *friends.* to **friends?**
- ⬭ Change *A computer* to **You can use a computer**
- ⬭ Change *A* to **a**
- ⬭ Make no change

5 What change, if any, should be made to sentence 7?

- ⬭ Change *for.* to **for?**
- ⬭ Change *for.* to **for!**
- ⬭ Change *for.* to **for,**
- ⬭ Make no change

Home Activity Your child prepared for taking tests on sentences. Ask your child to explain the difference between a sentence and a fragment.

✪ **3.22.C.1** Use complete simple sentences with correct subject-verb agreement.

Plurals -s, -es, -ies

Directions Use the plural form of each word in ( ) to complete each sentence. Write the word on the line.

_____ **1.** Tanya put her hands into her (pocket).

_____ **2.** She pulled out a handful of (penny).

_____ **3.** She also found two (pencil).

_____ **4.** She traded each pencil for two boxes of (paint).

_____ **5.** She used the money to buy two new (brush).

_____ **6.** She filled (glass) with water for cleaning her brushes.

_____ **7.** She painted a forest filled with trees and (bush).

_____ **8.** She made pictures of (beach) and waves.

_____ **9.** She showed (family) having fun together.

_____ **10.** Tanya gave away many (copy) of her pictures.

Directions Write the plural form of each word below.

11. lady _____   **16.** supply _____

12. dish _____   **17.** fox _____

13. class _____   **18.** boss _____

14. peach _____   **19.** list _____

15. kiss _____   **20.** book _____

Home Activity Your child wrote plurals—words naming more than one person, place, or thing. Ask your child to look around a room in your home and tell what he or she sees. Work with your child to write a list of twenty things in the room. Ask your child to write the plural form of each word.

3.1.A.1.iii Decode multisyllabic words in context by applying common spelling patterns including changing the final "y" to "i".

© Pearson Education, Inc., 3

Sequence

- The **sequence** is the order in which things happen in a story—what happens first, next, and last.
- Sometimes a writer uses **clue words** such as *first, so, then,* and *at last.*

Directions Read the following passage.

First, Cisco raked leaves for Mrs. Rey. He put the leaves into four piles on the lawn.

Cisco could not put the leaves in plastic bags by himself. So Cisco asked his brother Rico to help.

Rico held the bags open, and then Cisco dumped leaves inside. When a bag was full, Cicso tied it at the top.

At last they were done, and Mrs. Rey gave Cisco twenty dollars. Cisco gave Rico five dollars for helping.

Directions Write these sentences in the correct place on the organizer.

- Cisco put leaves in a bag.
- Cisco asked Rico to help.
- Mrs. Rey paid Cisco $20.
- Cisco raked the leaves.

1. First

2. Next

3. Then

4. Last

5. On another piece of paper, use the sentences to write a summary of the story.

Home Activity Your child put events from a story in the order they happened. Read a simple story to your child. Name events from the story by asking, "What are some things that happened in the story?" Then ask your child to retell the story putting the events in the order they happened.

3.11.A.3 Paraphrase what the reading was about, maintaining logical order.

Writing • Fable

Key Features of a Fable

- often has animals that talk and act like humans
- is usually very short and tells a simple story
- usually has a moral at the end

Mia Cleans House

Mia Mouse had a messy house. "How can you ever find anything?" asked her friend Gus Mouse.

"I can find what I need," Mia said.

That night Mia could not find any cheese.

"I know I have some," she said to herself. She could not find it and went to bed hungry.

The next day, Gus was surprised to see Mia cleaning.

"What are you doing?" he asked.

"Cleaning never hurt anyone," Mia replied. "Would you like some cheese?"

Moral: There are good reasons to be clean and organized.

1. Read the fable. Who and what are the characters?

_____

2. Why can't Mia find her cheese? How does she solve her problem?

_____

_____

Vocabulary

Directions Write the word from the box that best completes each sentence.

> ## Check the Words You Know
>
> __carpenter   __merchant
> __carpetmaker   __plenty
> __knowledge   __straying
> __marketplace   __thread

_____ 1. Sara had _____ of clothes to mend.

_____ 2. She needed to buy _____ for sewing.

_____ 3. She walked to the _____ to go shopping.

_____ 4. She found a _____ who sold what she wanted.

_____ 5. Later she talked to the _____ about a new rug.

Directions Write the word from the box that best matches each clue.

_____ 6. a person who builds with wood

_____ 7. a lot

_____ 8. wandering or roaming

_____ 9. facts and ideas

_____ 10. someone who makes rugs

Write an Interview

On a separate paper, write five questions you could ask a carpenter, merchant, or a carpetmaker. Answer each question. Use as many vocabulary words as possible.

Home Activity Your child identified and used vocabulary words from *What About Me?* With your child, act out a conversation that might have taken place in an old-time village marketplace. Use vocabulary words as you and your child discuss what you are buying or selling.

3.4.B.1 Use context to determine the relevant meaning of unfamiliar words.

Name _____

Subjects and Predicates

A sentence has a **subject** and **predicate**. The subject is the sentence part that tells whom or what the sentence is about. All the words in the subject are called the complete subject. The predicate is the sentence part that tells what the subject is or does. It includes a verb. All the words in the predicate are called the complete predicate.

In the following sentence, the complete subject is underlined once. The complete predicate is underlined twice. The verb is circled.

The market has many interesting things.

Directions Underline the complete subject of each sentence.

1. Many people buy beautiful carpets at the market.

2. Farmers bring goats to the market too.

3. The vegetables in the stalls look delicious.

4. Children run around the town square.

5. Everything happens at the town market!

Directions Underline the complete predicate of each sentence. Circle the verb.

6. A young boy asks for help.

7. The old man is wiser than the boy.

8. The students in a classroom learn lessons all the time.

9. Animals learn differently from people.

10. My parents teach me many lessons.

Home Activity Your child learned about subjects and predicates. Say a sentence. Have your child identify its complete subject and predicate.

🌐 **3.22.B.1** Use the complete subject in a sentence.
3.22.B.2 Use the complete predicate in a sentence.

Conventions Subjects and Predicates **55**

Plurals -s, -es, -ies

Categories Write the word that names each category.

Spelling Words

pennies
inches
plants
families
bodies
glasses
wishes
pockets

lists
copies
parties
bunches
crashes
supplies
pencils

1. Colored and sharpened are types of ___.

2. Paper and pens are types of school ___.

3. Birthday and graduation are types of ___.

4. Drinking and eye are types of ___.

5. Bushes and flowers are types of ___.

6. Grocery and Christmas are types of ___.

1. _____   2. _____

3. _____   4. _____

5. _____   6. _____

Writing Plurals Write the plural of the underlined word in each sentence.

7. Three <u>family</u> went on the camping trip.   7. _____

8. The snake was thirty <u>inch</u> long.   8. _____

9. Big <u>bunch</u> of balloons were tied to her bike.   9. _____

10. Our <u>body</u> need good food, exercise, and rest.   10. _____

11. My jeans have lots of <u>pocket</u>.   11. _____

12. I found some <u>penny</u> on the curb.   12. _____

13. She made three <u>wish</u> on her birthday.   13. _____

14. There were many <u>crash</u> during the ice storm.   14. _____

15. Let's make some <u>copy</u> of the map.   15. _____

© Pearson Education, Inc., 3

Home Activity Your child spelled plurals that end with -s, -es, and -ies. Ask your child to explain how he or she knows which ending to use when making a word plural.

⭐ **3.24.A.2** Use knowledge of word parts to spell. **3.24.B.1.iii** Spell words changing y to i before adding an ending. **3.24.B.1.v** Spell words with complex consonants.

Name _____

Story Sequence B

Title _____

> **Beginning**

↓

> **Middle**

↓

> **End**

Vocabulary • Compound Words

- Sometimes you may come across a word you don't know. The word may be a long **compound word** made up of two small words.

- If you know the meaning of the small words, it will help you figure out the meaning of the long compound word.

Directions Read the riddle. Then circle the compound word that solves the riddle.

1. I take care of goats. I watch them during the day. I watch them at night. Who am I?
goatkeeper   goaltender

2. I sit and weave all day. I make wonderful patterns of many colors. I make things you put on your floor and walk on. Who am I?
coverup   carpetmaker

3. I raise goats. When they are big, I sell them to people. Who am I?
cowboy   goatseller

4. I help people get married. I help men meet women. I help women meet men. Who am I?
matchmaker   firefighter

5. I am a place where people go to buy things. There are many people selling things here. There are many people buying things here. What am I?
doorknob   marketplace

6. I am a place for children. I have swings and monkey bars. I have many things that children can play on. What am I?
playground   outline

7. Birds live inside me. I have a perch for them to sit on. I have cups for food and water. What am I?
cardboard   birdcage

8. I own a store. I help my customers. I stand behind the counter. People who buy things in my shop pay me. Who am I?
shopkeeper   airport

© Pearson Education, Inc., 3

Home Activity Your child used word structure to figure out the meaning of unfamiliar compound words. Read a newspaper article or store advertisement with your child. Encourage your child to identify unfamiliar compound words by defining the small words that make up each compound word.

3.4.B.1 Use context to determine the relevant meaning of unfamiliar words.

Alphabetical Order

Entries or subjects in encyclopedias, dictionaries, and indexes are listed in **alphabetical order,** so you can find information quickly and easily. When two entries or subjects have the same first letter, alphabetize by the second letter. If the second letters are also the same, alphabetize by the third letter, and so on. See how these occupation entries have been alphabetized in an index.

Accountant, 12	Butcher, 35	Counselor, 14
Actor, 22	Carpenter, 18	Dancer, 23
Auto Mechanic, 32	Carpet Installer, 20	Dentist, 29
Bank Teller, 34	Cashier, 9	Designer, 24
Barber, 8	Chef, 7	Educator, 26
Bus Driver, 10	Computer Operator, 6	Engineer, 19

Directions Put these words from *What About Me?* in alphabetical order. Use the index example above to help you.

> master   carpet   work
> thread   spun

> moral   wise   weave
> spinner   merchant

1. _____

2. _____

3. _____

4. _____

5. _____

6. _____

7. _____

8. _____

9. _____

10. _____

School + Home

Home Activity Your child put words in alphabetical order. Give your child a list of 5 names of family members and/or friends. Ask him or her to put the names in alphabetical order.

★ Alphabetize a series of words.

Plurals -s, -es, -ies

Proofread a List Circle four spelling mistakes in Ben's school supply list. Write the words correctly. Write the last sentence, using correct grammar and punctuation.

Spelling Words

pennies
inches
plants
families
bodies
glasses
wishes
pockets

lists
copies
parties
bunches
crashes
supplies
pencils

School supplys I need
colored pencils
folders with pocketes
ruler with centimeters and inchs
snacks—extras for friens
lined paper
Remember to turn in them copies of doctor records

---

1. _____   2. _____

3. _____   4. _____

5. _____

_____

Frequently Misspelled Words

friends
presents
his

Proofread Words Fill in the circle to show the correctly spelled word. Write each word.

6. ○ familys   ○ families   ○ familes   6. _____

7. ○ crashs   ○ crashes   ○ crashies   7. _____

8. ○ lists   ○ listes   ○ listies   8. _____

9. ○ bunchs   ○ bunchies   ○ bunches   9. _____

10. ○ glassies   ○ glasses   ○ glasss   10. _____

11. ○ wishs'   ○ wishs   ○ wishes   11. _____

12. ○ plantes   ○ plants   ○ plantts   12. _____

© Pearson Education, Inc., 3

Home Activity Your child identified and corrected misspelled plural nouns. Have your child help you make a shopping list. Include some list words.

3.24.A.2 Use knowledge of word parts to spell. **3.24.B.1.iii** Spell words changing y to i before adding an ending. **3.24.B.1.v** Spell words with complex consonants. **3.24.C.1** Spell high-frequency words from a commonly used list.

Subjects and Predicates

Directions Read the selection. Then read each question that follows the selection. Decide which is the best answer to each question. Mark the space for the answer you have chosen.

The Market

(1) The market is a busy place. (2) Many people buy beautiful carpets at the market. (3) Farmers bring goats to the market, too. (4) People in the stalls sell fresh vegetables. (5) A woman yells out for her family. (6) _____ run around the market square. (7) You can have a lot of fun at the market!

1 What is the complete subject in sentence 1?
- ⬭ is
- ⬭ place
- ⬭ The market
- ⬭ exciting

2 What is the verb in sentence 2?
- ⬭ buy
- ⬭ people
- ⬭ carpets
- ⬭ the market

3 What is the complete subject in sentence 4?
- ⬭ People
- ⬭ the stalls
- ⬭ fresh vegetables
- ⬭ People in the stalls

4 What is the complete predicate in sentence 5?
- ⬭ A woman
- ⬭ family
- ⬭ yells out for her family
- ⬭ A woman yells

5 What subject makes the most sense in sentence 6?
- ⬭ Carpets
- ⬭ Children
- ⬭ Stalls
- ⬭ Picnic baskets

© Pearson Education, Inc., 3

Home Activity Your child prepared for taking tests on subjects and predicates. Say a sentence about your family. Ask your child to identify the complete subject and predicate of the sentence. Continue with other sentences.

3.22.B.1 Use the complete subject in a sentence. **3.22.B.2** Use the complete predicate in a sentence.

Base Words and Endings

Directions Add **-ed** and **-ing** to each word on the left. Remember that you may have to double the last consonant, drop the final **e**, or change **y** to **i**.

Word	-ed	-ing
plan	planned	planning
1. please	_____	_____
2. use	_____	_____
3. shop	_____	_____
4. worry	_____	_____
5. tug	_____	_____

Directions Add **-er** and **-est** to each word on the left. Remember that you may have to double the last consonant, drop the final **e**, or change **y** to **i**.

Word	-er	-est
heavy	heavier	heaviest
6. great	_____	_____
7. easy	_____	_____
8. thin	_____	_____
9. angry	_____	_____
10. big	_____	_____

School + Home

Home Activity Your child wrote words that end with *-ed, -ing, -er,* and *-est.* Work with your child to write a story using the words on the page above. Before the writing begins, ask your child to review the words he or she wrote and think about ways to use the words.

3.1.A.2.ii Decode multisyllabic words independent of context by applying common spelling patterns including doubling final consonants when adding an ending.

© Pearson Education, Inc., 3

Sequence

- **Sequence** is the order in which things happen in a story.
- **Clue words,** such as *first, second, then, next, finally,* and *last,* can tell you when something happens.

Directions Read the following passage. Draw a line under the words or phrases that help you follow the sequence of story events. Then answer the questions below.

Tina's mother liked to watch rainbows. Tina decided to make her mother a rainbow. First, she found a large piece of white fabric. She sewed a row of red buttons to the fabric. Next, she sewed a row of orange buttons under the red buttons.

Then Tina found some yellow and green glitter. She used glue and made a row of yellow glitter and then a row of green glitter under the buttons.

Next, Tina found some blue fabric scraps. She sewed the blue fabric under the green glitter.

Then Tina found some violet buttons. She sewed a row of violet buttons under the blue fabric.

Finally, Tina made fabric loops to hang her rainbow. Now her mother can see a rainbow any time.

1. When did Tina sew orange buttons to her fabric?

_____

2. What did Tina glue on the fabric after she sewed the red and orange buttons?

_____

3. When did Tina sew the violet buttons?

_____

4. What did Tina do last?

_____

5. Write the colors Tina used in the sequence she used them. Why do you think she did things in this order? _____

_____

School + Home **Home Activity** Your child answered questions about the order of events in a story. Write the events from a story on cards or pieces of paper. Mix them up. Then have your child put the cards in the correct order.

3.2.B.7 Locate details about stories.

Writing • Thank-You Note

Key Features of a Thank-You Note

- uses the format of a friendly letter
- has a friendly tone
- explains why the writer is grateful

2218 Magnolia Street
San Antonio, TX 78201
October 14, 2011

Dear Aunt Teresa,

Not a day has gone by that I haven't played the guitar you left with me. Thank you for trusting me to take care of your guitar while you are away. I practice every day, and I can already play a few songs.

Naturally, my goal is to learn that gorgeous song you played for us during your last visit. Do you remember it? I'm talking about the Spanish lullaby, of course! If I haven't learned the song by the time you get back, you will have to teach me.

Until then, I will miss you terribly. I hope you are having a great time on your trip! I am counting the days to your return.

With love,
Carmen

1. Identify the format features of a thank-you note by underlining the date, drawing a box around the greeting, and circling the name of the person who has written the note.

2. Why is Carmen writing this friendly thank-you note?

_____

_____

© Pearson Education, Inc., 3

Vocabulary

Check the Words You Know	
__gear	__twitch
__parka	__willow
__splendid	__yanked

Directions Draw a line to match each word with its definition.

1. gear   pulled with a sudden motion

2. parka   to move with a quick jerk

3. splendid   a heavy, waterproof coat or jacket with a hood

4. yanked   the equipment needed for some purpose

5. twitch   very good; excellent

Directions Write the word from the box that best completes each sentence.

_____ **6.** I put on my boots and _____ to go out in the snow.

_____ **7.** Tim put all his fishing _____ into his dad's truck.

_____ **8.** We sat by the pond under the huge _____ trees.

_____ **9.** Jassy _____ the weeds out of the garden by hand.

_____ **10.** It was a _____ day for a hike in the woods.

Write a Story

On a separate sheet of paper, write a story about a boy or girl who goes fishing. Use as many vocabulary words as possible.

© Pearson Education, Inc., 3

Home Activity Your child identified and used vocabulary words from *Kumak's Fish*. Play a game with your child in which you take turns pantomiming and guessing an action involving a vocabulary word, such as putting on a parka.

3.4.B.1 Use context to determine the relevant meaning of unfamiliar words.

Declarative and Interrogative Sentences

A sentence that tells something is a **statement.** It is also called a **declarative sentence.** A sentence that asks something is a **question.** It is also called an **interrogative sentence.**

    Statement   The lake has many fish.   **Question**   Did you catch a fish?

A statement begins with a capital letter and ends with a period. A question begins with a capital letter and ends with a question mark.

Directions Write each sentence. Add the correct end punctuation. Write *S* if the sentence is a statement, or declarative sentence. Write *Q* if the sentence is a question, or interrogative sentence.

1. Are the winters long in the Arctic

_____

2. Spring is a good season for fishing

_____

3. We have a good fishing pole

_____

Directions Add one word from the box to make each statement into a question. Write the new sentence. Use correct capitalization and punctuation.

can   will   should   do

4. The people catch fish in the frozen lake.

_____

5. They take them home for a feast.

_____

Home Activity Your child learned about statements and questions. Have your child make up one statement and one question about an animal he or she likes.

⊕ **3.22.C.1** Use complete simple sentences with correct subject-verb agreement.

Base Words and Endings

Rhymes Write a list word that rhymes with each underlined word.

1. Our <u>latest</u> invention is the ___.

2. Nobody is ___ to be <u>teased</u>.

3. Everyone who had been <u>weaving</u> was ___.

4. We <u>hopped</u> out of the car and ___.

5. He is <u>sneezing</u> because it is ___ outside.

6. The ___ cartoon was about the <u>sunniest</u> day.

1. _____ 2. _____

3. _____ 4. _____

5. _____ 6. _____

© Pearson Education, Inc., 3

Spelling Words

using
getting
easiest
swimming
heavier
greatest
pleased
emptied

leaving
worried
strangest
freezing
funniest
angrier
shopped

Word Endings Add an ending to each word in parentheses to form a list word that completes the sentence.

7. (heavy) This box is _____ than that one.

8. (swim) I take _____ lessons twice a week.

9. (get) He is _____ a watch for his birthday.

10. (strange) That is the _____ bug I have ever seen.

11. (easy) That is the _____ way to solve the puzzle.

12. (use) I am _____ three different colors on my poster.

13. (worry) He _____ that he would be late.

14. (empty) She _____ the wastebasket in her classroom.

15. (angry) She was _____ than I thought.

Home Activity: Your child wrote words that end in *-ed*, *-ing*, *-er*, and *-est*. Ask your child to find list words in which a consonant is doubled or an *e* is dropped before adding *-ing* (consonant doubled in *getting*, *e* dropped in *using*, *leaving*, *freezing*).

3.24.A.2 Use knowledge of word parts to spell. **3.24.B.1.i** Spell words with consonant doubling when adding an ending. **Also 3.1.A.1.i,** **3.1.A.1.ii, 3.24.B.1.ii.1, 3.24.B.1.iii.**

Spelling Base Words and Endings **67**

Outline Form A

Title _____

A. _____

    1. _____

    2 _____

    3. _____

B. _____

    1. _____

    2. _____

    3. _____

C. _____

    1. _____

    2. _____

    3. _____

Vocabulary • Reference Sources

- You can use a **glossary** or a **dictionary** to find the meanings of unknown words.
- Entries in glossaries and dictionaries are in **alphabetical order.** When two words have the same first and second letter, alphabetize by the third letter.

blizzard *NOUN.* a blinding snowstorm with very strong, cold winds

blow *VERB.* **1.** to make air come out of your mouth. **2.** to move in the wind

parka *NOUN.* a warm, heavy jacket with a hood

pattern *NOUN.* an arrangement or design

Directions Put these words in alphabetical order. Use the glossary example above to help you. Then answer the questions.

> wander   wake   waist
> walrus   wade

> waves   water   wax
> warm   was

1. _____

2. _____

3. _____

4. _____

5. _____

6. _____

7. _____

8. _____

9. _____

10. _____

11. Which word comes just before *warm* in the glossary?

_____

12. Which word comes just after *water* in the glossary?

_____

© Pearson Education, Inc., 3

School + Home   **Home Activity** Your child put words whose first two letters are the same in alphabetical order. Give your child a list of three names that begin with the same two letters, such as *Sam, Sandy,* and *Sally.* Have your child put the names in alphabetical order.

3.4.E.1 Alphabetize a series of words to the third letter.
3.4.E.2 Use a dictionary or glossary to determine meanings of unknown words.

Glossary

- Sometimes you come across a word you don't know. You can use a **glossary** to find the meaning of the unfamiliar word.

- A **glossary** has the meanings of important words in a book. It is usually found in the back of a book. The words are listed in alphabetical order.

Directions Study the sample from a glossary page below. Then use it to answer the questions.

---

spell • yanked

spell *v.* to write or say the letters of a word in order
splendid *adj.* very good; excellent
twitch *v.* to move with a quick jerk
vision *n.* the power of using the imagination to see what the future might bring
willow *n.* the wood of the willow tree

---

1. What are the guide words on this page? _____

2. Would the word *space* be on this page? How do you know?

_____

3. The abbreviation *n.* stands for *noun*. Which words shown are nouns?

_____

4. Where in a book is a glossary usually found? _____

5. Do you think this section of the glossary is at the beginning of the glossary or near the end? Why?

_____

_____

6. Write the meaning of the word *vision*: _____

_____

Home Activity Your child learned how to use a glossary. Ask your child to name the word on the sample glossary page above that is a verb and explain his or her answer.

3.4.E.1 Alphabetize a series of words to the third letter.
3.4.E.2 Use a dictionary or glossary to determine meanings of unknown words.

Base Words and Endings

Proofread a Thank-You Note Circle four misspelled words in Joe's thank-you note. Circle the word with the capitalization error. Write the words correctly.

dear Uncle Jim,

Thanks for geting me the swiming gear. I planned on useing my savings so I had emptied my piggy bank. However, there wasn't enough. That's why I was so pleased with your gift. You're the greatest!

Love,
Joe

1. _____   2. _____

3. _____   4. _____

5. _____

Complete the Sentence Circle the word that is spelled correctly. Then write the word.

6. I picked out the **easiest easyest** puzzle.   6. _____

7. Have you **shoped shopped** for a new bike?   7. _____

8. The box was **heavyier heavier** than I thought.   8. _____

9. Are you **leaving leaveing** before lunch?   9. _____

10. I'm **freezing freezeing**!   10. _____

11. Are you **worry worried** about the test?   11. _____

12. She was **pulesed pleased** with my report.   12. _____

Home Activity Your child identified misspelled words that end in -ed, -ing, -er, and -est. Name a base word and have your child explain how to add the ending.

© Pearson Education, Inc., 3

3.24.A.2 Use knowledge of word parts to spell. **3.24.B.1.i** Spell words with consonant doubling when adding an ending. **3.24.B.1.ii.1** Spell words dropping final "e" when endings are added. **Also 3.24.B.1.iii.**

Declarative and Interrogative Sentences

Directions Read the selection. Then read each question that follows the selection. Decide which is the best answer to each question. Mark the space for the answer you have chosen.

Fishing at the Lake

(1) What is your favorite lake for fishing? (2) My favorite lake is Mirror Lake. (3) I fish in the summer (4) how big are the fish you catch? (5) The fish smell good when they are cooked. (6) My family eats a lot of fish. (7) Does your lake freeze in the winter

1 What change, if any, should be made to sentence 1?
- ⬭ Change *What* to **what**
- ⬭ Change *fishing?* to **fishing.**
- ⬭ Change *fishing?* to **fishing**
- ⬭ Make no change

2 What change, if any, should be made to sentence 3?
- ⬭ Change *I* to **i**
- ⬭ Change *summer* to **summer.**
- ⬭ Change *summer* to **summer?**
- ⬭ Make no change

3 What change, if any, should be made to sentence 4?
- ⬭ Change *catch?* to **catch.**
- ⬭ Change *catch?* to **catch,**
- ⬭ Change *how big* to **How big**
- ⬭ Make no change

4 What type of sentence is sentence 5?
- ⬭ It is a statement.
- ⬭ It is a question.
- ⬭ It is an interrogative sentence.
- ⬭ It is an incomplete sentence.

5 What change, if any, should be made to sentence 7?
- ⬭ Change *winter* to **winter?**
- ⬭ Change *winter* to **winter!**
- ⬭ Change *winter* to **winter.**
- ⬭ Make no change

Home Activity Your child prepared for taking tests on statements and questions. Read a story together. Have your child identify statements and questions in the story.

⬇ **3.22.C.1** Use complete simple sentences with correct subject-verb agreement.

Long Vowel Digraphs

Directions Choose the word with the **long a**, **long e**, or **long o** sound that best matches each definition. Write the word on the line.

_____	**1.** all right	glad	okay	well
_____	**2.** a sound of pain	groan	sob	whimper
_____	**3.** free from dirt	clean	fresh	spotless
_____	**4.** toss	fling	pitch	throw
_____	**5.** go along with	accept	admit	agree
_____	**6.** reach or get	gain	gather	win
_____	**7.** heat until brown	cook	toast	broil

Directions Circle the word that has the **long a**, **long e**, or **long o** sound. Then underline the letters in the word that stand for that vowel sound.

8. chock	chop	cheep
9. best	blown	bought
10. flash	float	flock
11. braid	brick	build
12. school	sorry	stay
13. feast	flash	friend
14. dish	dream	droop
15. sand	screen	shoe
16. plain	plant	print

Home Activity Your child wrote words in which the long *a* sound is spelled *ay* and *ai*, the long *e* is spelled *ee* and *ea*, and the long *o* is spelled *oa* and *ow*. Ask your child to list words that rhyme with the long *a*, *e*, and *o* words on the page above. Write the rhyming words and have your child read them noting different spellings for the same sound.

© Pearson Education, Inc., 3

3.1.B.1.v.1 Use common syllabication patterns to decode words including vowel digraphs.

Compare and Contrast

- **Compare** by telling how two or more things are alike.
- **Contrast** by telling only how two or more things are different.

Directions Read the following article.

Dan, Tim, and Anna grocery shop for their family. Dan always heads for the supermarket. He likes lots of choices. Dan buys what he wants and leaves in a hurry. He thinks small stores are boring.

Tim prefers the small corner grocery. The store doesn't have much, but it has what Tim needs. Tim likes the store's owner, Mrs. Garza. When the store isn't busy, Tim stays and talks awhile. Tim likes cozy little stores. He thinks big stores are too noisy and crowded.

Anna likes both stores. She dashes to the corner when she needs basic supplies. She goes to the supermarket to find special foods.

Directions Fill in the chart to compare and contrast Dan's, Tim's, and Anna's shopping habits.

	Big Supermarket	**Corner Store**
Dan		
Tim		
Anna		

© Pearson Education, Inc., 3

Home Activity Your child compared and contrasted three shoppers. Talk with your child about shopping likes and dislikes. Discuss how your child's attitudes about shopping are like and unlike your own attitudes.

★ Compare and contrast ideas and information.

Writing • Description

Key Features of a Description

- uses sensory language
- includes important details
- creates a picture in the reader's mind

My Favorite Place to Shop

Our local thrift shop makes money for Children's Hospital. People bring in things they no longer need or want and the thrift shop sells them for a fair price. It's made for me!

Sometimes I see a game I've been wanting but don't want to pay $15 for. Other times there's a great looking pair of jeans that have hardly been worn. Mom always finds something to brighten up the house. Once she found a sparkly, red painting. Another time she found a tall, rectangular lamp. "Leave your wallets at home," Dad says as we head to the shop.

The woman who owns the shop likes to burn candles. The whole store smells like vanilla. It smells delicious! I hear the sound of the cash register and people talking about items to buy. The thrift shop is a great place to spend my money.

I wonder if every town has a thrift shop. I am so glad our town does!

1. List three sensory words or phrases from the selection.

_____

2. How many exclamatory sentences are included in the selection? How do you know?

_____

Name _____

Vocabulary

Directions Match the word with its meaning. Draw a line from the word to
its definition.

1. store

2. laundry

3. shelves

4. spoiled

5. traded

clothes that have been washed or need to be washed

thin flat pieces of wood or other material fastened to a
wall or frame to hold things

exchanged, bartered

a place where things are sold

became bad, not good to eat

Directions Choose a word from the list that best fits the meaning of the sentence and
write it on the line.

6. The milk _____ quickly in the warm weather.

7. My favorite part of the supermarket is the bakery _____.

8. You can find a huge _____ of fruit in a supermarket.

9. It seemed like there were _____ of cars in the parking lot.

10. It's fun to shop in the grocery _____.

Write a Grocery List

On a separate sheet of paper, write a description of a trip to the supermarket and list
what you bought. Include items from different sections of the supermarket. Use as
many vocabulary words as you can.

© Pearson Education, Inc., 3

Home Activity Your child identified and used vocabulary words from *Supermarket*. With your child discuss
your local supermarket and what things you buy there. Encourage your child to use vocabulary words in
your conversation.

🌟 **3.4.B.1** Use context to determine the relevant meaning of
unfamiliar words.

Imperative and Exclamatory Sentences

A sentence that tells someone to do something is a **command.** It is also called an **imperative sentence.** A sentence that shows strong feelings is an **exclamation.** It is also called an **exclamatory sentence.**

> **Command** Buy some apples.
> **Exclamation** What juicy peaches these are!

Some commands begin with *Please*. Commands usually end with periods. The subject of a command is *you*. The word *you* is not written or said, but it is understood. Exclamations can express feelings such as surprise, anger, or excitement. Exclamations begin with a capital letter and end with an exclamation mark.

Directions Write the sentences. Add the correct end punctuation. Write *C* if the sentence is a command, or imperative sentence. Write *E* if the sentence is an exclamation, or exclamatory sentence.

1. Please get a loaf of bread

_____

2. Wow! This supermarket is huge

_____

Directions Use a word from the box to complete each command or exclamation. Write the new sentence. Use correct capitalization and punctuation.

> What   Look   Talk   How

3. _____ on that shelf for cereal.

_____

4. _____ busy the workers are!

_____

Home Activity Your child learned about commands and exclamations. Have your child make up one command and one exclamation about saving money.

🌐 **3.22.C.1** Use complete simple sentences with correct subject-verb agreement.

Conventions Imperative and Exclamatory Sentences   **77**

© Pearson Education, Inc., 3

Vowel Digraphs

Rhymes Write the list word that rhymes with the underlined word.

Spelling Words

clean
agree
teeth
dream
grain
coach
display
window

shadow
cheese
peach
braid
Sunday
float
thrown

1. Did you ever meet a <u>goat</u> that knew how

to _____ ?

2. Did you ever <u>approach</u> the other

team's _____ ?

3. Did you ever <u>reach</u> for a big fuzzy _____ ?

4. Did you ever get a <u>pain</u> from eating

green _____ ?

5. Did you ever <u>scream</u> when you had a

bad _____ ?

6. Did you ever help <u>Jean</u> keep her room _____ ?

7. Did you ever get <u>paid</u> to wear your hair in a _____ ?

Context Clues Write the missing list word.

8. I like grilled _____ sandwiches.

9. Floss your _____ every day.

10. The first day of the week is _____ .

11. The tree cast a long _____ .

12. Let's open the _____ to get some fresh air.

13. Mom will _____ to drive us to the game.

14. I've _____ out all my old papers.

15. Let's make a _____ of our seashells.

Home Activity Your child wrote words with long vowel digraphs (letter combinations that stand for long vowel sounds). Ask your child to circle the digraphs *ai, ay, ee, ea, oa,* and *ow.*

✪ **3.24.A.1** Use knowledge of letter sounds to spell. **3.24.A.2** Use knowledge of word parts to spell. **3.24.A.3** Use knowledge of word segmentation to spell. **3.24.A.4** Use knowledge of syllabication to spell.

Main Idea

Main Idea

Supporting Details

Vocabulary • Context Clues

- **Multiple-meaning words** are words that have different meanings depending on how they are used.
- Use **context clues,** or the words around a multiple-meaning word, to figure out which meaning is used.

Directions Read the following passage. Then answer the questions below. Look for context clues that show the correct meanings of the multiple-meaning words as you read.

> It's hard to find **rich** soil in the city, so most city people can't **grow** their own food. Instead they go to the supermarket. Each kind of food is always in the same place. That way shoppers can go **right** to the items they need. Then they rush home and **store** the food in their kitchen so it won't get **spoiled.** It's not good to shop when you're hungry. Hungry shoppers buy everything they see!

1. What clue lets you know that *rich* means "having lots of nutrition," not "having lots of money"?

   _____

2. In this passage, does *grow* mean "to get bigger" or "to make something get bigger"?

   _____

3. What clue words tell you that *right* means "directly"?

   _____

4. What are two meanings for *store*? What clues tell you the word's meaning in this passage?

   _____

   _____

5. In this passage does *spoiled* describe people or pets who get everything they want or does it mean "became rotten"?

   _____

© Pearson Education, Inc., 3

Home Activity Your child used context clues to understand multiple-meaning words. Say sentences with multiple-meaning words, such as *run, place,* and *blue.* Ask your child to use context clues to determine the meaning of each word.

3.4.B.2 Use context to distinguish among multiple meaning words.

Imperative and Exclamatory Sentences

Directions Read the selection. Then read each question that follows the selection. Decide which is the best answer to each question. Mark the space for the answer you have chosen.

Shopping Trip

(1) There are so many kinds of foods here! (2) Please get a box of crackers. (3) Check the price of tomatoes (4) Please look for the grapes (5) What a good price that is (6) The bread smells so good! (7) _____ put the bags in the car.

1 What type of sentence is sentence 1?

- ⬭ a command
- ⬭ an imperative sentence
- ⬭ an exclamatory sentence
- ⬭ an interrogative sentence

2 What type of sentence is sentence 2?

- ⬭ an exclamation
- ⬭ an exclamatory sentence
- ⬭ a declarative sentence
- ⬭ an imperative sentence

3 What change, if any, should be made to sentence 4?

- ⬭ Change *grapes* to **grapes.**
- ⬭ Change *grapes* to **grapes!**
- ⬭ Change *Please* to **Please!**
- ⬭ Make no change

4 What change, if any, should be made to sentence 5?

- ⬭ Change *is* to **is.**
- ⬭ Change *is* to **is!**
- ⬭ Change *What* to **what**
- ⬭ Make no change

5 Which word makes the most sense in sentence 7?

- ⬭ Please
- ⬭ Please!
- ⬭ What
- ⬭ Shopping

Home Activity Your child prepared for taking tests on commands and exclamations. Have your child write a note about a chore to a family member, including a command and an exclamation. Ask your child to identify each kind of sentence.

3.22.C.1 Use complete simple sentences with correct subject-verb agreement.

Vowel Diphthongs

Directions Circle each word with **ou** or **ow** that has the same vowel sound as **out.** Then write the word on the line.

_____ 1. Jen slowly counted her money.

_____ 2. She had the amount she needed.

_____ 3. Jen was proud that she didn't have to borrow money.

_____ 4. She could buy her mother some bath powder.

_____ 5. Jen would also buy some yellow flowers.

Directions Circle each word with **oi** or **oy** that has the same vowel sound as **toy.** Then write the word on the line.

_____ 6. It was time for Al to make a choice.

_____ 7. Should he find a new employer?

_____ 8. Al wanted to avoid a long ride to work.

_____ 9. He wanted to enjoy his job.

_____ 10. He also hoped to work in an office that was not noisy.

Directions Circle each word with the same vowel sound as the first word. Then underline the letters in the circled word that stand for that vowel sound.

11. town	loyal	proud	snow
12. boy	sound	know	broil
13. choice	coat	plow	spoil
14. hour	crown	float	show
15. join	bay	annoy	brown

© Pearson Education, Inc., 3

 Home Activity Your child wrote words with the vowel sound in *out,* spelled *ou* as in *proud* and *ow* as in *shower,* and the vowel sound in *toy,* spelled *oi* as in *choice* and *oy* as in *voyage.* Have your child list other words that have the vowel sounds in *out* and *toy.* Tell your child to underline the letters that stand for the vowel sound in each word.

3.1.B.1.v.2 Use common syllabication patterns to decode words including diphthongs.

Author's Purpose

An **author's purpose** is the author's reason for writing. An author may write to inform or teach, to entertain, to persuade, or to express thoughts and feelings. Authors choose either a first-person narrator who is often one of the story's characters or a third-person narrator who tells the story without taking part in the events. First-person narrattors use language such as "I" and "me." Third-person narrators use language such as "he" and "she."

Directions Read the story. Then complete the web. Finish the sentences. Write the author's purpose in the middle circle.

Jamal wanted to go to soccer camp, so he asked his dad to pay for it. "Let's make a deal," his dad said. "If you save half the cost, I'll pay the rest." Jamal thought that was fair, so he agreed.

Right away, Jamal started to save, but sometimes it was hard. He put almost all of his allowance into the bank. He did jobs for the neighbors. He didn't spend one cent of his birthday money! Whenever Jamal wanted to buy something, he thought about his goal.

When it was time to pay for camp, Jamal had saved more than half the cost. He was proud that he had worked hard to reach his goal. You should save for something special too. You will feel great when you reach your goal!

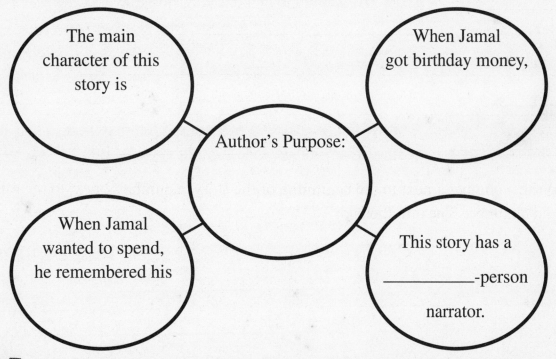

The main character of this story is

When Jamal got birthday money,

Author's Purpose:

When Jamal wanted to spend, he remembered his

This story has a _____-person narrator.

© Pearson Education, Inc., 3

School + Home

Home Activity Your child read a story and identified the author's purpose and the narrator. Read a story together. Discuss the author's purpose for writing and ask your child to tell whether the narrator is first person or third person.

3.8.C Identify whether the narrator of a story is first person or third person.

Comprehension 85

Writing • Writing for Tests

Aiming for the Moon

Every morning my mom gives me money to buy lunch at school. She gives me more money than I need, and she knows it. I usually buy something yummy to eat after school. I spend all the money I have.

Yesterday I saw a remote control moon, and I want one for my bedroom. My mom said, "Save your money to buy it." No more extra snacks for me! Instead I will put the money that I used to spend on treats in my bank. I can also use the money Grandpa gave me for my birthday. He told me to pick out something I really wanted. This moon looks like lots of fun, and I will give up extra treats for it.

1. Find the characters in the model. Draw a box around each one. How are the characters related?

_____

2. Describe the story's sequence of events.

Beginning: _____

_____

Middle: _____

_____

End: _____

_____

3. Write a number 1 next to the beginning of the story, a number 2 next to the middle, and a number 3 next to the end.

Name _____

Vocabulary

Directions Fill in the blank with the word that fits the meaning of the sentence.

1. Hold the ladder _____ so I can climb up.

2. I _____ often when I first learned to ride a bike.

3. He _____ his birthday presents after the party.

4. She did a few _____ to help her grandmother.

5. We tied our clothes in _____ and went to the laundry.

Directions Draw a line from the word to its definition.

6. dangerously   put in order

7. arranged   shook from side to side

8. excitedly   uncovered

9. unwrapped   in an unsafe way

10. wobbled   with strong, lively feelings

Write an Advertisement

On a separate sheet of paper, write an advertisement for a job. Write about someone who is looking for a student to work after school. Describe the job and how much it pays. Use as many vocabulary words as possible.

© Pearson Education, Inc., 3

Home Activity Your child identified and used words from *My Rows and Piles of Coins*. Read a story about a student who gets a job. Discuss the story with your child using this lesson's vocabulary words.

 3.4.B.1 Use context to determine the relevant meaning of unfamiliar words.

Name _____

Compound Sentences

A **simple sentence** has one subject and one predicate. A **compound sentence** contains two simple sentences joined by a comma and a word such as *and, but,* or *or.*

Simple Sentence	I rode my bike to Dan's house.
Simple Sentence	We rode to the park.
Compound Sentence	I rode my bike to Dan's house, and we rode to the park.

Directions Write *S* if the sentence is a simple sentence. Write *C* if the sentence is a compound sentence.

1. Bicycles are important to people in some countries. _____

2. People in some places do not have cars. _____

3. They ride bicycles to work, and they ride them to the store. _____

4. Bicycles cost less than cars, but they are not cheap. _____

5. Bicycles do not make the air dirty, but cars do. _____

Directions Choose one of the words in ( ) to combine each pair of simple sentences. Write the compound sentences on the lines.

6. Chris rode a bicycle up the hill. It was not easy. (but, or)

_____

7. Chris skinned his knee. He bumped his head. (but, and)

_____

8. Now Chris can ride to school. He can ride to the park. (or, but)

_____

Home Activity Your child learned about compound sentences. Say two short, related sentences describing your child. Have him or her combine the sentences to make a compound sentence.

✪ **3.22.C.1** Use complete simple sentences with correct subject-verb agreement. **3.22.C.2** Use complete compound sentences with correct subject-verb agreement.

Vowel Diphthongs

Classifying Write the list word that belongs with each group.

proud
shower
hour
amount
voyage
choice
avoid
thousand

prowl
employ
bounce
poison
annoy
appoint
broil

1. second, minute, ___

2. fry, grill, ___

3. rain, sprinkle, ___

4. journey, trip, ___

5. million, hundred, ___

6. jump, spring, ___

1. _____ 2. _____

3. _____ 4. _____

5. _____ 6. _____

Word Meanings Write the list word that means almost the same thing as the underlined word or phrase.

7. Don't <u>bother</u> me. 7. _____

8. The winners were too <u>boastful</u>. 8. _____

9. The bill was a large <u>sum</u>. 9. _____

10. Some spiders use <u>venom</u> to kill their prey. 10. _____

11. Will you <u>choose</u> an assistant? 11. _____

12. My cat likes to <u>roam</u> around at night. 12. _____

13. Summer camps <u>hire</u> many young people. 13. _____

14. My grandparents <u>keep away from</u> crowds. 14. _____

15. He was careful in his <u>selection</u> of players. 15. _____

© Pearson Education, Inc., 3

Home Activity Your child wrote words with the vowel sounds heard in *out* and *toy*. Ask your child to circle and pronounce *ou, ow, oi,* and *oy* in the list words.

3.24.A.1 Use knowledge of letter sounds to spell. **3.24.A.2** Use knowledge of word parts to spell.

Scoring Rubric: Writing for Tests: Realistic Fiction

	4	3	2	1
Focus/Ideas	Vivid narrative; well-developed characters and setting; realistic	Good narrative; adequate characterization and setting	Narrative lacking focus on characters or setting; somewhat unrealistic	Narrative with no focus on characters or setting; unrealistic
Organization	Clear series of events	Able to follow series of events	Unclear series of events	No series of events
Voice	Voice always matches word choice	Voice mostly matches word choice	Voice rarely matches word choice	Voice never matches word choice
Word Choice	Strong use of precise words	Some use of precise words	Weak use of precise words	No use of precise words; story lifeless
Sentences	Clear sentences of various lengths and types	Sentences of a few lengths and types	Sentences of similar length and type	No attempt at sentences of various lengths and types
Conventions	Few, if any, errors; correct use of compound sentences	Several small errors; correct use of compound sentences	Many errors; weak use of compound sentences	Many serious errors; incorrect or no use of compound sentences

Vocabulary • Prefixes and Suffixes

- Sometimes you may come across words you do not know. You can look to see if the base word has a **prefix** at the beginning or a **suffix** at the end that helps you figure out the meaning.
- The **prefix** *un-* makes a word mean "not" or "the opposite of." For example, *unhappy* means "not happy."
- The **suffix** *-ly* makes a word mean "in a ___ way." For example, *slowly* means "in a slow way."

Directions Read each sentence. One word is underlined in each sentence. Circle the prefix *un-* or suffix *-ly* in the underlined word. Then circle the correct meaning of the word.

1. When I <u>unloaded</u> the heavy things from the bike, it was easy to ride.
   took off   put on

2. I was <u>deeply</u> pleased when I won the prize.
   a strongly felt way very low

3. The boy stood <u>dangerously</u> close to the edge of the cliff.
   in an unsafe way in an angry way

4. She <u>unwrapped</u> the gift and found ice skates inside.
   took off the cover did not open

5. He laughed <u>gleefully</u> when he won the spelling bee.
   in a silly way in a happy way

6. After the hike, we returned <u>wearily</u> to our tents and went to sleep.
   very quickly in a tired way

7. My father <u>proudly</u> gave me a hug when he saw my report card.
   in a loud way in a pleased way

8. I <u>untied</u> the bundle of coins and gave my sister a dime.
   opened   spilled

Home Activity Your child used prefixes and suffixes to figure out the meaning of words. With your child, read a story about a person who gets a part-time job to earn money. Encourage your child to find words that have prefixes and suffixes and to use them to figure out the meaning of unfamiliar words.

3.4.A.2 Know how prefixes change the meaning of roots.
3.4.A.4 Know how suffixes change the meaning of roots.

Keyboarding

A **computer** can be used as a tool to help you learn. You can use it for research, to visit Web sites, or to send e-mail. Some people use it to keep an online journal, or blog, that others can read. You can use it to type and print a report or story.

You type on the computer, using the **keyboard.** You look at the computer screen, or **monitor.**

A **mouse** helps you move around on the computer screen.

A **cursor** shows you where you are on the screen.

You can put a **CD** or **DVD** into the data disk drive. You can use it to play a game or listen to music.

You may use a computer to access the **Internet.** The Internet is an extremely large network of computers. Using the Internet, people can exchange messages and information all over the world.

Directions Read the information above and study the diagram. Then answer the questions.

1. Which computer part helps you move around on the computer?

_____

2. Which computer part do you use to type?

_____

3. What does the cursor do?

_____

4. What is the disk drive for?

_____

5. What are three things you can use a computer for?

_____

_____

_____

© Pearson Education, Inc., 3

Home Activity Your child studied a diagram of a computer and answered questions. Either at home or at the library, explore with your child some of the things a computer is used for, how to use the keyboard and mouse, and some children's Web sites.

★ Demonstrate basic keyboarding skills and familiarity with computer terminology.

Name _____

Vowel Diphthongs

Proofread a Book Report Circle four spelling mistakes in Tom's book report. Write the words correctly. Then write the last sentence, adding the missing word.

Spelling Words

proud
shower
hour
amount
voyage
choice
avoid
thousand

prowl
employ
bounce
poison
annoy
appoint
broil

> **Book Report**
>
> My book is about a boy who makes a voyage of two thosand miles. He has to avood a thief on the proul, posion, and other dangers. Finally, he is _____ by a kind man.

1. _____   2. _____

3. _____   4. _____

5. _____

_____

Frequently Misspelled Words

found
house

Proofread Words Draw a line through the word that is **not** spelled correctly. Write the word correctly.

6. I'm so **proud   prowd** of you!   6. _____

7. Shall we **briol   broil** the meat?   7. _____

8. I have to practice for an **howr   hour.**   8. _____

9. Let's **bounce   bownce** on the trampoline. 9. _____

10. Do **appoint   appoynt** three people.   10. _____

11. The **choice   choise** was correct.   11. _____

12. The pup doesn't mean to **annoy   anoiy** you. 12. _____

Home Activity Your child spelled words with the vowel sounds heard in *out* and *toy*. Read a sentence on this page, and have your child spell the list word.

© Pearson Education, Inc., 3

⭐ **3.24.A.1** Use knowledge of letter sounds to spell. **3.24.A.2** Use knowledge of word parts to spell. **3.24.C.1** Spell high-frequency words from a commonly used list.

Name_____

Compound Sentences

Directions Read the selection. Then read each question that follows the selection. Decide which is the best answer to each question. Mark the space for the answer you have chosen.

Bicycles in Other Countries

(1) Bicycles are important to people in some countries. (2) People in many places do not have cars. (3) People ride their bicycles to work, and they ride them to the store. (4) Bicycles cost less than cars, but they are not cheap. (5) There are advantages to bicycles, too. (6) Bicycles do not hurt the environment, and they do not cause traffic jams.

1 What is the subject in sentence 1?
- ⬭ Bicycles
- ⬭ people
- ⬭ countries
- ⬭ important

2 What word joins the simple sentences in sentence 3?
- ⬭ but
- ⬭ or
- ⬭ and
- ⬭ too

3 What are the subjects in sentence 4?
- ⬭ Bicycles, cars
- ⬭ Bicycles, they
- ⬭ cars, cheap
- ⬭ hurt, cause

4 Which sentences in the paragraph are compound?
- ⬭ 3, 4
- ⬭ 3, 4, 5, 6
- ⬭ 3, 6
- ⬭ 3, 4, 6

5 What is the predicate in sentence 5?
- ⬭ There are advantages
- ⬭ are advantages to bicycles
- ⬭ bicycles
- ⬭ too

Home Activity Your child prepared for taking tests on compound sentences. Have your child find compound sentences in a magazine and identify the two simple sentences that make up each compound sentence and the word that joins the two sentences.

🔽 **3.22.C.1** Use complete simple sentences with correct subject-verb agreement. **3.22.C.2** Use complete compound sentences with correct subject-verb agreement.

© Pearson Education, Inc., 3

Name_____

Short Vowels; Syllables VC/CV

Spelling Words

happen	lettuce	basket	winter	sister
problem	supper	subject	lesson	spelling
napkin	collar	traffic	suggest	puppet

Syllable Match Cross out the extra syllable. Write the list word.

1. bas kin ket   1._____

2. les low son   2._____

3. hap pen per   3._____

4. sis col lar   4._____

5. sug ject gest   5._____

6. let pup pet   6._____

7. mon ster ter   7._____

8. sub per ject   8._____

9. hap nap kin   9._____

10. traf per fic   10._____

Opposites Write the list word that completes each phrase.

11. not a **brother,** but a ___   11._____

12. not **summer,** but ___   12._____

13. not **breakfast,** but ___   13._____

14. not **cabbage,** but ___   14._____

15. not **math,** but ___   15._____

Home Activity Your child is learning to spell words with short vowel sounds with the spelling pattern VC/CV. Choose a word. Write it, but leave out two letters, putting a blank in their places. Have your child write the missing letters and then write the whole word.

3.24.A.1 Use knowledge of letter sounds to spell. **3.24.A.4** Use knowledge of syllabication to spell. **3.24.D.1** Spell words with common syllable constructions.

Sentences

Directions Read the groups of words. Write the group of words that is a sentence.

1. We play many computer games.
   Other kinds of games, too.

   _____

2. High winds and heavy rain.
   A big storm blows power lines down.

   _____

3. We don't need power for board games.
   Played checkers all day.

   _____

4. Some kids got bored.
   No power to play video games.

   _____

5. Finished an art project.
   My friends painted a mural.

   _____

Directions Decide whether each group of words is a sentence or a fragment.
If it is a sentence, write the sentence with correct capitalization and punctuation.
If it is a fragment, write *F*.

6. we can play tag and soccer outdoors

   _____

7. people on the baseball field

   _____

8. looked everywhere for a battery

   _____

9. they discovered new games during the storm

   _____

🌐 **3.22.C.1** Use complete simple sentences with correct subject-verb agreement.

Base Words and Endings

Spelling Words				
using	getting	easiest	swimming	heavier
greatest	pleased	emptied	leaving	worried
strangest	freezing	funniest	angrier	shopped

Word Pairs Write the missing list word. Use the underlined word as a clue.

1. Sara's joke is <u>funny</u>, but Diego's is the ___ I've heard. _____

2. A hippo is <u>heavy</u>, but an elephant is ___. _____

3. That picture is <u>strange</u>, but this one is the ___ of all. _____

4. Brent is <u>angry</u>, but David is ___. _____

5. Math is <u>easy</u>, but Spelling is the ___ of all. _____

6. Many movies are <u>great</u>, but this movie is the ___ ever. _____

Analogies Write the list word that completes each phrase.

7. **Sit** is to **sitting** as **get** is to _____

8. **Ship** is to **shipped** as **shop** is to _____

9. **Run** is to **running** as **swim** is to _____

10. **Try** is to **tried** as **empty** is to _____

11. **Hurry** is to **hurried** as **worry** is to _____

12. **Sneeze** is to **sneezing** as **freeze** is to _____

13. **Come** is to **coming** as **leave** is to _____

14. **Save** is to **saving** as **use** is to _____

15. **Amuse** is to **amused** as **please** is to _____

© Pearson Education, Inc., 3

Home Activity Your child is spelling words that end in *-ed, -ing, -er,* and *-est*. To practice at home, spell each word together. Have your child say which ending is used at the end of the word.

3.24.A.2 Use knowledge of word parts to spell. **3.24.B.1.i** Spell words with consonant doubling when adding an ending. **3.24.B.1.ii.1** Spell words dropping final *"e"* when endings are added. **3.24.B.1.iii** Spell words changing y to i before adding an ending.

Declarative and Interrogative Sentences

Directions Write *statement* if the sentence is a statement. Write *question* if the sentence is a question.

1. Fish is a tasty, healthful food. _____

2. What is your favorite kind of fish? _____

3. Fish tastes good with all kinds of spices. _____

4. How shall we cook this big trout? _____

5. We can make tacos or soup with it. _____

Directions Write the sentences. Add the correct end punctuation. Write *S* if the sentence is a statement and *Q* if the sentence is a question.

6. Can we fish in this pond

_____

7. Has anyone caught anything

_____

8. The fish leap out of the water

_____

9. There are big fish and little fish

_____

10. Did you see that colorful fish

_____

11. It is tugging on my line

_____

12. How much does it weigh

_____

3.22.C.1 Use complete simple sentences with correct subject-verb agreement.

Name _____

Vowel Diphthongs

Spelling Words				
proud	shower	hour	amount	voyage
choice	avoid	thousand	prowl	employ
bounce	poison	annoy	appoint	broil

Words in Context Write the missing list word.

1. During the sea _____ the ship was in a storm.

2. The play lasted about one _____.

3. One way to cook meat is to _____ it.

4. The cat liked to _____ for mice.

5. I took a bath, not a _____.

6. Try to _____ that busy street.

Alphabetizing Write each group of words in ABC order.

| choice   amount   bounce |

7. _____

8. _____

9. _____

| employ   poison   appoint |

10. _____

11. _____

12. _____

| thousand   annoy   proud |

13. _____

14. _____

15. _____

© Pearson Education, Inc., 3

 Home Activity Your child has been learning to spell words with the vowel sounds in *out* and *toy*. Divide a sheet of paper into two columns. Have your child write words with the vowel sound in *out* in one column and words with the vowel sound in *toy* in the other column.

3.24.A.1 Use knowledge of letter sounds to spell.
3.24.A.2 Use knowledge of word parts to spell.

Spelling 103

Compound Sentences

Directions Write *S* if the sentence is a simple sentence. Write *C* if the sentence is a compound sentence.

1. Many people use bicycles for their jobs. _____

2. Some people deliver messages on their bikes. _____

3. James carries flowers on his bike, and Dave carries groceries. _____

4. Dave prefers heavy loads, but it is hard work. _____

5. Bicycles are fun, and they are also useful. _____

Directions Use the word *and, but,* or *or* to combine each pair of sentences. Write the compound sentence.

6. Kevin worked hard. He saved money for a skateboard.

_____

_____

7. The store had many skateboards. Kevin wanted a special one.

_____

_____

8. You buy a skateboard from the store. You order one from a catalog.

_____

_____

9. Kevin saw the perfect skateboard in a catalog. He ordered it right away.

_____

_____

10. Kevin waited a long time for his skateboard. It was worth the wait.

_____

_____

3.22.C.1 Use complete simple sentences with correct subject-verb agreement. **3.22.C.2** Use complete compound sentences with correct subject-verb agreement.

Notes for a Personal Narrative

Directions Fill in the graphic organizer with information about the event or experience that you plan to write about.

Summary

What happened? _____

When? _____

Where? _____

Who was there? _____

Details

Beginning

Middle

End

🌀 **3.17.A.1** Plan a first draft by selecting a genre appropriate for conveying the intended meaning to an audience. **3.17.A.2** Plan a first draft by generating ideas through a range of strategies.

Words That Tell About *You*

Directions How did you feel about your experience at the beginning, middle, and end? Choose one or two words from the word bank to describe each part of your experience. Then add details that *show* readers each feeling.

worried	excited	proud	sad
disappointed	embarrassed	satisfied	curious
puzzled	anxious	delighted	upset

Beginning _____

_____

_____

_____

Middle _____

_____

_____

_____

End _____

_____

_____

_____

© Pearson Education, Inc., 3

★ Develop drafts by choosing words that show rather than tell readers about feelings.

Name _____

Combining Sentences

When you write, you can combine short, choppy simple sentences to make compound sentences. The two sentences you combine must make sense together. You can combine the sentences using the words *and, but,* or *or.*

Directions Use the word in ( ) to combine the two sentences. Remember to capitalize the first word of the new sentence and to replace the first period with a comma.

1. (but) Many huge weeds grew in the garden. I pulled each weed out.

_____

_____

2. (and) The job was hard. It took me all afternoon.

_____

_____

3. (or) Pull out the weed's root. The weed will grow back.

_____

_____

4. (and) I earned five dollars. I felt good about my hard work.

_____

_____

5. (but) I was tired. The garden looked great.

_____

_____

3.17.C.2 Revise drafts for organization. **3.17.C.3** Revise drafts for use of simple sentences **3.17.C.4** Revise drafts for use of compound sentences.

Unit 1 Writing Process   **107**

Editing 1

Directions Edit these sentences. Look for errors in spelling, grammar, and mechanics. Use proofreading marks to show the corrections.

Proofreading Marks	
Delete (Take out)	⤳
Add	∧
Spelling	⬭
Uppercase letter	≡
Lowercase letter	/

1. My mom and me decided to adopt a dog from the granville Animal Shelter.

2. I was so excited I has wanted a dog forever.

3. But Mom said, "Youll have to help pay for the dog's supplys."

4. So i started a dog walking business in their neighborhood.

5. The neighbors listened to me as I explains my plan and my gole.

6. Soon little dogs, big dogs, and medium-sized dogs was pulling me around the

   block evry day after school.

7. I made enough money, to buy too bowls, some dog food, a bed, a leash, and a

   collar, for my new dog.

8. When we brought ranger home for the first time I wanted to jump for joy!

Now you'll edit the draft of your personal narrative. Then you'll use your revised and edited draft to make a final copy of your narrative. Finally, you'll share your written work with your audience.

3.17.D Edit drafts for grammar, mechanics, and spelling, using a teacher-developed rubric. **3.17.E.1** Publish written work for a specific audience.

Name _____

Syllables V/CV, VC/V

Directions Circle each word in the box with the **long vowel** sound in the **first syllable.** Underline each word in the box with the **short vowel** sound in the **first syllable.** Then write each word in the correct column.

| lady | lemon | finish | baby | robot |
| panel | spider | polish | moment | credit |

long vowel

1. _____

2. _____

3. _____

4. _____

5. _____

short vowel

6. _____

7. _____

8. _____

9. _____

10. _____

Directions Circle each word in the box with the **long vowel** sound in the **first syllable.** Underline each word in the box with the **short vowel** sound in the **first syllable.** Then use the words to complete the sentences. Write each word on the line.

| menu | female | motor | seven | zebra |

_____ **11.** A _____ horse is called a mare.

_____ **12.** A _____ has black and white stripes.

_____ **13.** A _____ is a list of food.

_____ **14.** There are _____ little chicks.

_____ **15.** A _____ is an engine.

Home Activity Your child identified words that have a long or short vowel sound in the first syllable. Ask your child to read the long and short vowel words he or she circled or underlined on the page above. Help your child use some of these words to write a story.

3.1.B.1.ii Use common syllabication patterns to decode words including open syllable (CV).

Main Idea and Details

- The **topic** is what a piece of writing is about. The **main idea** is the most important idea about the **topic**. **Supporting details** are small pieces of information about the **main idea**.

Directions Read the following passage. Complete the graphic organizer below.

What if you wanted to cross Antarctica? What would you need to take along?

You would need warm clothes, such as a parka and fur-lined boots. You'd also need bulky socks, thick pants, and the warmest mittens you could find!

Don't forget to bring your own food. You could warm frozen casseroles over a fire and eat nuts and snack bars during the day.

At night you'll need a sleeping bag. Take the warmest one you can find so you are sure to keep warm all night long!

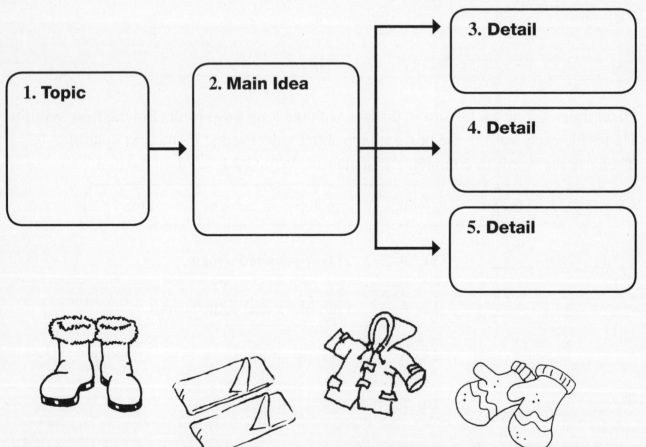

1. Topic

2. Main Idea

3. Detail

4. Detail

5. Detail

School + Home

Home Activity Your child found the topic, main idea, and details in a passage. Read a nonfiction book to your child. To find the topic, ask, "In one or two words, what is the book all about?" To find the main idea, help your child make a sentence that tells the most important part about the topic. Then ask your child to list several details that tell more about the main idea.

🟢 **3.13.A.1** Identify details or facts that support the main idea.

Writing • Cinquains

Key Features of Cinquains

- five-line poems that begin and end with a single word
- usually commas in the second and third line, separating the words

Play

**Puppy
Silly, happy
Running, jumping, playing
Now it's time for
Sleep**

1. Name one key feature that you see that makes this poem a cinquain.

_____

2. What images of puppies do you see in your mind when you read "Play"?

_____

_____

Vocabulary

Check the Words You Know

___hatch   ___pecks
___snuggles   ___preen
___flippers   ___frozen
___cuddles

Directions Choose the vocabulary word from the box and write it next to its meaning.

_____ **1.** taps at

_____ **2.** turned into solid ice

_____ **3.** limbs used for swimming

_____ **4.** to make yourself clean and neat

_____ **5.** curls up comfortably

Directions Write the word on the line that fits the meaning of the sentence.

6. Mother _____ the little baby penguin.

7. The chick is about to _____ out of its egg.

8. Penguins use their _____ to help them swim.

9. The penguins _____ their young until their feathers are clean.

10. It was so cold that we could ice skate on the _____ lake.

Write a News Report

On a separate sheet of paper, tell what happens when a penguin chick hatches.
Describe the setting and the sequence of events using as many vocabulary words
as possible.

Home Activity Your child identified and used vocabulary words from *Penguin Chick*. Read a story or a
nonfiction article about penguins with your child. Discuss the story using this week's vocabulary words.

⊕ **3.4.B.1** Use context to determine the relevant meaning of
unfamiliar words.

Common and Proper Nouns

A **common noun** names any person, place, or thing. A **proper noun** names a particular person, place, or thing. Proper nouns begin with capital letters. The names of days, months, places, and holidays are proper nouns. Historical periods and special events are also proper nouns.

Common Nouns	You can see penguins at some zoos.
Proper Nouns	On Labor Day, a penguin from Africa was displayed at the New York State Fair.

Capitalize each important word in a proper noun: Fourth of July, Civil War.

Directions Write *C* if the underlined noun is a common noun. Write *P* if the underlined noun is a proper noun.

1. There are not many emperor penguins in our country. _____

2. A sea park in San Diego has an emperor penguin. _____

3. Jon went to the zoo on Independence Day. _____

4. He saw penguins and other unusual animals. _____

5. Whales and penguins are popular sea park attractions. _____

Directions Underline the common nouns and circle the proper nouns in the sentences.

6. Alaska became a state on January 3, 1959.

7. Penguins do not come from the United States.

8. Seals and polar bears like the cold weather.

9. The Millers will visit Juneau at Thanksgiving.

10. The Iditarod Trail Sled Dog Race is held in March.

Home Activity Your child learned about common and proper nouns. Have your child write the names of friends and family members and explain why the names are proper nouns.

⊛ **3.22.A.1.ii.3** Use and understand nouns (common) in the context of reading, writing, and speaking. **Also 3.22.A.1.ii.4, 3.23.C.1.ii.2.**

Conventions Common and Proper Nouns   **113**

Syllables V/CV, VC/V

Missing Words Write the missing list word.

1. It is easy to _____ this camera.

2. The _____ of the plane has white hair.

3. My flute teacher has a new _____ .

4. The mother cat had two male kittens and one
   _____ kitten.

5. This type of _____ has two humps
   on its back.

6. You will be able to swim _____
   better after a little rest.

7. The song had a _____ beat.

8. I pulled the children in a _____ .

Syllables Find the list word that fits each word. Write the first
syllable, the second syllable, and the complete word.

	First Syllable	Second Syllable	Base Word
9. song	_____	_____	_____
10. flower	_____	_____	_____
11. fruit	_____	_____	_____
12. end	_____	_____	_____
13. vegetables	_____	_____	_____
14. quiet	_____	_____	_____
15. machine	_____	_____	_____

Home Activity Your child divided long vowel and short vowel words into syllables and wrote
them. Say a list word. Spell the first syllable, and have your child spell the second.

3.24.A.1 Use knowledge of letter sounds to spell. **3.24.A.4** Use
knowledge of syllabication to spell. **3.24.A.2** Use knowledge of word
parts to spell. **3.24.D.1** Spell words with common syllable constructions.

Writing • Diamante Poems

Key Features of Diamante Poems

- seven lines
- first and last lines have one noun, usually with opposite meanings
- second and sixth lines have adjectives
- third and fifth lines have verbs (*-ed* or *-ing*)
- fourth line has four nouns

Plants and Animals

Plants
Leafy, healthy
Watering, feeding, growing
Gardens, yards, forests, jungles
Running, hunting, surviving
Brave, wild
Animals

1. Name one key feature that you see that makes this poem a diamante.

_____

_____

2. What images of animals do you see in your mind when you read "Plants and Animals"?

_____

_____

Vocabulary • Synonyms

- Sometimes you come across a word you don't know. The author may give you a clue about its meaning. The clue may be a **synonym**, a word that means the same thing.
- Look for **synonyms** to figure out the meaning of unfamiliar words.

Directions Read the sentences. One word is underlined. Circle the synonym of the underlined word. Write the meaning of the underlined word on the line.

1. The chick <u>pecks</u> at the inside of the egg. After the chick taps a hole in the egg, the chick can leave the egg.

   _____

2. She made an <u>error</u> in her spelling, so she fixed the mistake.

   _____

3. Penguins use their <u>flippers</u> or their fins to swim quickly.

   _____

4. Penguins <u>preen</u> their chicks by cleaning and brushing them with their beaks.

   _____

5. The penguin chick must <u>stay</u> on its mother's feet to remain warm.

   _____

6. Penguins hunt <u>creatures</u> of the sea, such as the tiny animals called krill.

   _____

7. The newborn chick was very <u>fluffy</u>, with soft and fuzzy feathers all over it.

   _____

8. Like human children who love hugs, penguin chicks love to <u>cuddle</u>.

   _____

© Pearson Education, Inc., 3

Home Activity Your child used context clues such as synonyms to figure out the meaning of new words. Read a story together and encourage your child to find synonyms in the text that help to figure out the meaning of unfamiliar words.

🌀 **3.4.C.2** Identify synonyms.

Dictionary/Glossary

A **dictionary** is a book of words and their meanings. A **glossary** is a section of a book with a list of difficult words and their meanings from the book. A glossary is usually found at the end of a book. In both a dictionary and a glossary, words are listed in alphabetical order. **Guide words** are printed in large dark type at the top of each dictionary or glossary page. They show the first and last entry words on the page.

Directions Use the dictionary page to answer the questions.

romp • roost

rook, *n.*
  1 a large black European bird related to a
    crow, that lives in large flocks
  2 a cheat
  3 *v.* to cheat or trick someone

rookery, *n.* a breeding place for certain
  animals or birds, such as seals or penguins
rookie, *n.* a beginner, as on a police force or in
  a sport

1. Which word can be used to describe a baseball player during his or her first year on the team?

_____

2. Which entry word or words can be used as a verb?

_____

3. Find the entry word *rook.* Which meaning of *rook* is used in this sentence?
The rook flew into the tree.

_____

_____

4. What are the guide words on this page?

_____

5. Which of these words could also be found on this dictionary page: *round, roll, roof, rock?*

_____

_____

Home Activity Your child read entries in a dictionary and used them to answer questions. Have your child practice looking up words in a dictionary or a glossary with you.

 3.4.E.2 Use a dictionary or glossary to determine meanings of unknown words.

Syllables V/CV, VC/V

Spelling Words				
finish	pilot	even	wagon	music
silent	rapid	female	lemon	pupil
focus	robot	tulip	camel	salad

Proofread an Announcement Circle five misspelled words in this announcement about a special concert. Write the words correctly. Then write the word with a capitalization error.

> Don't miss Friday's concert! The musik will focus on early america. You will evin hear a jug band. The femail group will sing favorit songs about wagen trains, the Gold Rush, and California.

Frequently Misspelled Words

favorite
before
pretty

1. _____ 2. _____ 3. _____

4. _____ 5. _____ 6. _____

Proofread Words Fill in the circle to show the correctly spelled word. Write the word.

7. ○ saled   ○ salad   ○ salade   7. _____

8. ○ kamel   ○ camel   ○ camal   8. _____

9. ○ silent   ○ silant   ○ sylent   9. _____

10. ○ leman   ○ lemen   ○ lemon   10. _____

11. ○ finash   ○ finish   ○ fenish   11. _____

12. ○ rowbot   ○ robat   ○ robot   12. _____

Home Activity Your child identified misspelled multi-syllable words with long and short vowels. Ask your child to explain how to divide a multi-syllable word (immediately after a long vowel; after the consonant that follows a short vowel).

3.24.A.1 Use knowledge of letter sounds to spell. **3.24.A.4** Use knowledge of syllabication to spell. **3.24.A.2** Use knowledge of word parts to spell. **Also 3.24.C.1, 3.24.D.1.**

Name_____

Compare and Contrast

- **Compare** by telling how two or more things are alike or different.
- **Contrast** by telling only how two or more things are different.

Directions Read the following story.

Ron and Blake wanted a puppy, but Dad always said, "A dog is hard work." One day Dad surprised them. He said, "If you two can find a solution to the puppy care problem, we'll visit a breeder tomorrow."

Ron and Blake thought fast.

"Dogs need exercise," said Ron. "I'll take our puppy for walks."

"Dogs need love," said Blake. "I'll pet our puppy."

"Dogs make a mess," said Ron, "but I won't mind cleaning up after our puppy."

"Good!" smiled Blake. "And I'll feed it and keep its water dish filled."

"You boys have a good plan," Dad agreed. "Tomorrow we'll get our new pup."

Directions Fill in the chart to compare and contrast Ron and Blake.

Compare and Contrast	
Ron	**Blake**

© Pearson Education, Inc., 3

Home Activity Your child compared and contrasted two story characters. Read a story together. Discuss the characters with your child by comparing and contrasting them.

★ Compare and contrast ideas and information.

Writing • Fairy Tale

Key Features of a Fairy Tale

- imaginary story that may include heroic acts
- often begins "Once upon a time … "
- often ends " … and they lived happily ever after"
- characters are usually all good or all bad

The Skunk and the Mice

Once upon a time, in a quiet neighborhood, there lived a skunk. He was lonely. Each day, Skunk rested in a hole dug under the porch steps. Each evening, Skunk crept out to search for food.

There were others living under the porch steps. A group of mice lived there. All day long, they chattered and scurried about. At night they went out all together to find food. Skunk thought they looked very happy. One night, he asked if he could join them.

"No way," said the leader of the mice. "We are mice. You would make a funny looking mouse. You cannot come with us."

It so happened that cool weather was coming, and food was getting harder to find. The mice still went out at night, but they didn't find much to eat. Skunk became hungry, too. Once again he asked the mice if he could join them.

"No," said the leader of the mice. "We've told you before, and we'll tell you again. No! No! No!"

That night came a terrible storm. Snow and freezing rain came down in buckets. The mice huddled together, terrified of the sounds of the whipping wind. "How will we get food now!" they cried.

Skunk, without waiting a moment, went out in the storm to search for food for the mice. The cold wind almost blew him over, but he stayed close to the ground as best he could. Skunk finally found some morsels of food, and he rushed back to the porch.

When Skunk returned, the mice were so grateful for the food that they made him a special member of their family.

And they all lived happily ever after.

1. What problems does the Skunk have?

_____

_____

2. What happens that solves these problems?

_____

Vocabulary

Check the Words You Know

___adorable	___mature
___compassionate	___mention
___exactly	___trophies
___iguana	

Directions Fill in the blank with the word from the box that fits the meaning of the sentence.

1. Look at this _____ little kitten.

2. It is _____ the kind of pet I want.

3. My brother would rather have a spiky _____.

4. But a _____ cat is much smaller than a grown-up lizard.

5. I'll be sure to _____ that to Mom when I ask for the kitten.

Directions Draw a line from the word to its meaning.

6. compassionate   to talk briefly about someone or something

7. trophies   precisely

8. mature   with sympathy; wanting to help

9. exactly   fully grown; adult

10. mention   awards

Write a Speech

Imagine that you work in an animal shelter. Choose an animal that might be in the shelter and write a speech you could use to convince someone to adopt the animal. Use as many vocabulary words from this week as you can.

Home Activity Your child identified and used vocabulary words from *I Wanna Iguana*. Talk about pets you and your child have known. Use the vocabulary words on this page.

3.4.B.1 Use context to determine the relevant meaning of unfamiliar words.

© Pearson Education, Inc., 3

Name _____

Singular and Plural Nouns

A **singular noun** names only one person, place, or thing. A **plural noun** names more than one person, place, or thing.

Singular Nouns   The <u>boy</u> wanted a pet.

Plural Nouns   <u>Iguanas</u> and other <u>lizards</u> live in <u>deserts</u>.

Most nouns add -s to form the plural. Add -es to a noun that ends in *ch, sh, s, ss,* or *x: lunches, dishes, buses, dresses, boxes.* When a noun ends in a consonant and *y,* change the *y* to *i* and add -es: *bodies.*

Directions Write *S* if the underlined noun is a singular noun. Write *P* if the underlined noun is a plural noun.

1. Many <u>animals</u> live in the desert. _____

2. The desert is a very dry <u>place</u>. _____

3. People often keep <u>pets</u>. _____

4. Dogs and <u>cats</u> are popular. _____

5. A pet <u>store</u> sells food and supplies. _____

Directions Write the plural nouns in each sentence.

6. Many lizards eat bugs and vegetables.

_____

7. Snakes and buzzards live in the desert.

_____

8. The boy and his mother write notes.

_____

9. He thinks iguanas are cuter than hamsters.

_____

Home Activity Your child learned about singular and plural nouns. Say "I see a [something in your house]" and have your child say the plural form of the word.

⭐ **3.22.A.1.ii.1** Use and understand nouns (singular) in the context of reading, writing, and speaking. **3.22.A.1.ii.2** Use and understand nouns (plural) in the context of reading, writing, and speaking.

Compound Words

Directions Identify the two words that make up each compound word. Write the words on the lines.

1. _____ + _____ = sunglasses

2. _____ + _____ = railroad

3. _____ + _____ = haircut

4. _____ + _____ = firehouse

5. _____ + _____ = popcorn

6. _____ + _____ = myself

7. _____ + _____ = greenhouse

8. _____ + _____ = backyard

9. _____ + _____ = rainwater

10. _____ + _____ = sunflower

Directions Choose the compound word to complete each sentence. Write the word on the line. Draw a line between the two words that make up each compound word.

_____ **11.** My (grandfather/uncle) lives on a farm.

_____ **12.** I help him take care of his animals (whenever/when) I visit.

_____ **13.** Last winter I was with him during a terrible (snowstorm/blizzard).

_____ **14.** We had to work (outside/quickly) in the cold and snow.

_____ **15.** It's (sometimes/often) difficult to be a farmer.

Home Activity Your child wrote compound words—words formed by joining two shorter words—such as *homework*. With your child, read advertisements to find compound words (such as *everyday, something,* and *everyone*). Have your child identify the two words that make up each compound word.

★ Recognize compound words and their word parts.

Draw Conclusions

- A **conclusion** is a decision or opinion that makes sense based on facts and details.
- When you use new information you read or information you already know to make decisions, you are **drawing conclusions.**

Directions Read the following article.

Many people feel nervous when they're surrounded by clutter. They waste lots of time searching for what they need. If you need to get organized, follow these steps:

1. Discard or give away items you no longer need.

2. Sort the objects that are left into categories. For example, group your shoes,

pants, and shoes and put your homework supplies in a special place.

3. Take a few minutes each day to make sure your belongings are in their certain places.

You'll spend less time searching and more time doing what you want to do.

Directions Complete the graphic organizer by using the information from the article to write a conclusion.

Fact or detail from article
People surrounded by clutter often waste their time searching for the things they need.

Fact or detail from article
People who organize their belongings usually have more time to spend on activities they enjoy.

Conclusion:

Home Activity Your child drew a conclusion from information presented in a text. With your child, read a how-to article in a magazine or on the Internet. Have your child draw conclusions about the information and identify the facts and/or details that helped him or her reach the conclusions.

3.13.B.1 Draw conclusions from facts presented in text.

Writing • Persuasive Advertisement

Key Features of a Persuasive Advertisement

- states why a person would want to go somewhere or buy something
- gives reasons and details as evidence to support statements
- uses descriptive words and phrases
- connects with a reader's feelings

"The Prudy Museum of Indescribable Wonderment"

Where can you go to find ribbon collections, plastic lizards, and the most dog hair you've ever seen? You can go to The Prudy Museum of Indescribable Wonderment. It is the most interesting museum in the world. You will never see a collection like the one at the Prudy Museum.

Many museums have art or dinosaur ones. This museum is special. You can e amazing collections of gym socks, scarves, souvenir postcards, leaves, and old candy boxes. They have been carefully collected and organized by one young girl. This museum is the biggest tourist attraction in town and even includes a gift shop.

A visit to The Prudy Museum of Indescribable Wonderment will put you in a good mood. After your visit, you will see beauty in things you see around your house every day.

1. Read the advertisement. What is one statement made about the museum? What reasons and details support this statement?

_____

_____

_____

_____

2. How does the advertisement try to connect with readers' feelings?

_____

_____

Vocabulary

Directions Choose the vocabulary word from the box and write it next to its meaning.

> ### Check the Words You Know
> ___enormous ___shoelaces
> ___strain ___scattered
> ___collection ___butterflies

_____ **1.** spread over a large area

_____ **2.** a group of similar things a person gets and saves

_____ **3.** insects with brightly colored wings

_____ **4.** to stretch too much

_____ **5.** very big; huge

Directions Each sentence has a word missing. Circle the word at the end of each sentence that fits the meaning.

6. She brought new blue _____ for her old shoes.   shoelaces   butterflies

7. My sister _____ her leg in the race.   enormous   strained

8. We _____ the grass seed all over the front yard.   scattered   strained

9. The _____ dictionary in the library is too heavy to lift.
collection   enormous

10. My brother has a large _____ of baseball cards.   strain   collection

Write an Advertisement

On a separate sheet of paper, write an advertisement describing an item for sale. Tell why a person would want it in a collection. Use as many vocabulary words as possible.

 Home Activity Your child identified and used vocabulary words from *Prudy's Problem and How She Solved It*. Ask your child to explain Prudy's problem to you and how it was solved. Encourage your child to use as many vocabulary words as possible.

🌟 **3.4.B.1** Use context to determine the relevant meaning of unfamiliar words.

Name _____

Irregular Plural Nouns

A plural noun names more than one person, place, or thing. Most nouns add *-s* to form the plural. An **irregular plural noun** has a special form for the plural.

Singular Nouns   A goose and a deer ate a leaf.
Irregular Plural Nouns   Some geese and some deer ate some leaves.

Some nouns and their irregular plural forms are *child/children, deer/deer, foot/feet, goose/geese, leaf/leaves, life/lives, man/men, mouse/mice, ox/oxen, sheep/sheep, tooth/teeth,* and *woman/women.*

Directions Write *S* if the underlined noun is singular. Write *P* if the underlined noun is plural.

1. The children had a messy room. _____

2. Aunt Rose would not put a foot into the room. _____

3. There were leaves on the floor. _____

4. I've never seen such a sight in my life! _____

5. Mice could make a nest in there. _____

Directions Write the plural nouns in each sentence.

6. The men on the farm had a problem.

_____

7. Deer were eating vegetables from their fields.

_____

8. The farmers found holes in the lettuce leaves.

_____

9. The women tried to think of clever solutions.

_____

Home Activity Your child learned about irregular plural nouns. Say the words goose, mouse, and child and have your child say the plural form of each word.

3.22.A.1.ii.2 Use and understand nouns (plural) in the context of reading, writing, and speaking. **3.24.B.1.v** Spell words with complex consonants.

Conventions Irregular Plural Nouns   **135**

Compound Words

Missing Words Write the missing list word.

1. I squeezed toothpaste onto

   my _____ .

2. Do you like _____ muffins?

3. School was cancelled because of the

   _____ .

4. Our teacher asked us to turn in _____ .

5. She felt her ear and discovered she had lost an

   _____ .

6. A good pair of _____ will protect

   your eyes.

7. The _____ wore an old straw hat.

Spelling Words

sunglasses
football
homework
haircut
popcorn
railroad
snowstorm
earring

scarecrow
blueberry
butterflies
lawnmower
campground
sandbox
toothbrush

Combinations Underline the two words in the sentence that should be combined into a compound word. Write the compound word.

8. Carrie's mom gave her a hair cut.   8. _____

9. I ate pop corn at the theater.   9. _____

10. The lawn mower needs to be fixed.   10. _____

11. Look at the big blue butter flies!   11. _____

12. We should take our pails out of the sand box.   12. _____

13. Do you want to play foot ball after school?   13. _____

14. A train blocked the rail road crossing.   14. _____

15. We set up our tent at a great camp ground.   15. _____

© Pearson Education, Inc., 3

Home Activity Your child wrote compound words. Remind your child that no letters are dropped from the two words that are combined to make a compound word.

3.24.A.2 Use knowledge of word parts to spell. **3.24.C.2** Spell compound words from a commonly used list.

Outline Form A

Title _____

A. _____

    1. _____

    2 _____

    3. _____

B. _____

    1. _____

    2. _____

    3. _____

C. _____

    1. _____

    2. _____

    3. _____

Vocabulary • Compound Words

- Sometimes you may come across words you do not know. You can look to see if the word is a **compound word,** a word made up of two small words. Each word can stand on its own and still have meaning.

Directions Read the sentences and underline each compound word. Then write the words that make the compound word on the lines.

1. My grandmother lives in Florida. _____ + _____

2. Florida's nickname is the Sunshine State. _____ + _____

   _____ + _____

3. Gram always wears sunglasses when she goes out. _____ + _____

4. She is teaching me to waterski. _____ + _____

5. She says I should be careful not to get a sunburn. _____ + _____

6. Gram makes me put on sunscreen, too. _____ + _____

7. After supper we watch videotapes. _____ + _____

8. Sometimes we make popcorn. _____ + _____

Directions Read the clues. Think of a compound word that matches the clue and write it on the line.

9. You use it to cut the grass. _____

10. These keep your sneakers on your feet. _____

11. Some caterpillars turn into these. _____

12. This is jewelry you wear in your ear. _____

13. You use this to keep your teeth clean. _____

14. You sit in this to take a bath. _____

15. This berry is small and blue, and good to eat. _____

© Pearson Education, Inc., 3

Home Activity Your child identified and used compound words. Give your child words that are part of compounds, such as *sun, snow,* and *butter.* Have your child list as many compound words as possible that can be made from those words.

★ Recognize compound words and their word parts.

Name _____

Magazine

Directions Read the magazine article. Use it to answer the questions below.

Collector's Monthly	
How to Manage Your Collectibles *by Sara Vega* We all love our collectibles, but often there are too many items to manage. Here are some suggestions: • Set a goal or purpose for your collection. Get rid of items that don't meet this goal or purpose. • Buy or make storage containers. You want to be able to view each item. • Make a list of each item in your collection. Add and remove items from the list as needed. You may want to keep your list on a computer.	**FOR SALE** **Action Figures** More than 100 favorites. Call Mike 430-1874. **Rare Coins** Many hard-to-find U.S. coins. 555-7372 Ask for Marcia.

1. What is the title of the magazine?

_____

2. What is the title of the article?

_____

3. What is the article about?

_____

_____

4. Who might buy this magazine?

_____

_____

5. If you were looking for a rare coin or action figure, how might you use this magazine?

_____

_____

Home Activity Your child read a magazine page and answered questions about it. Look through a children's magazine. Ask your child to point out the different parts. Have him or her suggest other articles or materials that might be found in a magazine like this.

3.13.D.1 Use text features to locate information.

Compound Words

Proofread a Description Ann wrote about a family reunion. Underline two words that should have been a compound word. Circle three other spelling mistakes. Write the words correctly. Add the missing comma.

> All my relatives met at a camp ground. The grownups talked while the kids played football and chased butterflys. Then evryone ate chicken popcorn, bluebery pie, and other good food. Nobody wanted to say goodnight.

Spelling Words

sunglasses
football
homework
haircut
popcorn
railroad
snowstorm
earring

scarecrow
blueberry
butterflies
lawnmower
campground
sandbox
toothbrush

1. _____ 2. _____

3. _____ 4. _____

Proofread Words Fill in the circle to show the correctly spelled word.

Frequently Misspelled Words

outside
everyone
something
sometimes

5. Our family always has _____ on Sunday night.
   ○ popcorn   ○ pop korn   ○ pop corn

6. Manuel's grandma has a _____ in her garden.
   ○ scarecrow   ○ scarcrow   ○ scare crow

7. I do my _____ right after school.
   ○ homwork   ○ home work   ○ homework

8. Let's build a castle in the _____ .
   ○ sandbox   ○ sand box   ○ sandbocks

Home Activity Your child identified misspelled compound words. Have your child draw a line to divide each list word into its two parts.

3.24.A.2 Use knowledge of word parts to spell. **3.24.C.1** Spell high-frequency words from a commonly used list. **3.24.C.2** Spell compound words from a commonly used list.

© Pearson Education, Inc., 3

Irregular Plural Nouns

Directions Read the selection. Then read each question that follows the selection. Decide which is the best answer to each question. Mark the space for the answer you have chosen.

Different Collections

(1) All the <u>child</u> collect something. (2) Carlo has 20 <u>foot</u> of string. (3) Jo has 8 stuffed <u>mouse</u>. (4) Nick has all his baby <u>tooth</u>. (5) Jake has 100 toy army <u>man</u>. (6) Maria has 20 plastic <u>sheep</u>. (7) Nan has 15 pictures of fall <u>leaf</u>.

1 What is the plural form of the underlined noun in sentence 1?

- ⬭ childs
- ⬭ children
- ⬭ childe
- ⬭ childen

2 What is the plural form of the underlined noun in sentence 2?

- ⬭ foots
- ⬭ foves
- ⬭ fice
- ⬭ feet

3 What is the plural form of the underlined noun in sentence 3?

- ⬭ mice
- ⬭ mouses
- ⬭ meese
- ⬭ mousen

4 What is the plural form of the underlined noun in sentence 5?

- ⬭ manen
- ⬭ mans
- ⬭ men
- ⬭ manes

5 What is the plural form of the underlined noun in sentence 6?

- ⬭ sheep
- ⬭ sheeps
- ⬭ sheepes
- ⬭ shep

Home Activity Your child prepared for taking tests on irregular plural nouns. Have a discussion with your child about the families in your neighborhood. Ask your child to use the singular and plural forms of *man, woman,* and *child.*

🌐 **3.22.A.1.ii.2** Use and understand nouns (plural) in the context of reading, writing, and speaking. **3.24.B.1.v** Spell words with complex consonants.

Consonant Blends

Directions Read the story. Underline the words with the three-letter blends **squ, spl, thr,** and **str.** Then write the underlined words on the lines.

Emily threw on her coat and ran down the street. As she got to the town square, she saw three friends throwing water balloons at one another. Each time a balloon struck the ground, it split open. Water splashed everywhere. Then someone tossed a balloon with such strength that it flew through an open car window. Emily knew they had to find the owner and tell what they had done.

1. _____
2. _____
3. _____
4. _____
5. _____
6. _____
7. _____
8. _____
9. _____
10. _____

Directions Read each word and listen for the three-letter blend. Then write two more words that start with the same blend. Underline the three-letter blend in each word you write.

11. straw _____ _____

12. splurge _____ _____

13. squeak _____ _____

14. thread _____ _____

15. straight _____ _____

Home Activity Your child wrote words that begin with the three-letter blends *spl* (as in *splash*), *squ* (as in *square*), *str* (as in *strike*), and *thr* (as in *throw*). Challenge your child to name additional words that begin with these three-letter blends. For help in identifying words with these starting letters, you can use a dictionary.

★ Decode words by applying common spelling patterns.

Name _____

Author's Purpose

- An **author's purpose** is the author's reason for writing. An author may write to inform or teach, to entertain, to persuade, or to express thoughts and feelings.

Directions Read the following passage.

Planting Bushes

STOP and answer Question 1 below.

The Lopez family had just built a nice house in the desert. The only problem was that the hot sun shone through the huge windows on the south side.

Early one morning, Dad and Grandpa planted bushes along the south side of the house.

"I wonder why they did that," thought Lupe.

STOP and answer Question 2 below.

Every day, Dad or Grandpa watered the bushes. They began to grow. Soon the bushes got so tall they blocked the sun from coming in the windows.

"Now I know why they did that!" thought Lupe.

Directions Complete the graphic organizer to determine the author's purpose.

1. **Before You Read** Read the title. For which reason might the author write a passage with this title?

   _____

   ⬇

2. **As You Read** Think about the author's purpose. What new information have you learned?

   _____

   ⬇

3. **After You Read** Now what do you think the author's purpose was?

   _____

Home Activity Your child determined the author's purpose for writing a story. Purposes include to inform, to persuade, to entertain, or to express feelings or ideas. Talk about the author's purpose for writing tales your child is familiar with. Ask your child to give reasons for his or her answers.

★ Identify an author's purpose for writing.

Writing • Friendly Letter

Key Features of a Friendly Letter

- includes a date, salutation, and closing
- written in a friendly tone
- usually written to someone you know

September 15, 2008

Dear Bear,

I worked hard to grow vegetables this year. Now I have a lot of carrots and corn. I have enough to share with you. Would you like to come over for dinner?

We will have corn and carrots. We will have corn bread, too. Then we will have carrot cake for dessert. The cake's frosting will be sweet and creamy.

Please write back. Tell me if you want to come Tuesday or Thursday.

Your friend,
Hare

1. Read the letter. What is the purpose of Hare's letter to Bear?

_____

2. In the letter, what does Hare ask Bear to do?

_____

_____

Vocabulary

Directions Each sentence has an underlined word. Circle the word at the end of the sentence with the same meaning as the underlined word.

Check the Words You Know	
___lazy	___bottom
___crops	___clever
___cheated	___partners
___wealth	

1. My <u>lazy</u> brother hates to do his chores.   idle   young

2. Jill put the cookies on the <u>bottom</u> shelf.   lowest   long

3. Juan and I are <u>partners</u> in a lawn-mowing business.   co-workers   a class

4. Jim does well in school because he is very <u>clever</u>.   lazy   smart

5. A person with lots of money has lots of <u>wealth</u>.   riches   need

Directions Write a word from the box to complete each sentence below.

6. The farmer plants many _____ , including corn and wheat.

7. A farmer cannot be _____ because farming takes lots of work.

8. Ann is an honest student, so I don't think she _____ on the test.

9. The rich man had so much _____ , he owned five houses.

10. We will work together as _____ to build a business.

Write a Story

On a separate sheet of paper, write about two farmers working together on something special. Describe them and what happens. Use as many vocabulary words as possible.

Home Activity Your child identified and used vocabulary words from *Tops and Bottoms*. Visit the supermarket produce aisle together and have your child identify the vegetables whose tops or bottoms we eat. Encourage using as many vocabulary words as possible.

3.4.B.1 Use context to determine the relevant meaning of unfamiliar words.

© Pearson Education, Inc., 3

Singular Possessive Nouns

To show that one person, animal, or thing owns something, use a **singular possessive noun.** Add an apostrophe (') and the letter *s* to a singular noun to make it possessive.

Singular Noun	The <u>hare</u> planted corn.
Singular Possessive Noun	The bear wanted the <u>hare's</u> corn.

Directions Write the possessive noun in each sentence.

1. Aesop's fables tell stories about people and animals. _____

2. A fox takes a crow's cheese. _____

3. A mouse frees a lion's paw. _____

4. A wolf wears a sheep's fur. _____

5. People enjoy each story's lesson. _____

Directions Write the possessive form of the underlined noun in each sentence.

6. <u>Jeff</u> favorite fable is about the wind and the sun. _____

7. The wind challenges the <u>sun</u> power. _____

8. Which one can remove a <u>man</u> coat? _____

9. The man feels the <u>wind</u> chill, and he buttons his coat. _____

10. He pulls up his <u>coat</u> collar. _____

11. The <u>sun</u> heat makes the man warm, and he takes off his coat. _____

12. What do you think is the <u>fable</u> lesson? _____

© Pearson Education, Inc., 3

Home Activity Your child learned about singular possessive nouns. Have your child name objects in your home and use a possessive phrase to tell who they belong to, for example, *Dad's book.*

3.22.A.1.ii.1 *Use and understand nouns (singular) in the context of reading, writing, and speaking.* **3.23.C.1.i.3** *Recognize punctuation marks including apostrophes in possessives.* **Also 3.23.C.1.i.4.**

Words with *spl, thr, squ, str, scr*

Spelling Words				
splash	throw	three	square	scream
strike	street	split	splurge	thrill
strength	squeak	throne	scratch	squeeze

Rhyming Pairs Finish the sentence with a list word that rhymes with the underlined word.

1. He has a <u>batch</u> of itches to _____ .

2. Skiing down that <u>hill</u> was a _____ !

3. I don't think he has the _____ to swim the <u>length</u> of the pool.

4. See if you can _____ the ball to the <u>row</u> of trees.

5. The town _____ was <u>bare</u>.

6. The _____ has been occupied by six men and a <u>lone</u> woman.

7. There are _____ squirrels playing in the <u>tree</u>.

8. Let's <u>dash</u> into the water and make a big _____ .

Missing Blends Add a three-letter blend to finish the list word. Write the word.

9. The scared girl let out a ___ ___ ___ eam.   9. _____

10. The pitcher threw a ___ ___ ___ ike.   10. _____

11. Don't play in the ___ ___ ___ eet.   11. _____

12. I'd love to ___ ___ ___ urge on an expensive gift.   12. _____

13. Let's ___ ___ ___ it the last piece of pizza.   13. _____

14. Mom gave my hand a big ___ ___ ___ eeze.   14. _____

15. We heard the hinges ___ ___ ___ eak.   15. _____

Home Activity Your child wrote words with three-letter blends (*spl, thr, squ, str,* and *scr*). Have your child circle and pronounce the three-letter blends in the list words.

3.24.A.1 Use knowledge of letter sounds to spell. **3.24.A.2** Use knowledge of word parts to spell. **3.24.A.3** Use knowledge of word segmentation to spell. **3.24.B.1.v** Spell words with complex consonants.

Spelling Words with *spl, thr, squ, str, scr*   **147**

Web A

Vocabulary • Antonyms

- Sometimes you come across a word you don't know. The author may use a word with the opposite meaning—an **antonym**—as a clue to the word's meaning.
- Use **antonyms** as context clues to figure out the meaning of unfamiliar words.

Directions Read each sentence. One word is underlined. Circle the antonym of the underlined word. Write the meaning of the underlined word on the line.

1. Sue is always so busy that no one can say she is <u>lazy</u>.

_____

2. Put the glass on the top shelf because your sister may break it if it's on the <u>bottom</u>.

_____

3. Danny is so <u>clever</u>, he would never do a silly thing like that.

_____

4. The cat was <u>asleep</u>, but the dog was awake.

_____

5. Months after planting the seeds, the farmer can <u>harvest</u> the corn.

_____

6. Do not scatter the papers, but <u>gather</u> them into one pile.

_____

7. You look so nice when you smile that you should never <u>scowl</u>.

_____

8. Whisper the secret in my ear, don't <u>holler</u> it out loud.

_____

Home Activity Your child identified and used new words by understanding antonyms used in context. Read a story together and encourage identifying unfamiliar words. Then help look for antonyms in the text that might help figure out the words' meanings.

3.4.C.1 Identify antonyms.

Encyclopedia

An **encyclopedia** is a set of books, or **volumes,** that has **entries** and articles on many subjects. Volumes and entries are arranged in alphabetical order. **Guide words** show the first and last entries on a page or facing pages. **Electronic encyclopedias** display links to articles on subjects for which you search.

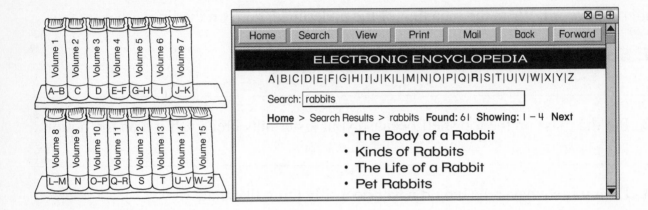

Directions Use the information above to answer the questions.

1. What word or words would you use to find information about the climate of the northeastern United States? Write the volume number you would use.

_____

2. The entry *tortoise* might be found between which guide words: **tidal wave/tiger, tornado/town,** or **toy/trampoline?** Write the volume number in which it would be found.

_____

3. You want to compare an alligator and a crocodile. Which volumes will you use?

_____

4. How many different articles on rabbits are shown in the electronic encyclopedia window? _____

5. Which article will you read to learn about the size of a rabbit?

© Pearson Education, Inc., 3

Home Activity Your child identified words and volume numbers to locate answers to questions about using an encyclopedia. Help your child write four or five questions about a topic of interest. Have your child use an encyclopedia, either print or electronic, to answer the questions.

⭐ **3.13.D.1** Use text features to locate information.

Words with *spl, thr, squ, str, scr*

Proofread a Report Circle four spelling mistakes in this report about the gray fox. Write the words correctly. Write the word that should be used instead of **don't** in the last sentence.

> A gray fox has a white belly. It can run fast and climb trees. It may splash into the water and swim if it is skared and needs to escape. It can also let out a high-pitched screem. When hunting, it listens for the sqeak of a mouse. If it sees movement, it srikes quickly. Sometimes, in bad weather, a gray fox don't leave its den for three or four days.

Spelling Words
splash
throw
three
square
scream
strike
street
split
splurge
thrill
strength
squeak
throne
scratch
squeeze

1. _____ 2. _____

3. _____ 4. _____

5. _____

Frequently Misspelled Words
scared
brother

Proofread Words Fill in the circle to show the correctly spelled word.

6. ○ thril   ○ thrill   ○ thill

7. ○ squeze   ○ sqeeze   ○ squeeze

8. ○ scatch   ○ scratch   ○ scrach

9. ○ throne   ○ trone   ○ throan

10. ○ stength   ○ strentgh   ○ strength

11. ○ streat   ○ steet   ○ street

12. ○ sqare   ○ square   ○ squar

© Pearson Education, Inc., 3

School + Home **Home Activity** Your child identified misspelled words with three-letter blends (*spl, thr, squ, str* and *scr*). Ask your child to use some of the list words to tell a story about a mouse.

3.24.A.1 Use knowledge of letter sounds to spell. **3.24.A.2** Use knowledge of word parts to spell. **3.24.A.3** Use knowledge of word segmentation to spell. **3.24.B.1.v** Spell words with complex consonants. **Also 3.24.C.1.**

Singular Possessive Nouns

Directions Read the selection. Then read each question that follows the selection. Decide which is the best answer to each question. Mark the space for the answer you have chosen.

A Favorite Fable

(1) Jeff favorite fable is about the wind and the sun. (2) In the story, the wind challenges the sun for power. (3) Which one can remove a man coat? (4) The wind blows hard to try to get the coat to fly off. (5) The man feels the wind chill, but it only makes him button his coat tighter. (6) He pulls up his coat collar. (7) The sun heat makes the man warm, and he pulls off his coat.

1 What change, if any, should be made to sentence 1?

- ⬭ Change *Jeff* to **Jeff's**
- ⬭ Change *fable* to **fables**
- ⬭ Change *wind* to **wind's**
- ⬭ Make no change.

2 What change, if any, should be made to sentence 3?

- ⬭ Change *one* to **one's**
- ⬭ Change *man* to **men's**
- ⬭ Change *man* to **man's**
- ⬭ Make no change.

3 What change, if any, should be made to sentence 4?

- ⬭ Change *blows* to **blow's**
- ⬭ Change *wind* to **winds**
- ⬭ Change *wind blows* to **wind's blow**
- ⬭ Make no change.

4 What change, if any, should be made to sentence 5?

- ⬭ Change *feels* to **feel's**
- ⬭ Change *wind* to **wind's**
- ⬭ Change *coat* to **coat's**
- ⬭ Make no change.

5 What change, if any, should be made to sentence 7?

- ⬭ Change *man* to **man's**
- ⬭ Change *pulls* to **pull's**
- ⬭ Change *sun* to **sun's**
- ⬭ Make no change.

Home Activity Your child prepared for taking tests on singular possessive nouns. Have your child think of a friend's name and something that friend owns and make up a sentence using the possessive form of the friend's name.

⊛ **3.22.A.1.ii.1** Use and understand nouns (singular) in the context of reading, writing, and speaking. **3.23.C.1.i.3** Recognize punctuation marks including apostrophes in possessives. **Also 3.23.C.1.i.4.**

Name _____

Consonant Digraphs

Directions Write **sh, th, ph, ch, tch,** or **ng** to complete each word. Write the whole word on the line to the left.

_____ **1.** Maria's family pur____ased a house.

_____ **2.** Her mo____er decided to paint it.

_____ **3.** She went to the store and bought bru____es and buckets.

_____ **4.** When she came home she put on old clo____ing.

_____ **5.** Then she pa____ed the cracks and nail holes.

_____ **6.** Maria didn't know what color her room was goi____ to be.

_____ **7.** She ____oned her friend to talk about it.

_____ **8.** Her friend helped Maria make the ____oice.

_____ **9.** Maria picked a beautiful ____ade of peach.

Directions Say the name of each picture. Write **sh, th, wh, ph, tch,** or **ng** to complete each word.

10. tro____y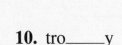

11. wa____

12. a____lete

13. ____ale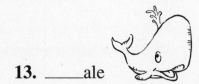

14. swi____

15. spla____

Home Activity Your child wrote words with the consonants *sh* (English), *th* (father), *wh* (wheel), *ph* (trophy), *ch* (chapter), *tch* (watch), and *ng* (wing). Have your child read the words on the page above. Ask your child to change one or more letters in some of the words to form new words. For example, substituting *t* for *p* in *peach* forms *teach*.

3.24.B.1.v Spell words with complex consonants.

Main Idea and Details

The **main idea** answers the question, "What is this story all about?" **Details** are small pieces of information that help tell what the story is about.

Directions Read the following passage.

John went into the woods on a snowy day, and his boots made tracks where he walked.

I can follow my tracks back out, thought John, so he didn't pay attention to where he was going.

But the sun came out and melted the snow, and when John wanted to leave, he couldn't see any tracks.

Then John saw an eagle overhead. "Eagle," said John, "please help me find my way out."

The eagle flew south, then west. John followed until he was out of the woods.

Directions Complete the graphic organizer to tell what the story is all about.

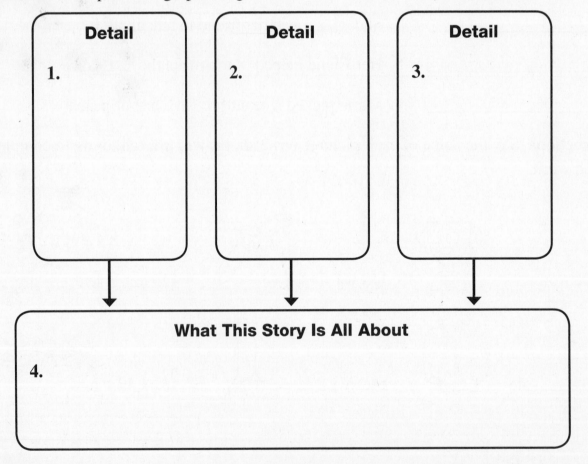

Detail

1.

Detail

2.

Detail

3.

What This Story Is All About

4.

© Pearson Education, Inc., 3

School + Home

Home Activity Your child found the main idea of a story. The main idea is a sentence that sums up what the story is all about. Read a story such as the one above with your child. Ask your child to name details from the story and then tell what the story is all about.

★ Summarize the main idea and supporting details in text.

Writing • Directions

Key Features of Directions

- gives a step-by-step explanation of how to perform a specific task
- provides necessary information and details
- explains a task fully
- often uses commands and sequence words

How to Make Pancakes

Pancakes are delicious, and they're not that hard to make. Let's find out how to make them in a few simple steps. Making pancakes requires using a hot stove, which can be dangerous. Be sure to have an adult help you with any steps that involve using the stove.

First, we should collect the ingredients and supplies we need. To mix the pancake batter, we want a bowl and a mixer. To cook the pancakes, we'll need a frying pan and a spatula. We also want a measuring cup to measure ingredients. The ingredients you need to make the pancakes are simple:

- 3 cups of flour   • ½ cup milk
- 1 cup of sugar   • water
- 1 egg   • butter

Next, we want to prepare the batter. Combine the flour, sugar, egg, and milk in the bowl. Mix them together until they form a smooth batter. Add water as necessary to make sure that the batter is not too thick. Stir through the batter carefully to make sure there are no lumps.

Now it's time to cook our pancakes. Again, be sure that there's an adult present. Put the frying pan on a lit burner and add a pat of butter. Once the butter has melted, pour the batter into the pan in order to form a pancake. If your pan is big enough, you can make more than one pancake at a time.

Once the pancakes begin to form bubbles and become dry on top, use the spatula to flip them over. Let the other side cook for two or three minutes. Then you can slide the pancakes out of the pan and onto your plate. Add some butter and syrup, and enjoy your breakfast!

1. What supplies do you need in order to make pancakes?

_____

_____

2. Put the following steps in making pancakes in the proper order:

_____

> 1. Pour batter into pan.
> 2. Eat pancakes.
> 3. Mix batter.
> 4. Gather supplies.

Vocabulary

Check the Words You Know

___bill   ___platform
___goo   ___tons
___hunters   ___twigs
___material

Directions Match the word with its meaning. Draw a line from the word to its definition.

1. bill   units of weight equal to 2,000 pounds

2. twigs   the hard part of a bird's mouth; beak

3. material   a raised level surface for people to stand or sit on

4. platform   very small branches of a tree or bush

5. tons   what a thing is made of

Directions Write the word from the box that best completes each sentence.

6. The mayor stood on the _____ to make his speech.

7. This bridge is strong enough to hold ten _____.

8. The rabbit hid from foxes and other _____.

9. I put my hand into the sticky _____.

10. The bird had a cherry in its _____.

Write a Journal Entry

Imagine you are watching a bird building its nest. On a separate piece of paper, write a journal entry telling about what the bird did. Use as many vocabulary words as you can in your writing.

Home Activity Your child identified and used vocabulary words from the selection *Amazing Bird Nests.* Find a library book on the same subject and read it together. Talk about the book using the week's vocabulary words.

🦃 **3.4.B.1** Use context to determine the relevant meaning of unfamiliar words.

Name _____

Plural Possessive Nouns

To show that two or more people share or own something, use a **plural possessive noun.**

Plural Noun	The <u>birds</u> built nests.
Singular Possessive Noun	One <u>bird's</u> nest was made of twigs.
Plural Possessive Noun	Some <u>birds'</u> nests are made of grass.

Add an apostrophe (') to plural nouns that end in *-s, -es,* or *-ies* to make them possessive. To make plural nouns that do not end in *-s, -es,* or *-ies* possessive, add an apostrophe and an *s.*

<u>children</u>   <u>children's</u> toys   <u>women</u>   <u>women's</u> books

Directions Write the plural possessive noun in each sentence.

1. Eagles' nests are huge. _____

2. Hummingbirds' nests hold their eggs. _____

3. The parents' job is to protect their chicks. _____

4. The trees' holes were made by woodpeckers. _____

5. The forest's trees are full of animals' homes. _____

Directions Write the possessive form of the underlined plural noun in each sentence.

6. There are good places for our <u>cities</u> birds to nest. _____

7. Some <u>pigeons</u> homes are on window ledges. _____

8. Sometimes they get in <u>people</u> way. _____

9. Their <u>babies</u> lives can be full of danger. _____

10. Some animals destroy the bird <u>families</u> homes. _____

Home Activity Your child learned about plural possessive nouns. Name some families in your neighborhood. Have your child make up sentences using the plural possessive form of each noun, such as *The Smiths' dog likes to play ball.*

3.22.A.1.ii.2 Use and understand nouns (plural) in the context of reading, writing, and speaking. **3.23.C.1.i.3** Recognize punctuation marks including apostrophes in possessives. **Also 3.23.C.1.i.4.**

Consonant Digraphs

Spelling Words				
father	chapter	other	alphabet	watch
English	weather	catch	fashion	shrink
pitcher	flash	athlete	trophy	nephew

Rhyme Clues Read the clue. Write the list word.

1. It rhymes with *patch,* but starts like *can.* _____

2. It rhymes with *link,* but starts like *shred.* _____

3. It rhymes with *feather,* but starts like *win.* _____

4. It rhymes with *mother,* but starts like *olive.* _____

5. It rhymes with *dash,* but starts like *flag.* _____

6. It rhymes with *stitcher,* but starts like *pencil.* _____

Making Connections Write a list word to fit each definition.

7. It's a list of letters. _____

8. It's something you might win. _____

9. It's a parent. It's not a mother. _____

10. It helps you tell the time. _____

11. It's a section of a book. _____

12. It's a sister's child. It's not a girl. _____

13. It's often spoken in Australia. _____

14. It could be a swimmer, a boxer, or a gymnast. _____

15. It's a trend in clothing. _____

© Pearson Education, Inc., 3

Home Activity Your child wrote words with *sh, th, ph, ch,* and *tch.* Point to a list word on this page. Ask your child to read the word and then look away and spell it correctly.

3.24.A.1 Use knowledge of letter sounds to spell. **3.24.A.2** Use knowledge of word parts to spell. **3.24.A.3** Use knowledge of word segmentation to spell. **3.24.B.1.v** Spell words with complex consonants.

Web A

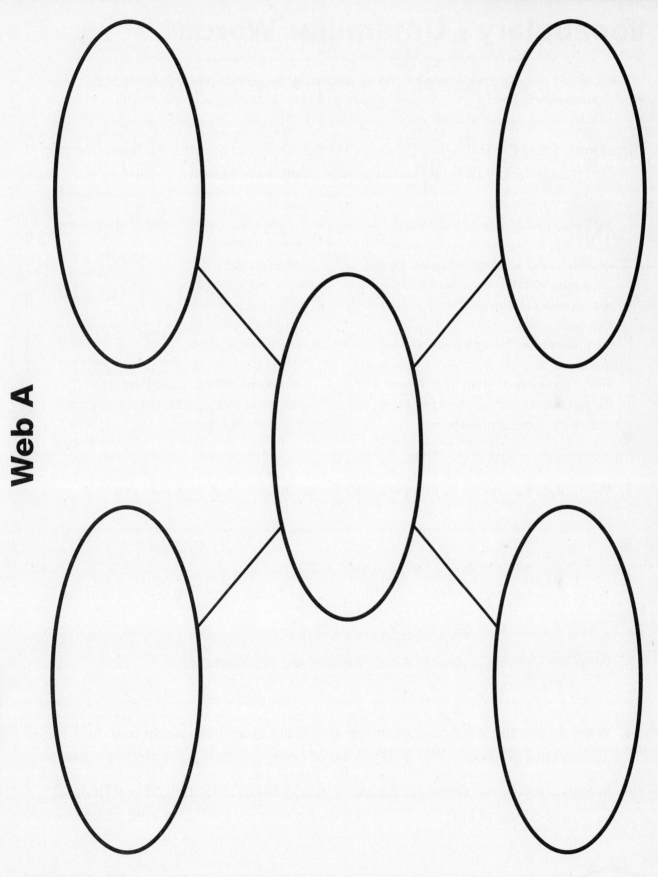

Vocabulary • Unfamiliar Words

- Context clues are the words around an **unfamiliar word** that help you figure out its meaning.

Directions Read the following passage. Then answer the questions below. Look for context clues to help you figure out any words you do not know.

Nancy loved living near the water. She loved sitting on her deck, looking out at the bay, and watching the boats. People often sailed small boats in the bay, because it was protected from the big waves out on the ocean.

Another thing Nancy loved about her house was the trees. Nancy's house was almost surrounded by tall trees. Except for the part of the yard that faced the water, there were trees on all sides.

The birds seemed to love the trees, too. Every morning when the sun came up, the birds woke her with their songs. When all the birds sang at dawn, it was like hearing a symphony of bird songs. Even now she could make out the sweet melody a bluebird was singing.

1. What does *bay* mean in this passage? What clues helped you find out?

_____

_____

2. What does *surrounded* mean in this passage? What clues helped you find out?

_____

3. What time of day is *dawn?* What clues helped you find out?

_____

4. What do you think a *symphony* might be? What clues helped you find out?
   ⬭ a kind of tree   ⬭ a kind of boat   ⬭ a kind of music

5. Which does the word *melody* probably mean? What clues helped you find out?
   ⬭ something to sing   ⬭ a kind of bird   ⬭ a kind of tree

Home Activity Your child used context clues to figure out the meaning of unfamiliar words. Read a book with your child that has some unfamiliar words. Have your child tell what he or she thinks the words mean, based on the context. Use a dictionary to confirm the meanings with your child.

🟊 **3.4.B.1** Use context to determine the relevant meaning of unfamiliar words.

Paraphrase Sources

- To **paraphrase** means to restate something in other words.

Directions Read the encyclopedia entry. Then paraphrase the information on the lines below.

Northern Mockingbird
(*Mimus polyglottos*)

The Northern Mockingbird is a medium-sized bird known for its unusual voice. Mockingbirds can imitate the songs of many kinds of birds, as well as other common sounds. Both male and female mockingbirds sing, although the males, especially males that are looking for a mate, sing most often. Unmated males may even sing at night. Male and female mockingbirds look alike. Both are gray on top and white underneath. Both have white patches on their wings and tails that can be seen when the bird is flying. Mockingbirds eat fruits and vegetables, but they also eat harmful insects. These birds are plentiful and are commonly found in a variety of habitats all over North America. The mockingbird is a popular bird that has been chosen as official state bird by Texas, Florida, and other states.

_____

_____

_____

_____

_____

_____

© Pearson Education, Inc., 3

Home Activity Your child read an encyclopedia entry about the Texas state bird and then paraphrased the information. Read another encyclopedia entry together and have your child tell about what you read in his or her own words.

★ Paraphrase information and ideas in texts.

Consonant Digraphs

Proofread Safety Tips Chad wrote some weather safety tips. Circle four spelling mistakes and one capitalization error. Write the words correctly.

➜ Don't let bad weatter cach you off guard. Listen to the forecast.

➜ Be ready to go to a basement if their is a tornado watch.

➜ Take shelter when you hear thunder. Don't wait for a flash of lightning.

➜ wear a cap, mittens, and othr warm clothes in freezing weather.

1. _____   2. _____

3. _____   4. _____

5. _____

Spelling Words

father
chapter
other
alphabet
watch
English
weather
catch

fashion
shrink
pitcher
flash
athlete
trophy
nephew

Frequently Misspelled Words

they
there
their

Proofread Words Circle the correctly spelled word. Write the word.

6. fashsun	fashion	**6.**	_____
7. pitcher	picher	**7.**	_____
8. trophy	trofy	**8.**	_____
9. english	English	**9.**	_____
10. shrink	shink	**10.**	_____
11. atlete	athlete	**11.**	_____
12. alpabet	alphabet	**12.**	_____

Home Activity Your child identified misspelled words with *sh, th, ph, ch,* and *tch.* Have your child underline and pronounce these letter combinations in the list words.

🌟 **3.24.A.1** Use knowledge of letter sounds to spell. **3.24.A.2** Use knowledge of word parts to spell. **3.24.A.3** Use knowledge of word segmentation to spell. **Also 3.24.B.1.v, 3.24.C.1.**

© Pearson Education, Inc., 3

Plural Possessive Nouns

Directions Read the selection. Then read each question that follows the selection. Decide which is the best answer to each question. Mark the space for the answer you have chosen.

City Birds

(1) There are good places for many <u>cities</u> birds to nest. (2) Some <u>pigeons</u> homes are on window ledges. (3) Robins' nests can be found under highways. (4) Living in the city can also be dangerous for a bird. (5) Sometimes these birds get in <u>people</u> way. (6) Their <u>babies</u> lives can be full of danger. (7) Some animals destroy bird families homes.

1 What is the possessive form of the underlined noun in sentence 1?

- ⊂⊃ cities
- ⊂⊃ city's
- ⊂⊃ citys'
- ⊂⊃ cities'

2 What is the possessive form of the underlined noun in sentence 2?

- ⊂⊃ pigeons'
- ⊂⊃ pigeon's
- ⊂⊃ pigeons
- ⊂⊃ pigeons's

3 What is the correct form of the underlined noun in sentence 5?

- ⊂⊃ peoples
- ⊂⊃ people's
- ⊂⊃ peoples'
- ⊂⊃ peoples's

4 What is the possessive form of the underlined noun in sentence 6?

- ⊂⊃ babie's
- ⊂⊃ babys'
- ⊂⊃ babies'
- ⊂⊃ baby's

5 What change, if any, should be made to sentence 7?

- ⊂⊃ Change *animals* to **animal's**
- ⊂⊃ Change *animals* to **animals'**
- ⊂⊃ Change *families* to **families'**
- ⊂⊃ Change *families* to **familie's**

Home Activity Your child prepared for taking tests on plural possessive nouns. Name some kinds of animals. Have your child write sentences using the plural possessive form of each animal name, such as *Zebras' stripes are black and white.*

3.22.A.1.ii.2 Use and understand nouns (plural) in the context of reading, writing, and speaking. **3.23.C.1.i.3** Recognize punctuation marks including apostrophes in possessives. **Also 3.23.C.1.i.4.**

Name _____

Syllables V/CV, VC/V

Spelling Words				
finish	pilot	even	wagon	music
silent	rapid	female	lemon	pupil
focus	robot	tulip	camel	salad

Crossword Puzzle Read each clue. Write the list word in the puzzle.

Across

2. to complete something
4. an animal with one or more humps
5. a sour fruit
8. a person who flies a plane
10. often made with lettuce
12. a kind of machine
13. very fast

Down

1. not odd but ___
2. the opposite of *male*
3. make no noise
6. songs
7. a toy with four wheels
8. a student
9. a spring flower
11. to adjust a camera lens

Home Activity Your child has been learning to spell words with long and short vowel sounds with these syllable patterns: V/CV VC/V. Give clues about a word from the list. Ask your child to guess the word and then spell it.

3.24.A.1 Use knowledge of letter sounds to spell. 3.24.A.2 Use knowledge of word parts to spell. 3.24.A.4 Use knowledge of syllabication to spell. 3.24.D.1 Spell words with common syllable constructions.

© Pearson Education, Inc., 3

Common and Proper Nouns

Directions Write *C* if the underlined noun is a common noun. Write *P* if the underlined noun is a proper noun.

1. Antarctica is an unusual <u>continent</u>.   _____

2. The <u>South Pole</u> is found there.   _____

3. The <u>weather</u> is harsh.   _____

4. It is one of the coldest places in the <u>world</u>.   _____

5. Yet some animals build <u>nests</u> on the land.   _____

6. The islands of <u>Antarctica</u> are home to many birds.   _____

7. Some <u>birds</u> live on the ocean.   _____

8. They find <u>fish</u> for food.   _____

9. Interesting birds live along the seashore of <u>America</u>. _____

10. Gulls and terns nest on the <u>coast</u> and fish at sea.   _____

Directions Underline the common nouns and circle the proper nouns in the sentences.

11. Ducks and geese make nests near the North Pole.

12. The animals come to the shores of North America in winter.

13. Many gulls live near the ocean in Canada.

14. They follow ships and eat trash that people throw out.

15. These birds also live on the Great Lakes.

© Pearson Education, Inc., 3

3.22.A.1.ii.3 Use and understand nouns (common) in the context
of reading, writing, and speaking. **3.22.A.1.ii.4** Use and understand
nouns (proper) in the context of reading, writing, and speaking.

Conventions **165**

Final Syllable -*le*

Spelling Words				
handle	trouble	simple	people	middle
table	little	gentle	poodle	pickle
noodle	saddle	juggle	uncle	riddle

Rhymes Write the list word that rhymes with the word shown.

1. nickel ___ ___ ___ ___ ___ ___

2. doodle ___ ___ ___ ___ ___ ___

3. label ___ ___ ___ ___ ___

4. paddle ___ ___ ___ ___ ___ ___

5. bubble ___ ___ ___ ___ ___ ___

6. steeple ___ ___ ___ ___ ___ ___

7. fiddle ___ ___ ___ ___ ___ ___

8. dimple ___ ___ ___ ___ ___ ___

Missing Words Write the list word that completes each phrase.

9. a door _____

10. not rough but _____

11. a barking _____

12. not my aunt but my _____

13. sit in the _____

14. _____ the balls

15. just a _____ bit more

handle	poodle
little	uncle
gentle	middle
juggle	

© Pearson Education, Inc., 3

Home Activity Your child is learning to spell words that end in -*le*. Together, say each word, spell it, clap, and loudly say "l, e" when you get to the end of a word.

3.24.A.2 Use knowledge of word parts to spell. **3.24.A.4** Use knowledge of syllabication to spell. **3.24.D.1** Spell words with common syllable constructions.

Singular and Plural Nouns

Directions Write *S* if the underlined noun is a singular noun. Write *P* if the underlined noun is a plural noun.

1. The desert is <u>home</u> to many animals. _____

2. <u>Kittens</u> are common house pets. _____

3. Mikey wants to give Alex his <u>iguana</u>. _____

4. A large <u>animal</u> needs a large house. _____

5. Lizards eat <u>flies</u> and other insects. _____

Directions Write the plural nouns in each sentence.

6. Cats and kittens make good pets.

_____

7. Birds live in special cages.

_____

8. Different animals eat different foods.

_____

9. Hamsters and gerbils are furry friends.

_____

10. Tiny sharks swim in special tanks.

_____

11. Pet owners have different jobs.

_____

12. We groom our dogs using brushes made for pets.

_____

3.22.A.1.ii.1 Use and understand nouns (singular) in the context of reading, writing, and speaking. **3.22.A.1.ii.2** Use and understand nouns (plural) in the context of reading, writing, and speaking.

Conventions 167

Compound Words

Spelling Words				
sunglasses	football	homework	haircut	popcorn
railroad	snowstorm	earring	scarecrow	blueberry
butterflies	lawnmower	campground	sandbox	toothbrush

Compound Match Up Draw a line to connect two words to make a compound word. Write the compound word.

1. tooth	corn	**1.** _____
2. pop	mower	**2.** _____
3. ear	berry	**3.** _____
4. lawn	brush	**4.** _____
5. foot	ring	**5.** _____
6. blue	work	**6.** _____
7. home	cut	**7.** _____
8. sand	ball	**8.** _____
9. rail	road	**9.** _____
10. hair	box	**10.** _____

Dividing Compounds Draw a line between the two words in each compound word. Write each word.

11. snowstorm   **11.** _____ + _____

12. campground   **12.** _____ + _____

13. sunglasses   **13.** _____ + _____

14. scarecrow   **14.** _____ + _____

15. butterflies   **15.** _____ + _____

© Pearson Education, Inc., 3

 School + Home **Home Activity** Your child has been spelling compound words. Together, look for compound words in a favorite book. Ask your child to name the two words that make up each compound word.

🌟 **3.24.A.2** Use knowledge of word parts to spell. **3.24.C.2** Spell compound words from a commonly used list.

Irregular Plural Nouns

Directions Write *S* if the underlined noun is singular. Write *P* if the underlined noun is plural.

1. The <u>women</u> next door had a problem in their barn. _____

2. Some <u>mice</u> had made homes there. _____

3. The little animals bothered the big <u>oxen</u> in the barn. _____

4. A noisy <u>goose</u> went into the barn. _____

5. Soon there were no mice under the people's <u>feet</u>. _____

Directions Write the plural nouns in each sentence.

6. The children had problems.

_____

7. They had loose teeth.

_____

8. They could not eat apples or carrots.

_____

9. Soon their teeth fell out, and their mouths felt better.

_____

10. They could eat snacks again.

_____

3.22.A.1.ii.2 Use and understand nouns (plural) in the context of reading, writing, and speaking. **3.24.B.1.v** Spell words with complex consonants.

Conventions 169

Words with *spl, thr, squ, str, scr*

Spelling Words				
splash	throw	three	square	scream
strike	street	split	splurge	thrill
strength	squeak	throne	scratch	squeeze

Question Clues Write the list word that answers each question.

1. How do you stop an itch?

1. _____

2. What is the name of that shape?

2. _____

3. What sound does a mouse make?

3. _____

4. Where does a queen sit?

4. _____

5. Where might you park a car?

5. _____

6. What might you do at a haunted house?

6. _____

7. What does a pitcher do with a ball?

7. _____

8. What number comes before four?

8. _____

9. What is it called when a batter swings
   and misses?

9. _____

10. What do you do to get toothpaste out of
    a tube?

10. _____

Proofreading Circle the list word that is spelled correctly. Write it.

11. splesh   splash

11. _____

12. thrill   thril

12. _____

13. stregth   strength

13. _____

14. splutt   split

14. _____

15. splurge   splurje

15. _____

Home Activity Your child learned words with the three-letter blends *spl, thr, squ, str,* and *scr.*
Divide a sheet of paper into four sections. Ask your child to sort and write the words according to
their beginning blends.

3.24.A.1 Use knowledge of letter sounds to spell. **3.24.A.2** Use
knowledge of word parts to spell. **3.24.A.3** Use knowledge of word
segmentation to spell. **3.24.B.1.v** Spell words with complex consonants.

© Pearson Education, Inc., 3

Name _____

Singular Possessive Nouns

Directions Write the singular possessive noun in each sentence.

1. The little hen used the farmer's wheat for bread.

   _____

2. The hen asked for each animal's help.

   _____

3. Each friend's answer was no.

   _____

4. The animals wanted the hen's good bread.

   _____

5. The hen enjoyed the bread's taste alone.

   _____

Directions Write the possessive form of the underlined singular noun in each sentence.

6. What is that <u>story</u> lesson?

   _____

7. Good bread comes from the <u>baker</u> hard work.

   _____

8. Everyone wants the <u>worker</u> food.

   _____

9. No one helps in the <u>cook</u> kitchen.

   _____

10. Each <u>person</u> help is needed.

   _____

3.22.A.1.ii.1 Use and understand nouns (singular) in the context of reading, writing, and speaking. **3.23.C.1.i.3** Recognize punctuation marks including apostrophes in possessives. **3.23.C.1.i.4** Use punctuation marks including apostrophes in possessives.

Conventions 171

Consonant Digraphs

Spelling Words				
father	chapter	other	alphabet	watch
English	weather	catch	fashion	shrink
pitcher	flash	athlete	trophy	nephew

Meaning Clues Read the clue. Write the list word the clue tells about. The letters in the boxes will answer this riddle:

What do you call cheese that's not yours?

1. get smaller   __ __ __ __ □ __

2. the ABCs   __ __ __ □ __ __ __ __

3. a clock for the wrist   __ __ __ □ __

4. a prize   __ __ __ □ __ __

5. a clothing trend   __ __ __ □ __ __ __

6. something that can hold water   __ __ □ __ __ __ __

7. not a niece but a _____   __ __ □ __ __ __

8. a dad   __ __ □ __ __ __

9. part of a book   __ __ □ __ __ __ __

10. a language   __ __ __ □ __ __ __

11. what it's like outside   __ __ __ __ □ __ __

Word Parts Write the list word that contains each small word.

12. ash   __ __ __ __ __

13. her   __ __ __ __ __ __

14. let   __ __ __ __ __ __ __

15. cat   __ __ __ __ __

School + Home **Home Activity** Your child learned to spell words with *sh*, *th*, *ph*, *ch*, and *tch*. Point to a word on the word list. Ask your child to circle the *sh*, *th*, *ph*, *ch*, or *tch* in the word. Then cover the word and have your child spell it out loud.

3.24.A.1 Use knowledge of letter sounds to spell. **3.24.A.2** Use knowledge of word parts to spell. **3.24.A.3** Use knowledge of word segmentation to spell. **3.24.B.1.v** Spell words with complex consonants.

Name _____

Plural Possessive Nouns

Directions Write the plural possessive noun in each sentence.

1. The chicks' fur is so soft.

_____

2. Hummingbirds' bills are long and thin.

_____

3. Weaverbirds' nests are cleverly built.

_____

4. The robins' eggs lie safely in nests.

_____

5. Building nests is the females' job.

_____

Directions Write the possessive form of the underlined plural noun in each sentence.

6. The students saw <u>eagles</u> nests in the treetops.

_____

7. They found <u>woodpeckers</u> eggs in tree trunks.

_____

8. Take pictures of some <u>sparrows</u> nests.

_____

9. Look carefully at the <u>nests</u> materials.

_____

10. Some <u>animals</u> homes are lined with feathers.

_____

11. The <u>feathers</u> colors are black and brown.

_____

12. The <u>students</u> day was full of interesting sights.

_____

3.22.A.1.ii.2 Use and understand nouns (plural) in the context of reading, writing, and speaking.
3.23.C.1.i.3 Recognize punctuation marks including apostrophes in possessives. **Also 3.23.C.1.i.4.**

Conventions 173

How-to Chart

Directions Fill in the graphic organizer with information about your project.

Task _____

Materials _____

Introduction _____

_____

_____

_____

_____

Steps _____

_____

_____

_____

_____

Conclusion _____

_____

_____

_____

3.17.A.2 Plan a first draft by generating ideas through a range of strategies. **3.17.B.1** Develop drafts by categorizing ideas.

Time-Order Words

Directions Add a time-order word to each of the five steps below. Write each sentence. Then add a final sentence using a time-order word. Tell what you could do with the flowers.

1. Find a pretty vase.

_____

_____

2. Pick some wildflowers from a field.

_____

_____

3. Put water in the vase.

_____

_____

4. Place the flowers in the water.

_____

_____

5. Arrange the flowers in an attractive pattern.

_____

_____

6. _____

_____

3.22.A.1.viii.1 Use and understand time-order transition words in the context of reading, writing, and speaking.

Vivid Words

When you write, use vivid, precise words to make your how-to report clearer and easier to follow.

General Words   Watch that kite go in the air.
Precise Words   Watch that kite soar up in the clouds.

Directions Replace each underlined word with a vivid, precise word. Write each sentence.

1. Cut paper for your kite in a shape.

   _____

   _____

2. Make your kite a good color.

   _____

   _____

3. Put some sticks on your kite.

   _____

   _____

4. Put your kite high in the air.

   _____

   _____

5. Use your kite with some people.

   _____

   _____

3.17.C.1 Revise drafts for coherence. **3.17.C.5** Revise drafts for audience.

Peer and Teacher Conferencing
How-to Report

Directions Read your partner's report. Refer to the Revising Checklist as you write your comments or questions. Offer compliments as well as revision suggestions. Then take turns talking about each other's draft. Give your partner your notes. After you and your teacher talk about your report, add your teacher's comments to the notes.

Revising Checklist

Focus/Ideas

☐ Is the how-to report focused on explaining one task or activity?

☐ Are there enough details in the steps to explain the process?

Organization

☐ Are the steps of the process arranged in a logical order?

☐ Does the report have opening and concluding paragraphs?

Voice

☐ Does the writer show enthusiasm and knowledge?

Word Choice

☐ Do time-order words and vivid, precise words help make the steps and their sequence clear and coherent to the audience?

Sentences

☐ Are commands with strong verbs used to explain the steps?

Things I Thought Were Good _____

_____

Things I Thought Could Be Improved _____

_____

Teacher's Comments _____

_____

★ Revise final drafts in response to feedback from peers. ★ Revise final drafts in response to feedback from teacher.

Contractions

Directions Use each pair of words to make a contraction. Write the contraction on the line.

_____ 1. have not

_____ 2. when is

_____ 3. did not

_____ 4. they will

_____ 5. she is

_____ 6. you will

_____ 7. we would

_____ 8. I would

_____ 9. let us

_____ 10. they are

_____ 11. that is

_____ 12. he would

_____ 13. was not

_____ 14. you would

Directions: Use the words in ( ) to make a contraction to complete each sentence. Write the contraction on the line.

_____ 15. Judy (has not) planted a garden before.

_____ 16. This year she decided (she would) like to grow some plants.

_____ 17. Her mom said that (they would) work together.

_____ 18. Judy's mom told her that it (was not) yet time to plant the garden.

_____ 19. She explained that seeds can't grow if (it is) too cold.

_____ 20. She also said that plants (would not) grow without water.

© Pearson Education, Inc., 3

Home Activity Your child formed contractions by using an apostrophe to take the place of letters that are left out. Ask your child to think of at least ten other word pairs that can be used to form contractions, such as *she is (she's), we will (we'll),* and *are not (aren't).* Ask your child to write sentences using these contractions.

3.1.D.1 Identify contractions. **Also 3.1.D.2.**

Draw Conclusions

- A **conclusion** is a decision you reach after thinking about facts and details you read.
- You can also use what you already know to help draw a **conclusion.**
- Then ask yourself, "Does my **conclusion** make sense?"

Directions Read the following passage. Then complete the chart to draw a conclusion.

> The Bradfords left home early in the morning. It took them most of the morning to get to the beach.
>
> When they got there, everyone scrambled out of the car. Joey and Cindy ran into the water. Kevin hiked along the beach to collect some rocks. Miranda played in the sand. They barely stopped to eat lunch.
>
> Finally, the sun was setting. Mom and Dad called them to go home, but no one wanted to leave.

Fact or Detail
1. What happens at lunchtime?

Fact or Detail
2. What happens when it's time to go home?

CONCLUSION about the Bradfords

3.

4. Does your conclusion make sense? Tell why.

_____

_____

© Pearson Education, Inc., 3

Home Activity Your child drew a conclusion by using two facts or details from a story. Good readers draw conclusions as they read, using both facts in the story and their own prior knowledge. Provide your child with two facts or details, such as "Sam fills up a tub with water" and "the dog runs away." Ask your child to use the information to draw a conclusion. (The dog does not want to have a bath.)

🌐 **3.13.B.1** Draw conclusions from facts presented in text.

Writing • Fiction

Key Features of Fiction

- tells an imagined story
- includes characters
- includes a setting
- follows a sequence of events that builds up to a climax

Lessons Learned on the Raisin Farm

Last week we got some new workers on the raisin farm. But these new workers did not know how to do everything correctly. Out in the field I found paper trays with grapes that weren't ripe enough to become raisins. I couldn't put these grapes back on the vine. Other trays had the right grapes. But these trays didn't have enough grapes on them.

I gathered the new workers together. I stood on a crate and spoke to them. I explained that some things were being done incorrectly. I showed them how to choose only ripe grapes from the vine, and I showed them how many grapes could fit on a tray. They promised to do better.

It was good that I talked to the new workers. The next day, I found just the right amount of the best grapes on all the paper trays in the field!

1. Read the story. The **setting** is when and where a story takes place. What is the setting in the story?

_____

2. Why does the narrator talk to the new workers? What happens the next day?

_____

_____

_____

_____

_____

Vocabulary

Check the Words You Know

___area   ___proof
___artificial   ___raise
___grapevine   ___raisin
___preservative

Directions Fill in the blank with the word from the box that fits the meaning of the sentence.

1. Most natural foods are healthier than _____ ones.

2. When you _____ your own crops, you know exactly what you are getting.

3. If the _____ has warm winters, people grow food all year.

4. They don't need _____ to keep their food fresh.

5. They can pull grapes off the _____, wash them, and eat them right away.

Directions Draw a line from the word to its meaning.

6. raisin   not found in nature

7. raise   additive that keeps food from spoiling too quickly

8. proof   a dried grape

9. preservative   evidence that shows that a fact is true

10. artificial   to grow, as on a farm

Write a Commercial

Write a commercial for raisins. Use as many of this week's vocabulary words as you can.

Home Activity Your child identified and used vocabulary words from *How Do You Raise a Raisin?* Talk with your child about foods in your kitchen or at the grocery store. Use the vocabulary words on this page.

Action and Linking Verbs

> A **verb** is a word that tells what someone or something is or does. **Action verbs** are words that show action. **Linking verbs,** such as *am, is, are, was,* and *were,* do not show action. They link a subject to a word or words in the predicate.
>
> **Action Verb**   Grapes <u>grow</u> on tall vines.
> **Linking Verb**   The grapes <u>are</u> red and juicy.

Directions One of the underlined words in each sentence is a verb. Write that word.

1. Amy <u>puts</u> the <u>seed</u> in the ground. _____

2. She <u>covers</u> it with <u>dirt</u>. _____

3. <u>It</u> <u>is</u> a pumpkin seed. _____

4. Pumpkins <u>grow</u> in <u>summer</u>. _____

5. They <u>are</u> good <u>for</u> decorations. _____

Directions Write the sentences. Underline the verb in each sentence.

6. Farmers grow grapes in warm places.

_____

7. They cut the ripe grapes from the vines.

_____

8. Many people gather the grapes.

_____

9. Raisins are dried grapes.

_____

10. We buy raisins at the supermarket.

_____

Home Activity Your child learned about action verbs and linking verbs. Have your child name some action verbs that describe something you have done or are doing together today.

3.22.A.1.i.1 Use and understand verbs (past) in the context of reading, writing, and speaking. **3.22.A.1.i.2** Use and understand verbs (present) in the context of reading, writing, and speaking. **3.22.A.1.i.3** Use and understand verbs (future) in the context of reading, writing, and speaking.

Contractions

Spelling Words				
let's	he'd	you'll	can't	I'd
won't	haven't	hasn't	she'd	they'll
when's	we'd	should've	wasn't	didn't

Contractions Write the underlined words as a contraction.

1. I wish <u>she had</u> stayed a few more days.

1. _____

2. If <u>you will</u> build a doghouse, I'll paint it.

2. _____

3. I <u>will not</u> be going to the party.

3. _____

4. I <u>can not</u> reach the top shelf.

4. _____

5. He <u>did not</u> go to the library.

5. _____

6. I knew <u>we had</u> put too much water in the paint.

6. _____

7. She <u>has not</u> finished writing the invitations.

7. _____

8. We <u>have not</u> played softball since Monday.

8. _____

Joining Words Write the contraction.

9. let + us

9. _____

10. they + will

10. _____

11. he + would

11. _____

12. when + is

12. _____

13. should + have

13. _____

14. was + not

14. _____

15. I + would

15. _____

Home Activity Your child wrote contractions. Pronounce a list word. Have your child name the words that were combined and then spell the contraction.

3.24.F.1 Spell complex contractions.

© Pearson Education, Inc., 3

Story Sequence B

Title	
Characters	**Setting**

↓

Events **1. First**	

↓

2. Next	

↓

3. Then	

↓

4. Last	

© Pearson Education, Inc., 3

Vocabulary • Homophones

- **Homophones** are words that sound the same but have different spellings and meanings.
- Use the words and sentences around the homophone to help you figure out what it means.

> **knead** to work dough with the hands
> **need** to be unable to do without something
>
> **does** plural of *doe,* a female deer
> **doze** to sleep lightly
>
> **scent** odor or smell
> **sent** the past tense of *send*
>
> **peace** calmness
> **piece** a part of
>
> **flour** the fine powder or meal made by grinding wheat or other grains
> **flower** the part of a plant that produces seeds

Directions In each sentence below, underline the word in the ( ) that makes sense in the sentence. Use context clues to help you choose the right word.

1. Plants (knead, need) water and nutrients to live.

2. The rose is my favorite (flour, flower).

3. The rose has a beautiful (scent, sent).

4. You have to (knead, need) the dough twice to make good bread.

5. Sometimes I like a little (peace, piece) and quiet.

6. There were two (does, doze) and two fawns in my backyard.

7. Put the (flour, flower) into a large bowl and add the milk and eggs.

8. My dad likes to (does, doze) in his chair after dinner.

9. We (scent, sent) the photos of the party to Grandma in an e-mail.

10. Do you want a (peace, piece) of pie?

Home Activity Your child used sentence context to identify the meanings of homophones, words which sound alike but are spelled differently and have different meanings. Take turns with your child naming words that sound alike (such as *read* and *red*) and making up sentences to show the meaning.

3.4.C.4 Identify homophones.

Card Catalog

Libraries use a **card catalog** or a computerized **library database** to organize their materials. You can search for a book using the **author, title,** or **subject.** Look for the author's last name followed by the first name. When the book is located, either on the card or computer, there will be a **call number.** Each book in the library has its own call number that appears on the spine of the book.

Directions A database entry for a book on gardening is shown below. Use the entry to answer the questions.

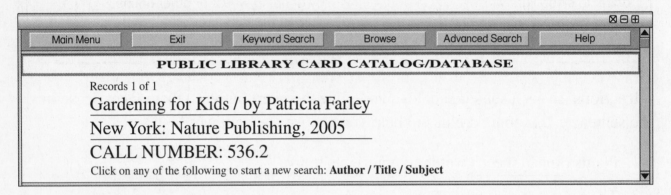

Main Menu	Exit	Keyword Search	Browse	Advanced Search	Help

PUBLIC LIBRARY CARD CATALOG/DATABASE

Records 1 of 1
Gardening for Kids / by Patricia Farley
New York: Nature Publishing, 2005
CALL NUMBER: 536.2
Click on any of the following to start a new search: **Author / Title / Subject**

1. What would you type to search the database by author to find this book?

_____

2. What is the call number for this book?

_____

3. What would you type to search the database by subject to find this book?

_____

4. You want to find a book about gardening. Which word will you click on to begin your search?

_____

5. In which year was this book published?

_____

Home Activity Your child answered questions about a library database. If possible, visit the library with your child to review the computerized database. If not, look at some books and have your child tell how to search for it by subject, author, and title.

3.26.A.1.ii.3 Follow the research plan to collect information from multiple sources of oral and written information, including online searches.

Name _____

Contractions

Proofread a Report To find out what happened in a playground accident, Tim's teacher had everyone write about it. Circle four spelling mistakes in Tim's report. Write the words correctly. Rewrite the compound sentence with a comma.

> I havn't been playing ball lately, so I did'nt see the accident with the bat. I was playing tag with Dan. He said hed been playing ball earlier.
>
> I'd tell you more but thats all I know. I hope Julian wasn't hurt badly.

Spelling Words

let's
he'd
you'll
can't
I'd
won't
haven't

hasn't
she'd
they'll
when's
we'd
should've
wasn't
didn't

1. _____ 2. _____

3. _____ 4. _____

5. _____

_____

Frequently Misspelled Words

that's
they're
didn't
it's

Proofread Words Circle the correct word and write it on the line.

6. Do you think **we'd we'ld** like the movie? 6. _____

7. I **cant can't** play right now. 7. _____

8. Before we go, **lets' let's** say goodbye. 8. _____

9. I know **they'll theyl'l** love this gift! 9. _____

10. He **has'nt hasn't** found his dog yet. 10. _____

11. I think **you'll you'l** be the winner. 11. _____

12. The team **won't wo'nt** make the playoffs. 12. _____

School + Home **Home Activity** Your child identified misspelled contractions. Point to a spelling word. Ask your child to name the letters that were replaced by the apostrophe (').

© Pearson Education, Inc., 3

3.24.C.1 Spell high-frequency words from a commonly used list.
3.24.F.1 Spell complex contractions.

Action and Linking Verbs

Directions Read the selection. Then read each question that follows the selection. Decide which is the best answer to each question. Mark the space for the answer you have chosen.

Raisins: From Farms to Markets

(1) Farmers grow grapes in warm places. (2) When it is time, they cut the ripe grapes from the vine. (3) It takes many people to gather the grapes. (4) Some grapes are dried. (5) This is how they become raisins. (6) Farmers ship raisins off to stores. (7) We buy raisins at the supermarket, and they are delicious.

1 What is the verb in sentence 1? Is it an action verb or a linking verb?

- ⬭ in; linking
- ⬭ grow; action
- ⬭ grow; linking
- ⬭ in; action

2 What is the action verb in sentence 2?

- ⬭ cut
- ⬭ is
- ⬭ they
- ⬭ from

3 What is the verb in sentence 4? Is it an action verb or a linking verb?

- ⬭ grapes; linking
- ⬭ grapes; action
- ⬭ are; action
- ⬭ are; linking

4 What is the action verb in sentence 6?

- ⬭ ship
- ⬭ farmers
- ⬭ off
- ⬭ to

5 What is the linking verb in sentence 7?

- ⬭ buy
- ⬭ raisins
- ⬭ they
- ⬭ are

Home Activity Your child prepared for taking tests on action verbs and linking verbs. Have your child make up some sentences about a job that interests him or her. Have your child identify the verb in each sentence.

3.22.A.1.i.1 Use and understand verbs (past) in the context of reading, writing, and speaking. **3.22.A.1.i.2** Use and understand verbs (present) in the context of reading, writing, and speaking. **3.22.A.1.i.3** Use and understand verbs (future) in the context of reading, writing, and speaking.

© Pearson Education, Inc., 3

Prefixes *un-, re-, mis-, dis-, non-*

Directions Add the prefix **un-, re-, mis-, non-,** or **dis-** to each base word. Write the new word on the line.

1. un- + load = _unload_

2. re- + learn = _relearn_

3. mis- + direct = _misdirect_

4. non- + sense = _nonsense_

5. dis- + like = _dislike_

Directions Write the word from the box that best fits each definition.

misspell **6.** to spell wrong

nonstop **7.** without stopping

unknown **8.** not known

rewrite **9.** to write again

dishonest **10.** not honest

> nonstop
> dishonest
> misspell
> rewrite
> unknown

Directions Add the prefix **un-, re-, mis-,** or **dis-** to the word in ( ) to complete each sentence. Write the new word on the line.

unable **11.** Last night I was (able) to see the stars.

disappeared **12.** The sky was so dark, I thought they had (appeared).

misplced **13.** I couldn't find the telescope. Someone had (placed) it.

recall **14.** When I asked who had used the telescope last, no one could (call).

unlikely **15.** It's (likely) that I will see the stars tonight.

© Pearson Education, Inc., 3

Home Activity Your child wrote words with the prefixes *un-* (unhappy), *re-* (recall), *mis-* (mistake), *non-* (nonsense), and *dis-* (dislike). Ask your child to choose words from the box above and use them in sentences. Then ask your child to remove the prefix from each word and use the new words in sentences.

✦ 3.1.A.1.iv.1 Decode multisyllabic words in context by applying common spelling patterns including using knowledge of common prefixes.

Phonics Prefixes **189**

Character, Setting, and Plot

- **Characters** are the people or animals in a story.
- We can learn about characters by what they do and say.
- The **setting** is where and when a story takes place.

Directions Read the following play. Then answer the questions below.

NARRATOR: Maureen and Lynn help Ms. Kominski clean the classroom whenever they can. One Friday after school, they were helping to clean the bookcases, when someone came to call Ms. Kominski to the office.

MS. KOMINSKI: I'll be right back, girls.

NARRATOR: The two girls kept working, dusting the bookcase and straightening the books. Suddenly Maureen bumped into Lynn, and Lynn's arm hit the vase of flowers. The vase went crashing to the floor and broke!

LYNN: Oh, no! Quick, let's leave before Ms. Kominski comes back.

MAUREEN: That's silly! She will know it was us! Let's just tell her.

LYNN: You're right.

NARRATOR: Just then Ms. Kominski returned, and Lynn and Maureen told her what had happened. They offered to buy a new vase.

MS. KOMINSKI: I'm glad you told me. The vase was not expensive, so we won't worry about your paying for it. Just help me clean up the spilled water.

1. What is the setting of this story? _____

2. How do you know the girls like their teacher and enjoyed helping her?

_____

3. Why do you think Lynn says they should leave when the vase breaks?

_____

4. Why did the girls offer to pay for the vase?

_____

5. How do you think they felt after Ms. Kominski said the vase was not expensive?

Home Activity Your child answered questions about characters in a story. Read a story together, or watch a television program, and discuss why the characters did the things they did in the story.

3.7.A.1–2 Explain elements of plot and character as presented through dialogue in scripts that are read, viewed, written, or performed.

Writing • Play

Key Features of a Play

- has characters with speaking and sometimes nonspeaking parts who act out the story
- speaking characters have lines to say called *dialogue*
- includes a description of the setting
- has a central problem that must be solved (plot)

The Moose and the Gadfly

[Setting: At the riverbank. Moose is drinking from the river. Beaver, Bear, Duck, and Gadfly are gathered nearby.]

Narrator: The animals were worried. Moose had been drinking from the river for a very long time, and they were concerned that he would soon drink the river dry. Then Beaver would have no place to build his dam, Bear would have no fish to catch, and Duck would have no place to swim.

Beaver: What else can we do to stop Moose from drinking the river? The logs I rolled down the river only bounced off of him.

Bear: My angry growls don't frighten him.

Duck: And my furious quacks Moose ignores.

Gadfly: I will stop Moose from drinking the river dry!

Beaver, Bear, and Duck: What! How can a little fly frighten away a big moose? You are not clever, or strong, or brave!

Gadfly: [*buzzes toward Moose*] You'll see!

Narrator: As the other animals watched in disbelief, Moose suddenly stopped drinking the river. He began to swish his tail and gnaw his neck, and finally became so angry at Gadfly's biting that Moose ran far away, stomping his great feet and creating deep holes in the river as he went. This is how the Grand Canyon was formed, with steep sides and the river at the bottom. When Gadfly returned, all the animals cheered for him and never doubted the little fly again.

1. What is the problem in the story? Circle the paragraph that tells you.

_____

_____

2. How is the problem solved? Circle the paragraph that tells you.

_____

_____

Vocabulary

Check the Words You Know

___overhead   ___poked

___imagined   ___narrator

___antlers   ___languages

Directions Write the vocabulary word from the box next to its meaning.

_____ **1.** jabbed with a finger or stick

_____ **2.** someone who tells a story

_____ **3.** bonelike growths on an animal's head, such as a deer

_____ **4.** the words and grammar people use to communicate

_____ **5.** formed a picture in your mind about something

Directions Fill in the word from the box that fits the meaning of the sentence.

6. The deer had huge, pointed _____ on its head.

7. We looked at the clouds _____ to see if it would rain.

8. The boy _____ that he would grow up to be a great ball player.

9. My brother _____ me in the arm to wake me up.

10. Rafael speaks two _____, English and Spanish.

Write a Poem

On a separate sheet of paper, write a poem about something wonderful you imagine. Use as many vocabulary words as possible.

Home Activity Your child has identified and used vocabulary words from *Pushing Up the Sky*. Play a game with your child in which you take turns imagining something, with each of you adding to what the other imagined. Use as many vocabulary words as you can.

3.4.B.1 Use context to determine the relevant meaning of unfamiliar words.

© Pearson Education, Inc., 3

Main Verbs and Helping Verbs

A **verb phrase** is a verb that has more than one word. The **main verb** shows action. A **helping verb** shows the time of the action. In the following sentence, *planting* is the main verb, and *are* is the helping verb.

The girls are planting corn with the women.

The helping verbs *am, is,* and *are* show present time. *Was* and *were* show past time. *Will* shows future time. The helping verbs *has, have,* and *had* show that an action happened in the past. In the following sentences, *had* and *will* are helping verbs.

They had planted in spring. We will harvest in fall.

Directions Underline the verb phrase in each sentence.

1. The chief is carving a beautiful pole.

2. He will place it at the entrance of the village.

3. The little boys are learning from the chief.

4. Someday they will carve a pole.

5. They have made many small animals already.

Directions Look at the underlined verb in each sentence. Write *M* if it is a main verb. Write *H* if it is a helping verb.

6. Everyone in the village is <u>helping</u> with the crops. _____

7. The women <u>had</u> planted the seeds. _____

8. The girls have <u>watered</u> the plants. _____

9. The boys <u>are</u> picking the beans. _____

10. The men <u>will</u> plow the fields. _____

Home Activity Your child learned about main verbs and helping verbs. Have your child answer the following question: *What were you doing at 3:00 today?* Then have your child identify the main verb and the helping verb in the answer.

⭐ **3.22.A.1.i.1** Use and understand verbs (past) in the context of reading, writing, and speaking. **3.22.A.1.i.2** Use and understand verbs (present) in the context of reading, writing, and speaking. **3.22.A.1.i.3** Use and understand verbs (future) in the context of reading, writing, and speaking.

Prefixes

Spelling Words				
unhappy	recall	disappear	unload	mistake
misspell	dislike	replace	mislead	disagree
rewrite	unroll	unknown	dishonest	react

Adding Prefixes Add a prefix to the underlined base word to make a list word. Write the list word. Read the sentence both ways.

1. Let's all help <u>load</u> the truck.

2. Our coach really knows how to <u>lead</u> the team.

3. We all <u>like</u> getting an allowance.

4. The class will <u>agree</u> with whatever you say.

5. I know I can <u>spell</u> that word.

6. You can count on that salesman to be <u>honest</u>.

7. I like to <u>write</u> letters.

8. Did you see the rabbit <u>appear</u> in the hat?

1. _unload_

2. _mislead_

3. _dislike_

4. _disagree_

5. _misspell_

6. _dishonest_

7. _rewrite_

8. _disappear_

Word Meanings Write the list word that means almost the same thing as each word or phrase.

9. unfamiliar

10. error

11. remember

12. spread out

13. respond

14. get another

15. sad

9. _unknown_

10. _mistake_

11. _react_

12. _unroll_

13. _recall_

14. _replace_

15. _unhappy_

react
mistake
recall
unhappy
unknown
replace
unroll

© Pearson Education, Inc., 3

Home Activity Your child spelled words with the prefixes *un-*, *re-*, *mis-*, and *dis-*. Point to a list word. Have your child spell the prefix and the base word separately.

3.24.A.2 Use knowledge of word parts to spell. **3.24.D.1** Spell words with common syllable constructions.

Three-Column Chart

Vocabulary: Dictionary/Glossary

- You can use a **glossary** or a **dictionary** to find the meaning, syllabication, and pronunciation of unknown words.

---

ant • ler (ant′ lər) *NOUN.* a bony, branching growth on the head of a male deer elk, or moose • *PLURAL* **ant • lers**

i • mag • ine (i maj′ ən) *VERB.* to make a picture or idea of something in your mind • *VERB* **i • mag • ines, i • mag • ined, i • mag • in • ing**

lan • guage (lan′ gwij) *NOUN.* human speech, spoken or written • *PLURAL* **lan • guag • es**

nar • ra • tor (nar′ āt ər) *NOUN.* the person who tells a story or tale

o • ver • head (ō′ vər hed′) *ADVERB.* over the head; on high; above

poke (pōk) *VERB.* to push with force against someone or something; jab • *VERB* **pokes, poked, pok • ing**

Directions Read the story. Use the glossary entries to answer the questions.

> In ancient times, people did not yet understand science. They had many questions, though. They wondered why deer had antlers, why the sun rose overhead every day, or how raindrops poked through the clouds. Ancient people imagined reasons for things they did not understand. They made up stories and chose a narrator to tell and retell the stories. Over time, the stories were translated into different languages. They are still fun to retell today.

1. How many syllables are in the word *narrator*? _____

2. Does the second *e* in *overhead* have a long or short sound? _____

3. Does the *g* in *imagined* have a hard sound as in *game* or a soft sound as in *giant*?

_____

4. What does *poked* mean? _____

5. Between which two letters would you divide the word *antlers* at the end of a line?

_____

 Home Activity Your child used a glossary to understand meanings, syllabication, and pronunciation of words. Find unknown words in a dictionary. Make up questions about the words and have your child use a dictionary or glossary to find the answers.

3.4.E.2 Use a dictionary or glossary to determine meanings of unknown words.
3.4.E.3 Use a dictionary or glossary to determine syllabication of unknown words.
3.4.E.4 Use a dictionary or glossary to determine pronunciation of unknown words.

Name _____

Thesaurus

A **thesaurus** includes entry words with synonyms (words with the same or similar meanings) and antonyms (words with opposite meanings). Most word processing programs have a thesaurus to help you choose just the right word.

Directions Use the thesaurus entry to answer the questions.

Entry Word   **Definition**

Quiet means making little or no noise. *Children are quiet at the library.*

Synonyms → **Silent** means not talking or making no sound. *The room became silent when the principal entered.*

Still means not moving. *The crowd was still as the last shot of the game was made.*

Antonym → ANTONYM: loud

Look up: Quiet

Synonyms: silent still

Antonym: loud

1. What is the entry word for this thesaurus example? _____

2. Which synonym of *quiet* best completes this sentence?
   Peter stood very _____ as the angry dog approached. _____

3. Which word could you use to replace the underlined phrase in this sentence?
   The children on the playground were <u>not quiet</u>. _____

4. How could you use a thesaurus to find more antonyms for *quiet*?

   _____

   _____

5. What is one way that you could use a thesaurus for schoolwork?

   _____

   _____

Home Activity Your child answered questions about a thesaurus entry. Read a book or story with your child. Select appropriate words for him or her to look up in a thesaurus to find synonyms and antonyms.

3.26.A.1.ii.2 Follow the research plan to collect information from multiple sources of oral and written information, including reference texts.

Prefixes

Proofread a Letter Circle four misspelled words and write them correctly. Rewrite the second sentence, adding the missing helping verb.

Dear Mayor,

    We think it's a misteak to close the swimming pool. That make alot of children unhappy. We don't dislike playgrounds, but we dissagree with changing the pool into a playground area. If you can't fix the pool, please replac it.

                        The Third Graders

1. _____   2. _____

3. _____   4. _____

5. _____

_____

Spelling Words
unhappy
recall
disappear
unload
mistake
misspell
dislike
replace
mislead
disagree
rewrite
unroll
unknown
dishonest
react

Frequently Misspelled Words
a lot
off
said

Missing Words Fill in the circle to show the correctly spelled word. Write the word.

6. Can you _____ what we did with the flashlight?   6. _____

○ reacl   ○ recall   ○ ricall

7. I'll try not to _____ any words.   7. _____

○ misspell   ○ mispell   ○ misspel

8. Did you see that deer _____ into the woods?   8. _____

○ desappear   ○ disapear   ○ disappear

Home Activity Your child identified misspelled words with the prefixes *un-*, *re-*, *mis-*, and *dis-*. Name a base word. Have your child spell the list word.

🌟 **3.24.A.2** Use knowledge of word parts to spell. **3.24.C.1** Spell high-frequency words from a commonly used list. **3.24.D.1** Spell words with common syllable constructions.

Main Verbs and Helping Verbs

Directions Read the selection. Then read each question that follows the selection. Decide which is the best answer to each question. Mark the space for the answer you have chosen.

In the Village

(1) The chief is carving a beautiful pole. (2) He will place it at the entrance of the village. (3) The little boys are learning from the chief. (4) Someday they will carve a pole. (5) The children have made many small animal carvings already. (6) The village is famous for its poles. (7) People have come from all around to see their poles.

1 What is the main verb in sentence 1?
- ⬭ chief
- ⬭ is
- ⬭ carving
- ⬭ pole

2 What is the helping verb in sentence 2?
- ⬭ will
- ⬭ place
- ⬭ it
- ⬭ of

3 What word could you use to replace the main verb in sentence 4?
- ⬭ are
- ⬭ is
- ⬭ make
- ⬭ made

4 What is the helping verb in sentence 5?
- ⬭ made
- ⬭ have
- ⬭ many
- ⬭ carvings

5 The helping verb in sentence 7 shows that the action took place in what time?
- ⬭ past
- ⬭ present
- ⬭ future
- ⬭ It does not show time.

Home Activity Your child prepared for taking tests on main verbs and helping verbs. Have your child make up two sentences about what he or she will do next weekend. Ask your child to identify the main verb and the helping verb in each sentence.

3.22.A.1.i.1 Use and understand verbs (past) in the context of reading, writing, and speaking. **3.22.A.1.i.2** Use and understand verbs (present) in the context of reading, writing, and speaking. **3.22.A.1.i.3** Use and understand verbs (future) in the context of reading, writing, and speaking.

Conventions Main Verbs and Helping Verbs   **199**

Spellings of /j/, /k/, /s/

Directions Underline the letter or letters that stand for the sound /j/ in **jar**, **large**, and **edge**. Then write a sentence using each word.

1. damage

_____

2. bridge

_____

3. banjo

_____

4. village

_____

Directions Circle the words in the box that have the sound /k/ spelled *k*, *c*, *ck*, and *ch* as in **mark**, **cost**, **pick**, and **school**. Write the words on the lines below.

> brake   branch   cellar   decide   locket
> merchant   peaceful   stomach   stretch   stuck

5. _____   **7.** _____

6. _____   **8.** _____

Directions Choose the words with the sound /s/ as in **person** and **pencil**. Write the word on the line.

_____ **9.** acid   is   picture

_____ **10.** become   catch   inside

_____ **11.** coat   dance   was

_____ **12.** account   bacon   once

Home Activity Your child wrote words with the /j/ sound in *jar*, *large*, and *edge*, the /s/ sound in *person* and *pencil*, and the /k/ sound in *mark*, *cost*, *pick*, and *chorus*. Encourage your child to identify other words with the /j/, /s/, or /k/ sounds. Together, make a list of these words and use them in sentences.

⊕ **3.24.B.1.v** Spell words with complex consonants.

Graphic Sources

- **Graphic sources** include maps, charts, illustrations, and captions.
- Graphic sources help you understand information in the text.

Directions Read the following passage. Study the graphic source.

There are many things to see in the sky. In the daytime, you can see the Sun. On a clear night, you might see the Moon and lots of stars. You might also see some of the planets.

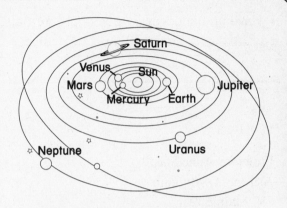

The Sun seems to travel around Earth, but that is not true. Earth is a planet, and planets orbit the Sun. The Sun, like other stars, stays in one place.

Directions Complete the chart to tell how the illustration and caption help you understand the text.

Type of Graphic Source	What It Shows	How It Helps You Understand Information
	the name of each planet	shows how many planets there are
illustration	the path each planet travels	
caption		helps readers understand the difference between stars and planets

Home Activity Your child used graphic sources such as captions and illustrations to understand a short passage. Flip through magazines and nonfiction books with your child. Discuss different graphic supports and how they help in understanding the text.

3.15.B.1 Locate specific information in graphic features of text. **3.15.B.2** Use specific information in graphic features of text.

Comprehension 201

Writing • Formal Letter

Key Features of a Formal Letter

- Are written in correct letter format: heading, inside address, salutation, body, closing, and signature
- Are short and to the point
- Have a respectful tone
- Have no unnecessary personal information

---

805 Oak Street
Pine Plains, NY 12523
January 24, 20 _____

Professor Anne Shea
Astronomy Museum
789 Main Street
Pine Plains, NY 12523

Dear Professor Anne Shea,

My third grade class has been learning about stars. I am writing because I have a question about pulsating stars. Is it true that these stars can expand and contract like beating hearts? And so some of these stars pulse with steady beats while others pulse with uneven beats?

I would appreciate it if you could please answer my questions about these stars. I would like to write a school report about them. Thank you for your time.

Sincerely,

Ben Chung

---

1. Which words make up the salutation?

_____

2. Circle where the writer shows respect in the letter.

3. List two examples of subject-verb agreement in the letter.

_____

Vocabulary: Reference Sources

- You can use a **glossary** or a **dictionary** to find the meanings of unknown words.
- Entries in glossaries and dictionaries are in **alphabetical order.** When two words have the same first and second letter, alphabetize by the third letter.

gigantic *ADJECTIVE.* huge
ginormous *ADJECTIVE.* so large that it is both gigantic and enormous

telescope *NOUN.* a tool to make distant objects appear nearer
temperature *NOUN.* the degree of heat or cold in something

Directions Put each set of words in alphabetical order. Use the glossary example above to help you. Then answer the questions.

shine   shapes   shrink
shoulder   shelf

thousands   these
that's   this   through

1. _____

2. _____

3. _____

4. _____

5. _____

6. _____

7. _____

8. _____

9. _____

10. _____

11. Which word comes just before *shoulder* in the glossary?

_____

12. Which word comes just after *this* in the glossary?

_____

Home Activity Your child put words whose first two letters are the same in alphabetical order. Use a dictionary, glossary, or telephone book to find three words that begin with the same two letters, such as *star*, *stem*, and *sting*. Have your child put the words in alphabetical order.

3.4.E.1 Alphabetize a series of words to the third letter.
3.4.E.2 Use a dictionary or glossary to determine meanings of unknown words.

Almanac

An **almanac** is a book of facts published once a year. There are two types of almanacs. The **farmer's almanac** contains facts about weather, astronomy, and the tides of the ocean. The **general information almanac** contains facts, figures, and information in many categories.

Directions Use the page from the almanac to answer the questions.

2007 Almanac

Awards and Prizes

The Newbery Medal, 2000–2006

The Newbery Medal of the American Library Association was first awarded in 1922. It is given to the author of the year's best children's book. Only American authors can win the Newbery Medal. The medal is named for John Newbery, the first English publisher of children's books.

2000   Christopher Paul Curtis, *Bud, Not Buddy*
2001   Richard Peck, *A Year Down Yonder*
2002   Linda Sue Park, *A Single Shard*
2003   Avi, *Crispin: The Cross of Lead*
2004   Kate DiCamillo, *The Tale of Despereaux*
2005   Cynthia Kadohata, *Kira-Kira*
2006   Lynne Rae Perkins, *Criss Cross*

1. Who won the Newbery Medal in 2001? _____

2. Under what broad category is this information listed?

_____

3. Is this page from a farmer's almanac or a general information almanac? How do you know?

_____

_____

4. What was the title of the best children's book of 2005?

_____

5. Name one fact you might find in a farmer's almanac.

_____

Home Activity Your child answered questions about a page of information from an almanac. Show your child an almanac. Have your child examine the different sections, such as the index.

3.26.A.1.ii.2 Follow the research plan to collect information from multiple sources of oral and written information, including reference texts.

Spellings of /j/, /s/, /k/

Proofread a Supply List Jon and Ted are organizing an overnight camping trip for the scouts. Circle four spelling mistakes. Write the words correctly. Write the item with the incorrect verb correctly.

Spelling Words

clock
large
page
mark
kitten
judge
crack
edge

pocket
brake
change
ridge
jacket
badge
orange

Bring these things:
- jackit
- raincoat or larg plastic bag
- pocket compass if you has one
- a chang of clothing
- signed permission page

Jon and I will bring are tents.

1. _____ 2. _____

3. _____ 4. _____

5. _____

Frequently Misspelled Words

our
I
I'm
until

Proofread Words Circle the word that is spelled correctly. Write it.

6.	citten	kitten	_____
7.	badg	badge	_____
8.	orange	orandge	_____
9.	rigde	ridge	_____
10.	brake	bracke	_____
11.	poket	pocket	_____
12.	edge	edje	_____

Home Activity Your child spelled words with *ge*, *dge*, *ck*, and *k*. Give clues about a list word. Have your child guess and spell the word.

3.24.A.1 Use knowledge of letter sounds to spell.
3.24.B.1.v Spell words with complex consonants.
3.24.C.1 Spell high-frequency words from a commonly used list.

Spelling Spellings of /j/, /s/, /k/ **209**

Subject-Verb Agreement

Directions Read the selection. Then read each question that follows the selection. Decide which is the best answer to each question. Mark the space for the answer you have chosen.

The Night Sky

(1) Juan <u>learn</u> all about stars. (2) He <u>use</u> his dad's telescope. (3) Juan's friends <u>is</u> interested in stars, too. (4) They <u>go</u> to the planetarium. (5) The planetarium has programs about the stars. (6) <u>Everyone</u> learn a lot on each visit.

1 What verb agrees with the subject in sentence 1?

- ⬭ learn
- ⬭ learns
- ⬭ learning
- ⬭ learnes

2 What verb agrees with the subject in sentence 2?

- ⬭ use
- ⬭ using
- ⬭ useses
- ⬭ uses

3 What verb agrees with the subject in sentence 3?

- ⬭ is
- ⬭ was
- ⬭ are
- ⬭ be

4 What verb agrees with the subject in sentence 4?

- ⬭ go
- ⬭ goes
- ⬭ going
- ⬭ gone

5 What subject agrees with the verb in sentence 6?

- ⬭ Everyone
- ⬭ Juan
- ⬭ Juan's dad
- ⬭ His friends

© Pearson Education, Inc., 3

School + Home

Home Activity Your child prepared for taking tests on subject-verb agreement. Point out a sentence in a newspaper. Have your child identify the subject and verb in the sentence and explain why they agree.

3.22.C.1 Use complete simple sentences with correct subject-verb agreement.

Suffixes *-ly, -ful, -ness, -less, -able, -ible*

Directions Add the suffix **-ly, -ful, -ness, -able, -ible,** or **-less** to each base word. Write the new word on the line.

1. grace   +   -ful   = _____

2. bare   +   -ly   = _____

3. depend   +   -able = _____

4. fair   +   -ness = _____

5. convert   +   -ible = _____

6. wire   +   -less = _____

7. rare   +   -ly   = _____

8. neat   +   -ness = _____

Directions Add **-ly, -ful, -ness, -able,** or **-less** to the base word in ( ) to best complete each sentence. Use the word box for help. Write the new word on the line.

> careful   careless   illness   quickly   safely   dependable   thickness

_____ **9.** A (care) mistake can cause an oil spill at sea.

_____ **10.** This can (quick) cause problems for seabirds.

_____ **11.** We can all help, by being (depend).

_____ **12.** If the oil is not (safe) removed, the birds cannot fly.

_____ **13.** If a seabird swallows oil, it can develop an (ill).

_____ **14.** The (thick) of a bird's eggshell can also change.

_____ **15.** To protect the sea and its wildlife, ships' captains must be (care).

Home Activity Your child wrote words with the suffixes *-ly (safely), -ful (playful), -ness (illness),* and *-less (worthless).* Name some base words such as *slow, thank, harm, kind,* and *help.* Ask your child to make new words using the suffixes he or she practiced on this page.

3.1.A.1.iv.2 Decode multisyllabic words in context by applying common spelling patterns including using knowledge of common suffixes. **Also 3.1.A.2.iv.2.**

Generalize

- Ideas in what you read are sometimes alike in several ways. To **generalize**, you can make a general statement about them together.
- Look for **clue words** such as *most*, *many*, *all*, *some*, or *few*.

Directions Read the following passage.

Mammals are animals that need to breathe air. Most mammals give birth to live babies. Mammal mothers also give milk to their babies.

Gray whales live in the ocean. Mothers-to-be find a safe place, such as a lagoon, to give birth. After the calf is born, a female helper pushes it up to the surface so it can breathe. Then the mother feeds the baby.

Directions Are gray whales mammals? Complete the chart. Make a generalization.

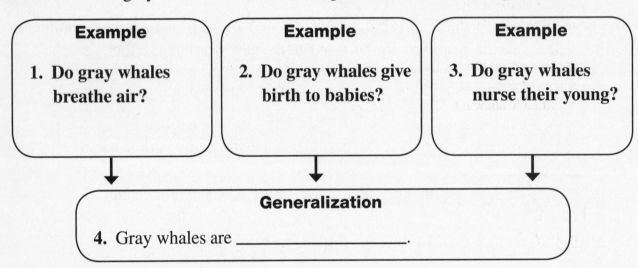

Example

1. Do gray whales breathe air?

Example

2. Do gray whales give birth to babies?

Example

3. Do gray whales nurse their young?

Generalization

4. Gray whales are _____.

5. How did answering the questions in the examples help you make a generalization?

_____

© Pearson Education, Inc., 3

Home Activity Your child made a generalization by finding examples of the ways things are alike. Draw a graphic organizer like the one above. Write examples about the ways dogs are alike in the three example boxes (dogs bark, wag tails, have hair). Then help your child write a generalization about dogs.

★ Make and support generalizations about text.

Writing • News Article

Key Features of a News Article

- has a headline and a short introduction that grab attention
- answers the five Ws and How?
- describes a current event and includes important information about the event

---

Baby Finds New Home by Jess Salvatore

Diego Salvatore didn't know what it was at first. It was small and pink. It was lying at the bottom of the tree in his backyard. It looked like it needed his help.

Saturday Surprise

Diego found the baby animal on Saturday morning. He wrapped it carefully in an old towel, and he placed it in a shoebox. He talked to other kids on his street, but none of them knew what it was. "I thought it was a puppy," Diego's friend Brandon said. They decided to show it to Mrs. Sing. Mrs. Sing lives next door to Diego. She loves animals. She has many birds, fish, and a tank of hermit crabs.

Mystery Solved

Mrs. Sing told them the animal was a baby squirrel. She called the Wildlife Center. The Center said they would care for the squirrel. "We rescue many baby squirrels each spring," said Alice, who works at the Center. "They often fall out of their nests."

After lunch, Mrs. Sing and Diego drove to the Center. They left the baby squirrel with Alice. They also made a donation to the Center. Their donation will help the Center rescue more young and wounded animals.

---

1. What is the action verb in the headline? What parts of the introduction grab your attention?

   _____

   _____

2. Write the first sentence in the model that tells you **what** happened.

   _____

3. Write the quotes from the news article. Put a star next to the name of the person who is an expert.

   _____

   _____

Name _____

Vocabulary

Directions Read the pairs of sentences below. Use one word from the box to fill in the blank in each pair of sentences. Use context clues to help you fill in the correct word.

1. This winter was very snowy. We had four _____ in December alone!

2. The bird sang a beautiful tune. The _____ was sweet and sad.

3. The children gathered all around the teacher. She was _____ by her class.

4. She was worried about her grade on the test. She waited _____ as the tests were handed back.

5. The water flowed along a narrow stream. The stream was a _____ that carried the water to the sea.

Directions In each sentence below, two words are underlined. Circle the word that makes sense. Use context clues in the sentence to help you choose the correct word.

6. The ship sailed into the large bay / blizzard that is near our town.

7. Before we went on the hike, I put a big bay / supply of water in my backpack.

8. Dan surrounded / chipped at the wood with a small ax.

9. We heard many musical instruments playing a beautiful symphony / channel together.

10. I heard a song on the radio, and I have been humming the symphony / melody all day.

Write a Scene from a Play

On a separate sheet of paper, write a short scene from a play about a person communicating with an animal. Use as many vocabulary words as possible.

Home Activity Your child identified and used vocabulary words from *A Symphony of Whales*. Read a story or article about animals to your child. Have your child point out unfamiliar words. Work together to try to figure out the meaning of each word by using other words that appear near it.

3.4.B.1 Use context to determine the relevant meaning of unfamiliar words.

© Pearson Education, Inc., 3

Present, Past, and Future Tenses

Verbs can show when an action happens. This is called **tense.** Different verb tenses have different forms. Many present tense verbs end in -*s.* Form the past tense of many verbs by adding -*ed.* Add the helping verb *will* to a verb to make it a future tense verb.

Present Tense	A whale <u>stays</u> near the beach.
Past Tense	The whale <u>jumped</u> out of the water.
Future Tense	The other whales <u>will jump</u> out soon.

- When a verb ends with *e,* drop the *e* before adding -*ed: glide   glided*
- When a one-syllable verb ends with one vowel followed by one consonant, double the final consonant before adding -*ed: shop   shopped*
- When a verb ends with a consonant followed by *y,* change the *y* to *i* before adding -*ed: hurry   hurried*

Directions Tell the tense of the underlined verb in each sentence. Write *present, past,* or *future.*

1. I <u>like</u> the humpback whales. _____

2. You <u>will enjoy</u> the whales' music. _____

3. Those whales <u>traveled</u> from the Arctic Ocean. _____

4. They <u>will return</u> next year. _____

Directions Write the verb in ( ) that correctly completes each sentence.

5. Last year Sammy's class (learn, learned) about whales. _____

6. Whales cannot breathe underwater, so they (jump, jumped) out of the water for air.

_____

7. Each time a mother whale gives birth, she (stays, stayed) close to the baby for a

year. _____

8. After a year, the baby (cared, will care) for itself. _____

Home Activity Your child learned about present, past, and future tenses. Ask your child to make up a sentence about something he or she saw on the way home from school and identify the tense of the sentence's verb.

3.22.A.1.i.1 Use and understand verbs (past) in the context of reading, writing, and speaking. **Also 3.22.A.1.i.2, 3.22.A.1.i.3.**

Conventions Present, Past, and Future Tenses   **215**

Suffixes

Spelling Words				
beautiful	safely	kindness	finally	spotless
worthless	illness	helpful	daily	suddenly
wireless	quietly	fairness	cheerful	painful

Word Endings Add an ending to the underlined word.
Then write the list word.

1. Do you floss your teeth <u>day</u>?

2. We've <u>final</u> finished our treehouse!

3. We sneaked <u>quiet</u> up the steps.

4. Cell phones are <u>wire</u>.

5. Isn't <u>fair</u> important in any game?

6. His bicycle was <u>spot</u>.

7. Holding the door open is a <u>help</u> thing to do.

8. His broken leg is <u>pain</u>.

9. Her <u>kind</u> made everyone feel better.

10. Then <u>sudden</u> the boat turned over.

11. She is always <u>cheer</u> when she gets up.

1. _daily_

2. _finally_

3. _quietly_

4. _wireless_

5. _fairness_

6. _spotless_

7. _helpful_

8. _painfull_

9. _kindness_

10. _suddenly_

11. _cheerful_

Context Clues Write a list word to complete the phrase.

12. drive _safely_

13. _spotless_ as a wooden nickel

14. contagious _illness_

15. _beautiful_ as a swan

Home Activity Your child spelled words with the suffixes -ly, -ful, -ness, and -less. Have your child pronounce each list word and identify the suffix.

3.24.A.2 Use knowledge of word parts to spell. **3.24.D.1** Spell words with common syllable constructions.

Five Ws and How?

What happened?

Who was there?

Where did it happen?

When did it happen?

Why did it happen?

How did it happen?

Vocabulary: Unfamiliar Words/Context Clues

- **Context clues** are the words and sentences around an unfamiliar word.
- When you come to an unfamiliar word, read the words around the word you don't know and use them to figure out the word's meaning.

Directions Read the following passage about helping water birds. Then answer the questions below. Look for context clues as you read.

When a huge ship spilled oil into the bay, people in the nearby village rushed anxiously to the water. They were sad to see ducks surrounded by floating oil. Their feathers were covered with the black, slimy stuff. Without help, the ducks would die!

The people grabbed their supplies. They cleaned the ducks with soap and towels. After the ducks were rested and dry, the people took them back to the water. The school band played a happy melody while the ducks were released. Everyone cheered as the ducks swam away.

1. What words in the first sentence are clues that the word *bay* names a body of water?

_____

2. Does *anxiously* mean "nervously" or "happily"? How do you know?

_____

_____

3. Does *surrounded* mean "underneath" or "in the middle of"?

_____

4. What two words in the second paragraph are clues to the meaning of *supplies*?

_____

5. How can you tell that a melody is a tune?

_____

Home Activity Your child used context clues to figure out the meanings of unfamiliar words. Read a story with your child. Stop when you come to an unfamiliar word and ask your child to use context clues to determine the word's meaning.

3.4.B.1 Use context to determine the relevant meaning of unfamiliar words.

Take Notes and Record Findings

As you research a subject, **taking notes** and **recording findings** of important information helps give your research a focus. You may want to organize your notes by main ideas and details or as answers to questions you have about the subject.

Directions Look at the chart below. Read the paragraph and highlight or underline important information as you read. Then record your findings in the lists to complete them.

> **Albino Animals**
>
> Imagine seeing an animal that looks like a deer, but it's different. It has white fur and pink eyes! The tail, the ears, and everything else look the same. Just the color is different. This animal is an albino deer. Albinos have a trait that is different from that of others of its species. An albino animal has no pigment in its skin, hair, or eyes. That's why the skin, fur, or feathers are white. Deer are not the only albino animals. Many others have been discovered. There are albino dogs, squirrels, leopards, and even birds.

Why It Is White	Features	Kinds of Animals
has different traits	looks like others	dogs
		leopards
1. _____	2. _____	squirrels
	_____	
	3. _____	4. _____
		5. _____

Home Activity Your child read a paragraph and recorded important information about it in categories. Help your child find a paragraph in a reference book, nonfiction text, or from a Web site. Ask your child to take notes about the important information in the paragraph.

3.26.C.2 Sort evidence into provided categories.

Name _____

Suffixes

Spelling Words				
beautiful	safely	kindness	finally	spotless
worthless	illness	helpful	daily	suddenly
wireless	quietly	fairness	cheerful	painful

Proofread a Note Christy sent a note to her neighbor who is in the hospital. Circle four spelling mistakes. Write the words correctly. Add the missing punctuation mark.

Dear Mrs Nelson,

Please get well soon! I hope your illnes is not very painful.

I've been watering your roses dayly. The yellow ones finnally bloomed. They look beautiful and very cheerfull.

Love,
Christy

Frequently Misspelled Words

finally
really

1. _____ 2. _____

3. _____ 4. _____

Proofread Words Fill in the circle next to the word that is spelled correctly. Write the word.

5. ○ suddennly ○ suddenly ○ suddenily 5. _____

6. ○ worthyles ○ worthles ○ worthless 6. _____

7. ○ safly ○ safely ○ safelly 7. _____

8. ○ quietly ○ quietily ○ qiuetly 8. _____

9. ○ kindnes ○ kinness ○ kindness 9. _____

10. ○ spotless ○ spotles ○ spottless 10. _____

School + Home **Home Activity** Your child spelled words with the suffixes -ly, -ful, -ness, and -less. Have your child underline the base word in each list word. Remind your child to change i back to y when necessary.

⊕ **3.24.A.2** Use knowledge of word parts to spell. **3.24.C.1** Spell high-frequency words from a commonly used list. **3.24.D.1** Spell words with common syllable constructions.

© Pearson Education, Inc., 3

Present, Past, and Future Tenses

Directions Read the selection. Then read each question that follows the selection. Decide which is the best answer to each question. Mark the space for the answer you have chosen.

Whales

(1) I _____ humpback whales. (2) Last summer, I _____ to the ocean to see them. (3) My jaw _____ when I saw them. (4) The whales traveled from the Arctic Ocean. (5) They _____ thousands of miles every year. (6) They _____ next year.

1 What present tense verb can be used in sentence 1?

- ⬭ like
- ⬭ liked
- ⬭ would like
- ⬭ liking

2 What past tense verb can be used in sentence 2?

- ⬭ travel
- ⬭ traveling
- ⬭ traveled
- ⬭ will travel

3 What past tense verb can be used in sentence 3?

- ⬭ dropping
- ⬭ will drop
- ⬭ dropped
- ⬭ droped

4 What present tense verb can be used in sentence 5?

- ⬭ will swim
- ⬭ swim
- ⬭ swimmed
- ⬭ swimed

5 What future tense verb can be used in sentence 6?

- ⬭ return
- ⬭ returning
- ⬭ returned
- ⬭ will return

Home Activity Your child prepared for taking tests on present, past, and future tenses. Point out a sentence in a book you are reading together. Have your child tell whether the sentence is in present, past, or future tense.

3.22.A.1.i.1 Use and understand verbs (past) in the context of reading, writing, and speaking. **Also 3.22.A.1.i.2, 3.22.A.1.i.3.**   **Conventions** Present, Past, and Future Tenses   **221**

Consonant Patterns *wr, kn, gn, st, mb*

Directions Choose the word in ( ) with the silent consonant, as in **wr, kn, st, mb,** or **gn,** to complete each sentence. Write the word on the line.

_____ **1.** It seemed like the perfect winter day for a (climb/hike) up the mountain.

_____ **2.** Jan packed water and snacks in a (cooler/knapsack).

_____ **3.** She put on her coat and (knit/new) cap.

_____ **4.** She grabbed the scarf with the blue and yellow (design/stripes).

_____ **5.** Then she (tossed/wrapped) it around her neck.

_____ **6.** Jan began to (close/fasten) her coat.

_____ **7.** The radio was on, and Jan stopped to (hear/listen).

_____ **8.** The reporter said there were (calls/signs) that a big snowstorm was on its way.

_____ **9.** Jan (learned/knew) she would have to go hiking another day.

Directions Circle each word in the box that has a silent consonant. Write the circled words in alphabetical order on the lines below.

gnaw relax castle wrong basket no comb knot humid water trap numb

10. _____ **13.** _____

11. _____ **14.** _____

12. _____ **15.** _____

© Pearson Education, Inc., 3

Home Activity Your child wrote words with the silent consonants *wr (write), kn (knight), st (listen), mb (thumb),* and *gn (gnaw).* Work with your child to see how many words with those silent letters you can name together. Write the words and take turns making sentences using each word.

★ Decode words by applying common spelling patterns.

Cause and Effect

- A **cause** tells why something happened.
- An **effect** is what happened.
- Words such as *because* and *so* are clues that can help you figure out a cause and its effect.

Directions Read the following article.

Some people have backyards that are full of animals. Their yards are almost like private zoos. That's because these nature-loving people have taken the time and trouble to plant trees. The trees attract birds, so the birds rush to build nests in the branches. Squirrels like trees, too, so they'll often be seen climbing the trunks and leaping from branch to branch. When people plant trees, they can enjoy watching wildlife in their backyards for years to come.

Directions Fill in the chart to show cause and effect. Then list two clue words from the passage that helped you figure out the cause and effect.

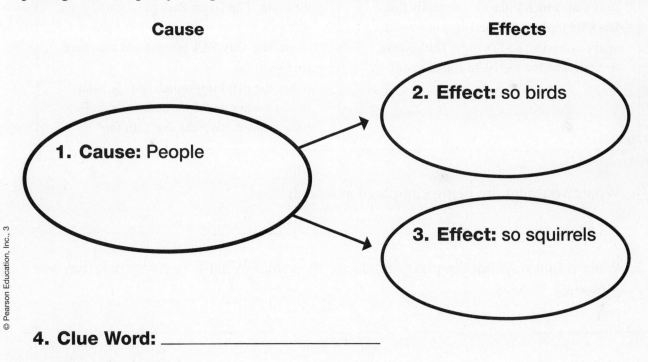

Cause

1. Cause: People

Effects

2. Effect: so birds

3. Effect: so squirrels

4. Clue Word: _____

5. Clue Word: _____

© Pearson Education, Inc., 3

School + Home **Home Activity** Your child identified cause and effect in an article. Talk with your child about things that happen around your home every day. Talk about what causes those things to happen.

3.13.C.1 Identify explicit cause and effect relationships among ideas in texts.

Writing • Compare-and-Contrast Composition

Key Features of a Compare-and-Contrast Composition

- shows how two things are similar and different
- includes supporting facts, details, and explanations
- ends with a concluding sentence or paragraph

A Tale of Two Playgrounds

There are two playgrounds I like to go to. The first is in Grant Park. The other one is in City Park. They have some things in common, but they also have differences.

The two playgrounds are the same in some ways. The Grant Park playground has a slide and swings. The slide is very tall. The playground also has a merry-go-round, which I like to spin really fast. The City Park playground also has a slide, merry-go-round, and swings. The slide is also tall, and the merry-go-round is just as fun.

The playgrounds have some differences too. Grant Park is near my house. We can walk to that playground. City Park is downtown, so we have to drive to get there. In the Grant Park playground, the ground is gravel. The City Park playground has sandy ground. The playgrounds are also different because the swings are different. The Grant Park playground uses soft swings that bend when you sit on them. The City Park playground uses hard, stiff swings.

So, the two playgrounds are the same in some ways and different in others. But most importantly, they are both fun!

1. What two things are being compared and contrasted?

_____

2. What is one way that the playgrounds are the same? What is one way that they are different?

_____

_____

_____

Name _____

Vocabulary

Directions Draw a line from the word to its meaning.

1. incredible   without moisture; dry

2. noble   not noticed

3. lofty   unbelievable

4. unseen   high up

5. waterless   impressive

Directions Fill in the blank with the word from the box that fits the meaning of the sentence.

6. It's fun to go in _____ of nature's secrets.

7. You may discover tricks animals use to be _____ in a harsh world.

8. Some birds keep their babies safe by building nests in _____ branches.

9. Some insects protect themselves by _____ their enemies.

10. Nature is always a good _____ of conversation.

Write a Journal Entry

Write a journal entry about a day spent observing nature. Use as many vocabulary words from this week as you can.

Home Activity Your child identified and used new vocabulary words from *Around One Cactus.* Talk with your child about animals and plants in your neighborhood. Use the vocabulary words on this page.

3.4.B.1 Use context to determine the relevant meaning of unfamiliar words.

© Pearson Education, Inc., 3

Irregular Verbs

Usually you add *-ed* to a verb to show past tense. **Irregular verbs** do not follow this rule. Instead of having *-ed* forms to show past tense, irregular verbs change to other words.

Present Tense	We <u>do</u> a report on water.
Past Tense	We <u>did</u> a report on water.
Past with *has, have,* or *had*	We <u>have done</u> reports on water.

Irregular verbs have a special form when they are used with *has, have,* and *had.* Use the special past forms in the third column of the chart only with these helping verbs.

Here are some irregular verbs and their past forms:

Present Tense	Past Tense	Past with *has, have,* or *had*
begin	began	*(has, have, had)* begun
do	did	*(has, have, had)* done
find	found	*(has, have, had)* found
give	gave	*(has, have, had)* given
go	went	*(has, have, had)* gone
run	ran	*(has, have, had)* run
see	saw	*(has, have, had)* seen
take	took	*(has, have, had)* taken
think	thought	*(has, have, had)* thought
wear	wore	*(has, have, had)* worn

Directions Choose the correct form of the irregular verb in ( ) to complete each sentence. Write the verb on the line.

1. My family (went, gone) for a hike in the desert. _____

2. We had (began, begun) hiking in the morning. _____

3. We (seen, saw) many desert creatures. _____

4. I had (think, thought) animals could not live there. _____

5. I (took, taken) lots of pictures. _____

© Pearson Education, Inc., 3

Home Activity Your child learned about irregular verbs. Ask your child this question: *What did you wear to school today?* Have your child answer with a sentence using *wear* in the past tense (*wore*).

⭐ **3.22.A.1.i.1** Use and understand verbs (past) in the context of reading, writing, and speaking. **Also 3.22.A.1.i.2.**

Consonant Patterns *wr, kn, gn, st, mb*

Spelling Words				
thumb	gnaw	written	know	climb
design	wrist	crumb	assign	wrench
knot	wrinkle	lamb	knob	knit

Words in Context Write the list word that completes each sentence.

1. A pup is a young dog. A _____ is a young sheep.

2. Your leg bends at the ankle. Your arm bends at the _____ .

3. You walk on a sidewalk. You _____ up a tree.

4. A bit of paper is a scrap. A bit of toast is a _____ .

5. You can weave a tablecloth. You can _____ a sweater.

6. Your big toe is on your foot. Your _____ is on your hand.

7. Music is composed. Books are _____ .

8. Chickens peck at corn. Dogs _____ on bones.

9. A carpenter uses a hammer. A plumber uses a _____ .

10. A gate has a latch. A door has a _____ .

Finishing Sentences Complete each sentence with a list word.

11. The artist painted a striped _____ on the vase.

12. I _____ how to dive.

13. He ironed every _____ out of his shirt.

14. She tied her shoelace in a _____ .

15. My teachers never _____ a lot of homework.

Home Activity Your child spelled words with *wr, kn, mb,* and *gn.* Have your child pronounce each list word and identify the "silent letter" (*w* in *wr, k* in *kn, b* in *mb, g* in *gn*).

3.24.A.1 Use knowledge of letter sounds to spell.
3.24.B.1.v Spell words with complex consonants.

Spelling Consonant Patterns *wr, kn, gn, st, mb*   **227**

Scoring Rubric: Writing for Tests: Expository Composition

	4	3	2	1
Focus/Ideas	Strong composition; compares and contrasts effectively	Good composition; compares and contrasts	Weak composition; poorly compares and/or contrasts	Poor composition; neither compares nor contrasts
Organization	Similarities and differences in clear order; includes strong concluding statement	Similarities and differences in fairly clear order; includes concluding statement	Similarities and differences in confused order; vague or weak conclusion	No similarities and differences; no conclusion
Voice	Writer shows interest in the subject	Writer shows some interest in the subject	Writer shows very little interest in the subject	Writer shows no interest in the subject
Word Choice	Strong use of compare/contrast words	Good use of compare/contrast words	Weak use of compare/contrast words	Poor or no use of compare/contrast words
Sentences	Sentences with different lengths and beginnings	Sentences with a few different lengths and beginnings	Sentences with similar lengths and beginnings	No variety in sentence lengths and beginnings
Conventions	Few or no errors; strong use of irregular verbs	Several minor errors; use of irregular verbs	Many errors; weak use of irregular verbs	Numerous errors; no use of irregular verbs

Name _____

Vocabulary: Word Structure

- A **prefix** is a syllable added at the beginning of a base word to change its meaning.
- A **suffix** is a syllable added to the end of a base word to change its meaning or the way it is used in a sentence.
- Recognizing prefixes and suffixes will help you figure out a word's meaning.

Directions Read the following passage about animals in hiding. Then answer the questions below. Look for prefixes and suffixes as you read.

> Many animals hide so well that they remain unseen unless we know how to find them. Some land turtles that live in a waterless environment crawl slowly along the ground. The slow movements don't attract our attention. Large birds may sit in lofty perches at the tops of tall trees. They are hidden by leaves, and we have to look hard to see them. Animals that can stay out of sight are most likely to be survivors in the harsh world of nature.

1. Does *unseen* have a prefix or a suffix? What does *unseen* mean?

_____

2. What is the base word in *waterless*? What does *waterless* mean?

_____

3. What is the base word in *slowly*? What is the suffix?

_____

4. What is the suffix in *lofty*? What does *lofty* mean?

_____

5. Is the *or* in *survivors* a prefix or suffix? What are survivors?

_____

_____

© Pearson Education, Inc., 3

Home Activity Your child used prefixes and suffixes to read and define unfamiliar words. Read an article about nature with your child. Ask your child to point out words with prefixes or suffixes.

3.1.A.1.iv.1 Decode multisyllabic words in context by applying common spelling patterns including using knowledge of common prefixes. 3.1.A.1.iv.2 Decode multisyllabic words in context by applying common spelling patterns including using knowledge of common suffixes.

Vocabulary 229

Newspaper

A **newspaper** is just what its name sounds like. It is the day's news printed on paper.

Directions Read the following article about newspapers. Then answer the questions.

Newspapers are printed on very large sheets of paper that are folded together in a packet. They include photographs and advertisements as well as articles. Advertisements pay for the cost of publishing newspapers.

There are many newspapers all across the country. Some are in big cities and some are in small towns. Some come out every day and others only publish once a week.

Every newspaper article has a headline. The headline is like the title of a book. It tells you in a few words what the article is about. Read the headline first to see if you want to read the article.

Newspapers are divided into sections by category. The front page usually contains a table of contents that gives the page numbers for each section. Sections usually include the following:

- **Front Page**—articles about important issues and events in the U.S. and the world
- **Local News**—articles about the city, town, or neighborhood in which the paper is published
- **Sports**—yesterday's scores and articles about games and athletes
- **Business**—articles about major events in the financial world
- **Entertainment**—movie reviews, entertainment stories, comic strips, crossword puzzles, and games

1. What is the purpose of a headline?

_____

2. Underline the section where you might find an article about who won the election for your town's mayor.

3. Draw a box around the section where you would look for yesterday's baseball scores.

4. In which section might you find an article about a nationwide strike by airline pilots?

_____

Home Activity Your child learned about the different sections of a newspaper. Show your child today's newspaper. Go through the sections together and have your child explain to you what he or she might find in each section.

3.13.D.1 Use text features to locate information.

Name _____

Consonant Patterns *wr*, *kn*, *gn*, *st*, *mb*

Proofread a Poster Circle four spelling mistakes on
the poster. Write the words correctly. Then write the
day and date correctly.

Art Fair!
Choose from four projects!

a. Make a wris or ankle knot bracelet.
b. Design a kite.
c. Learn an easy way to nit.
d. Make a thum puppet.

Where and wen: Room 103 on
wednesday january, 15

1. _____ 2. _____
3. _____ 4. _____

5. _____

**Frequently
Misspelled
Words**

know
when
where
what

Proofread Words Circle the correct word and write
it on the line.

6. Shall we **climb** **clim** to the top of the hill? 6. _____

7. I **know** **kow** where to find the glue. 7. _____

8. The **lam** **lamb** slept by her mother. 8. _____

9. He used a **wrench** **rench** to fix the leaky pipe. 9. _____

10. Did Mr. Rice **assin** **assign** the entire page? 10. _____

11. You have a **crum** **crumb** on your chin. 11. _____

12. The mouse will **gnaw** **naw** on the wires. 12. _____

School + Home

Home Activity Your child spelled words with *wr, kn, gn, st,* and *mb*. Have your child circle these
letter combinations in the list words.

3.24.A.1 Use knowledge of letter sounds to spell.
3.24.B.1.v Spell words with complex consonants.
3.24.C.1 Spell high-frequency words from a commonly used list.

Spelling Consonant Patterns *wr, kn, gn, st, mb* **231**

© Pearson Education, Inc., 3

Irregular Verbs

Directions Read the selection. Then read each question that follows the selection. Decide which is the best answer to each question. Mark the space for the answer you have chosen.

Learning About the Desert

(1) Jamie has <u>see</u> the desert. (2) He <u>give</u> a speech about the desert in class. (3) He <u>take</u> pictures of the desert plants and animals. (4) He showed us a path where a river had <u>wear</u> through the desert. (5) I had <u>think</u> the desert was empty. (6) Now I understand how amazing the desert really is.

1 What irregular verb is correct in sentence 1?
- ⬭ saw
- ⬭ sees
- ⬭ seen
- ⬭ sawen

2 What irregular verb is correct in sentence 2?
- ⬭ has gave
- ⬭ gave
- ⬭ giving
- ⬭ will go

3 What irregular verb is correct in sentence 3?
- ⬭ took
- ⬭ taken
- ⬭ taking
- ⬭ tooked

4 What irregular verb is correct in sentence 4?
- ⬭ wore
- ⬭ wearing
- ⬭ wored
- ⬭ worn

5 What irregular verb is correct in sentence 5?
- ⬭ thinked
- ⬭ thought
- ⬭ thinks
- ⬭ thoughted

© Pearson Education, Inc., 3

Home Activity Your child prepared for taking tests on irregular verbs. In a magazine or newspaper, point out a verb. Have your child tell whether the verb is regular or irregular.

✪ **3.22.A.1.i.1** Use and understand verbs (past) in the context of reading, writing, and speaking. **Also 3.22.A.1.i.2.**

Contractions

Spelling Words				
let's	he'd	you'll	can't	I'd
won't	haven't	hasn't	she'd	they'll
when's	we'd	should've	wasn't	didn't

Making Contractions Write the contraction for each pair of words.

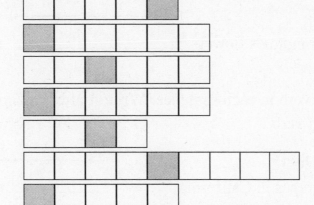

1. will not

2. has not

3. when is

4. you will

5. he would

6. should have

7. let us

Mystery Contractions Look at the shaded boxes. Write the letters and the apostrophe to make another contraction. Then write the two words that make up the contraction.

8. _____ = _____ + _____

Contraction Equations Write a contraction by solving each math word problem. Write an apostrophe in place of the letter or letters you subtract.

9. was + not – o = _____

10. I + would – woul = _____

11. she + had – ha = _____

12. have + not – o = _____

13. can + not – no = _____

14. did + not – o = _____

15. we + had – ha = _____

 Home Activity Your child has been learning to spell contractions. Use a newspaper or a magazine to hunt for contractions together. See how many can be found and circled in five minutes. Work together to figure out what two words make up each contraction.

Action and Linking Verbs

Directions Write the verb in each sentence.

1. Grandma plants bulbs every fall. _____

2. The plants grow in spring. _____

3. That plant is a lily. _____

4. These lilies are white. _____

5. This bulb is a tulip. _____

6. Everyone loves Grandma's flowers. _____

Directions Write the verb in each sentence. Write *A* after an action verb. Write *L* after a linking verb.

7. A raisin is a dried grape. _____

8. My uncle grows grapes in California. _____

9. I helped my uncle on the farm. _____

10. Plants need water and sunlight. _____

11. The grapes were ripe on the vines. _____

12. Workers laid them in the sun. _____

13. Raisins bake in the sun for two weeks. _____

14. Machines remove the dirt. _____

15. I packed some raisins. _____

16. The factory was busy. _____

17. Raisins are good snacks. _____

18. People buy my uncle's raisins. _____

3.22.A.1.i.1 Use and understand verbs (past) in the context of reading, writing, and speaking. **Also 3.22.A.1.i.2, 3.22.A.1.i.3.**

Prefixes

Spelling Words				
unhappy	recall	disappear	unload	mistake
misspell	dislike	replace	mislead	disagree
rewrite	unroll	unknown	dishonest	react

Context Clues Write the list word that correctly completes the sentence. Use the underlined word as a clue.

1. To not <u>spell</u> a word correctly is to ___misspell___ it.
2. If you don't <u>like</u> something, you ___dislike___ it.
3. To put something in its <u>place</u> again is to ___replace___ it.
4. To not <u>agree</u> is to ___disagree___.
5. To <u>call</u> back a memory of someone again is to ___recall___ that person.
6. For something to <u>appear</u> and then to pass from sight is for it to ___disappear___.
7. If you <u>take</u> something the wrong way, you ___mistake___ it.
8. A person who is not <u>honest</u> is ___dishonest___.
9. To <u>lead</u> someone the wrong way is to ___mislead___ that person.
10. To <u>write</u> something over is to ___rewrite___ it.
11. To <u>act</u> in response to something is to ___react___.

Making Opposites Use the base form of a list word. Add the prefix <u>un-</u> to make a word with the opposite meaning.

unknown	unroll	unload	unhappy

12. Dennis will roll the towel and lay it on the sandy beach. ___unroll___
13. Lily was happy about her broken computer. ___unhappy___
14. The stranger is known to me. ___unknow___
15. Please load the groceries and bring them into the house. ___unload___

School + Home **Home Activity** Your child has been spelling words with the prefixes *un-*, *re-*, *mis-*, and *dis-*. To practice the words together, help your child write each list word as an equation, like this: un + roll = unroll.

3.24.A.2 Use knowledge of word parts to spell. **3.24.D.1** Spell words with common syllable constructions.

Spelling   235

© Pearson Education, Inc., 3

Main Verbs and Helping Verbs

Directions Write the main verb and the helping verb in each sentence.

1. The men are hunting for deer in the forest.

   Main verb: _____

   Helping verb: _____

2. The women have planted corn in the field.

   Main verb: _____

   Helping verb: _____

3. The boys were fishing in the clear lake.

   Main verb: _____

   Helping verb: _____

4. The girl has sewn a pretty dress.

   Main verb: _____

   Helping verb: _____

5. I am learning about Native American life.

   Main verb: _____

   Helping verb: _____

Directions Look at the underlined verb in each sentence. Write *M* if it is a main verb. Write *H* if it is a helping verb.

6. A woman was <u>weaving</u> a basket. _____

7. She <u>will</u> make a necklace with beads. _____

8. The girls had <u>cut</u> the deerskin in pieces. _____

9. They are <u>making</u> shoes for everyone. _____

10. The boy <u>is</u> gathering pretty feathers. _____

⊕ **3.22.A.1.i.1** Use and understand verbs (past) in the context of reading, writing, and speaking. **Also 3.22.A.1.i.2, 3.22.A.1.i.3.**

Spellings of /j/, /s/, /k/

Spelling Words				
clock	large	page	mark	kitten
judge	crack	edge	pocket	brake
change	ridge	jacket	badge	orange

Silly Sentences Read each silly sentence. Write the list word that rhymes with the underlined word and makes sense in the sentence.

1. I looked at a <u>sock</u> to tell the time.   1. _____

2. My <u>mitten</u> likes milk.   2. _____

3. There is a big black <u>park</u> on my paper.   3. _____

4. The <u>fudge</u> is in court right now.   4. _____

5. There is a <u>barge</u> hippo in the zoo.   5. _____

6. This book <u>stage</u> has many words on it.   6. _____

7. My <u>racket</u> has a zipper and two pockets.   7. _____

8. Dad stepped on the <u>rake</u> to stop the car.   8. _____

9. Please <u>range</u> the TV channel.   9. _____

10. I have a dime in my <u>rocket</u>.   10. _____

Letter Directions Follow each direction. Write the new word.

11. Add **ge** to **bad**.   11. _____

12. Add **o** to **range**.   12. _____

13. Subtract **pl** from **pledge**.   13. _____

14. Add **c** to **rack**.   14. _____

15. Subtract **f** from **fridge**.   15. _____

Home Activity Your child learned words spelled with *ge*, *dge*, *ck*, and *k*. To help you practice the list words with your child, say each word and ask your child to spell it. Then take turns naming words that rhyme with it.

🌟 **3.24.A.1** Use knowledge of letter sounds to spell.
3.24.B.1.v Spell words with complex consonants.

Subject-Verb Agreement

Direction Choose the verb in ( ) that agrees with the subject. Write the verb.

1. The city lights (hide, hides) the stars. _____

2. Stars (gleam, gleams) brightly in the country. _____

3. They (seem, seems) close enough to touch. _____

4. The Big Dipper (look, looks) huge. _____

5. Our galaxy (is, are) amazing. _____

Directions Choose the verb in ( ) that agrees with the subject. Write the sentence.

6. This telescope (work, works) well.

_____

_____

7. We (see, sees) millions of stars.

_____

_____

8. Rigel (is, are) one of the brightest stars.

_____

_____

9. Hot gases (make, makes) it sparkle.

_____

_____

10. Astronomers often (find, finds) new stars.

_____

_____

3.22.C.1 Use complete simple sentences with correct subject-verb agreement.

Suffixes

Spelling Words				
beautiful	safely	kindness	finally	spotless
worthless	illness	helpful	daily	suddenly
wireless	quietly	fairness	cheerful	painful

Choosing Suffixes Circle the suffix needed to make a list word. Write the list word.

Base Word	**Suffix**		**List Word**
1. kind	ful	ness	**1.** _____
2. quiet	ly	ful	**2.** _____
3. cheer	ful	ness	**3.** _____
4. spot	ly	less	**4.** _____
5. worth	less	ful	**5.** _____
6. sudden	ful	ly	**6.** _____
7. ill	ly	ness	**7.** _____
8. safe	ful	ly	**8.** _____
9. help	ful	ness	**9.** _____
10. final	less	ly	**10.** _____

Meaning Clues Write a list word for each meaning clue.

11. full of beauty   __ __ __ __ __ __ __ ▢ __ __

12. full of pain   __ ▢ __ __ __ __ __

13. done each day   __ __ ▢ __ __ __

14. with no wire   __ __ ▢ __ __ __ __ __

Mystery Word Write the mystery word formed by the boxes. Then write the list word by adding the suffix *-ness* to the mystery word.

15. _____   _____

Home Activity Your child is learning to spell words with the suffixes *-ly*, *-ful*, *-ness*, and *-less*. Help your child write list words with two different suffixes, such as *painless, painful* and *kindly, kindness.*

3.24.A.2 Use knowledge of word parts to spell.
3.24.D.1 Spell words with common syllable constructions.

Spelling 239

Name _____

Present, Past, and Future Tenses

Directions Tell the tense of the underlined verb in each sentence.
Write *present, past,* or *future.*

1. Scientists <u>discovered</u> some smart mammals. _____

2. The mammals <u>live</u> in the ocean. _____

3. Many dolphins <u>learned</u> tricks. _____

4. Scientists <u>will study</u> dolphins more. _____

Directions Write the verb in ( ) that correctly completes each sentence.

5. These dolphins live at the sea park, and they (perform, performed) each day.

    _____

6. A few minutes ago, a dolphin (leaps, leaped) out of the water.

    _____

7. Tomorrow the dolphins (invented, will invent) a new trick.

    _____

8. In next week's show, a dolphin (tossed, will toss) a ball into a net.

    _____

9. Yesterday the dolphins (played, play) happily with their trainers.

    _____

10. I (enjoyed, will enjoy) dolphins in the future.

    _____

11. In yesterday's show, a dolphin (pushed, will push) a ball across the pool.

    _____

12. People watch the dolphins and (clapped, clap) loudly.

    _____

© Pearson Education, Inc., 3

3.22.A.1.i.1 Use and understand verbs (past) in the context of reading, writing, and speaking. **Also, 3.22.A.1.i.2, 3.22.A.1.i.3, 3.22.C.2.**

Cause-and-Effect Chart

Directions Most events in nature have more than one cause and effect. Fill in the chart with each cause and effect that helps explain the event you are planning to write about in your essay.

Natural Event	
Cause	**Effect**

3.17.A.1 Plan a first draft by selecting a genre appropriate for conveying the intended meaning to an audience. **3.17.B.1** Develop drafts by categorizing ideas.

Use Logical Order

Directions Choose a sentence from the box that logically follows each numbered sentence below. Write the letter of the second sentence on the line. Then write a third sentence that logically follows the first two sentences.

A. The house is very dirty.
B. The house was crowded.
C. The house is too small.

D. The house was completely dark.
E. The house was very quiet.
F. The house is vacant.

---

1. We lost our electricity for six hours last night.

   Second sentence: _____

   Logical conclusion:

   _____

2. Our neighbors moved away last year.

   Second sentence: _____

   Logical conclusion:

   _____

3. No one was home when Jim returned from baseball practice that morning.

   Second sentence: _____

   Logical conclusion:

   _____

4. The vacuum cleaner has stopped working.

   Second sentence: _____

   Logical conclusion:

   _____

3.17.B.1 Develop drafts by categorizing ideas.

Combining Sentences

When you revise, you can combine two short simple sentences to make a compound sentence. Make sure the ideas in the two sentences are related. Use one of these conjunctions: *and, but,* or *or.* Put a comma before the conjunction.

Simple Sentences The fire lasted three days. Most of the forest was destroyed.
Compound Sentence The fire lasted three days, and most of the forest was destroyed.

Directions Combine each pair of simple sentences with the conjunction *and, but,* or *or* to make a compound sentence. Don't forget to add a comma.

1. Flames raced from tree to tree. Black smoke filled the sky.

_____

_____

2. People could stay in their homes. They could go to shelters.

_____

_____

3. Firefighters worked day and night. They could not control the blaze.

_____

_____

4. No rain had fallen in weeks, and the forest was very dry.

_____

_____

5. The forest will return. It is hard to imagine trees growing here.

_____

_____

3.17.C.2 Revise drafts for organization.
3.17.C.3 Revise drafts for use of simple sentences.
3.17.C.4 Revise drafts for use of compound sentences.

Unit 3 Writing Process **245**

Editing 2

Directions Edit these sentences. Look for errors in spelling, grammar, and mechanics. Use proofreading marks to show the corrections.

Proofreading Marks	
Delete (Take out)	⌐
Add	∧
Spelling	⬭
Uppercase letter	≡
Lowercase letter	/

1. Farmers plant seeds in there fields and grew many different crops.

2. how are seeds in nature planted to grow into new plants

3. Nature has it's own sistem of planting its seeds.

4. Scattered in many ways

5. Some seeds has parachutes or wings that take flite on a windy day.

6. Seeds that float may fell into water and be carried to a new place.

7. Other seeds are taken to new places by animals that eat fruit contain seeds.

8. Some seeds' travel on animals or people by sticking to it.

Now you'll edit the draft of your cause-and-effect essay. Next, you'll use your revised and edited draft to make a final copy of your essay. Finally, you'll share your written work with your audience.

3.17.D Edit drafts for grammar, mechanics, and spelling, using a teacher-developed rubric. **3.17.E.1** Publish written work for a specific audience.

Irregular Plurals

Directions Use the plural form of each word in ( ) to complete each sentence.
Write the word on the line.

_____ **1.** Timmy wasn't like the other (mouse).

_____ **2.** He was missing all his (tooth).

_____ **3.** He couldn't chew into the (loaf) of bread in the bakery
where he lived.

_____ **4.** Using his (foot) to pull off tiny pieces of bread didn't
work.

_____ **5.** Of course the (woman) who worked in the bakery would
never feed him.

_____ **6.** When the delivery (man) came, Timmy would run and
hide.

_____ **7.** Timmy finally solved his problem when he saw some
(child) dropping crumbs.

_____ **8.** Now he stores the crumbs behind the (shelf) so he can eat
them whenever he wants.

Directions Write the plural form of each word below.

9. wife _____

10. wolf _____

11. scarf _____

12. hero _____

13. cuff _____

14. calf _____

15. banjo _____

16. elf _____

17. half _____

18. goose _____

19. knife _____

20. sheep _____

© Pearson Education, Inc., 3

Home Activity Your child wrote plurals—words naming more than one person, place, or thing. Ask your child to review the plural forms of the words on the page above. Work together to write a silly poem or song using these and other plural words.

3.24.A.1 Use knowledge of letter sounds to spell.

Generalize

- An **autobiography** is a book in which the author tells the story of his or her own life. It is written in the **first person**. The author uses pronouns such as *I, me, my, our, us,* and *we.*

- A **biography** is a life story written about someone other than the author. It is written in the **third person**. The author uses pronouns such as *he, she, him, her, his, hers, they,* and *them.*

- When you read autobiographies, biographies, and other types of literature, you can sometimes use what you have read to make a **general statement,** or **generalization.** When you generalize, you use individual examples to make a general rule about a subject.

Directions Read the following life stories. Think about generalizations you can make from what you have read. Then answer the questions.

When she was little, Bonnie never sat still. She turned somersaults. She jumped on the bed. She did splits. Finally her mother took her to gymnastics class. Bonnie loved it. She practiced and practiced. She dreamed of being an Olympic star.

Dad bought a little basketball when I was born. Maybe that's why I grew up loving the game. I practiced all the time because I loved to play, but all that practice made me better and better. I began to wonder whether I could be a professional player.

1. Which passage is an autobiography?

_____

2. How do you know?

_____

3. Think about what you read in both passages. What generalization can you make about when many star athletes probably begin learning their sport?

_____

4. Think about what you read in both passages. What generalization can you make about what most star athletes probably do that makes them successful?

_____

5. Reread your answer to question 4. What generalization can you make about why star athletes do this?

_____

Home Activity Your child read a biographical passage and an autobiographical passage and used the ideas to make generalizations. With your child, read two or more biographical articles about successful people. Then ask your child to make a generalization about how people become successful.

★ Make and support generalizations about text.

Writing Persuasive Text

Key Features of Persuasive Text

- take a position on a subject
- tries to influence the reader's opinion
- provides details or evidence to support the opinion
- might urge the reader to take action

Fun on the Ice

Curling is a fun, unique sport that everyone should try. It is a sport you play on an icy surface, such as a frozen pond or an ice rink. To play, one person throws a large, heavy stone toward a target called a "tee." Other players sweep the ice in front of the stone to make it go faster or slower.

Curling is a good sport for people who live in places with long winters. It is especially popular where ponds and lakes freeze over in the winter. If you like other winter sports like hockey, ice skating, or skiing, you will probably like curling.

In curling, sportsmanship is very important. Before you play, your team shakes hands with the other team and says "Good Curling." After you play, you shake hands again. You can learn a lot about being a good sport from curling.

Curling is also a good way to spend time with friends. You and your teammates have to practice a lot to become good at "throwing," sliding, the stones and getting them to stop in just the right places. Teams have to learn to work together.

So next time you want to have some fun on the ice, try curling!

1. What is the purpose of this persuasive essay?

_____

2. What reasons does the author use to achieve his or her purpose?

_____

_____

3. Which reason do you think is most persuasive?

_____

Vocabulary

Directions Draw a line from the word to its meaning.

Check the Words You Know

___basketball	___popular
___disease	___sports
___freeze	___study
___guard	___terrible

1. disease   enjoyed by many people

2. freeze   a game in which teams toss a ball into a basket

3. guard   illness

4. basketball   to keep an opponent from scoring points

5. popular   to get very, very cold

Directions Fill in the blank with the word from the box that fits the meaning of the sentence.

6. What are your favorite ____sports____?

7. One of my favorites is ____basketball____.

8. It is very ____popular____ with my friends, too.

9. We ____study____ our favorite players and then try to play the way they do.

10. A day when we can't play our favorite game is a ____freeze____ day.

Write Copy for a Sports Card

Think about sports you like. Write about your favorite player. Use as many vocabulary words from this week as you can.

Home Activity Your child identified and used new vocabulary words from *The Man Who Invented Basketball*. Talk with your child about favorite sports. Encourage your child to use the vocabulary words on this page.

3.4.B.1 Use context to determine the relevant meaning of unfamiliar words.

© Pearson Education, Inc., 3

Singular and Plural Pronouns

Pronouns are words that take the place of nouns. Pronouns that take the place of singular nouns are **singular pronouns**. *I, me, he, she, him, her,* and *it* are singular pronouns.

Singular Pronoun The <u>man</u> can run fast. <u>He</u> can run fast.

Pronouns that take the place of plural nouns are **plural pronouns**. *We, us, they,* and *them* are plural pronouns.

Plural Pronoun <u>Turtles</u> cannot run. <u>They</u> cannot run.

You can be used as a singular and a plural pronoun.

<u>Sam and Sara</u>, where do <u>you</u> like to run?

<u>Sara</u>, <u>you</u> are the fastest runner.

Directions Write the pronoun in each sentence.

1. People like to have fun, so we invent games. _____

2. Games and exercise are important to us. _____

3. People long ago had ideas, and they created games. _____

4. My sister and I invented a game. _____

5. She is a lot of fun. _____

Directions Write *S* if the underlined pronoun is singular. Write *P* if it is plural.

6. James Naismith was clever, and <u>he</u> invented a game. _____

7. The game was fast, and <u>it</u> was fun. _____

8. Two teams played the game, and <u>they</u> tried to make baskets. _____

9. <u>We</u> still play the game today. _____

10. Mike's team got new uniforms and wore <u>them</u> to the game. _____

Home Activity Your child learned about singular and plural pronouns. Make up sentences about one or more members of your family. Have your child repeat the sentences using pronouns in place of people's names.

★ Understand and use pronouns.

© Pearson Education, Inc., 3

Irregular Plurals

Spelling Words				
wolves	knives	feet	men	children
women	sheep	heroes	scarves	mice
geese	cuffs	elves	banjos	halves

Seeing Relationships Write list words to complete the comparisons.

1. arms and hands, legs and _____   1. _____

2. cats and lions, dogs and _____   2. _____

3. feet and shoes, necks and _____   3. _____

4. milk and cows, wool and _____   4. _____

5. boys and girls, men and _____   5. _____

6. tubas and trumpets, violins and _____   6. _____

7. grown and adults, young and _____   7. _____

8. fur and rabbits, feathers and _____   8. _____

9. leaders and followers, cowards and _____   9. _____

10. four and fourths, two and _____   10. _____

Rhyming Plurals Write a list word that rhymes with the underlined word.

11. The _____ on my coat look like <u>puffs</u> of fur.   11. _____

12. The _____ in this story live on toy <u>shelves</u>.   12. _____

13. We've found _____ in the garage <u>twice</u>.   13. _____

14. The _____ put the cattle back in the <u>pen</u>.   14. _____

15. They carry _____ on <u>dives</u> in dangerous water.   15. _____

Home Activity Your child spelled plural words. Name a list word. Ask your child to explain how the plural was formed.

3.24.A.1 Use knowledge of letter sounds to spell. **3.24.A.2** Use knowledge of word parts to spell. **3.24.A.3** Use knowledge of word segmentation to spell.

© Pearson Education, Inc., 3

Main Idea

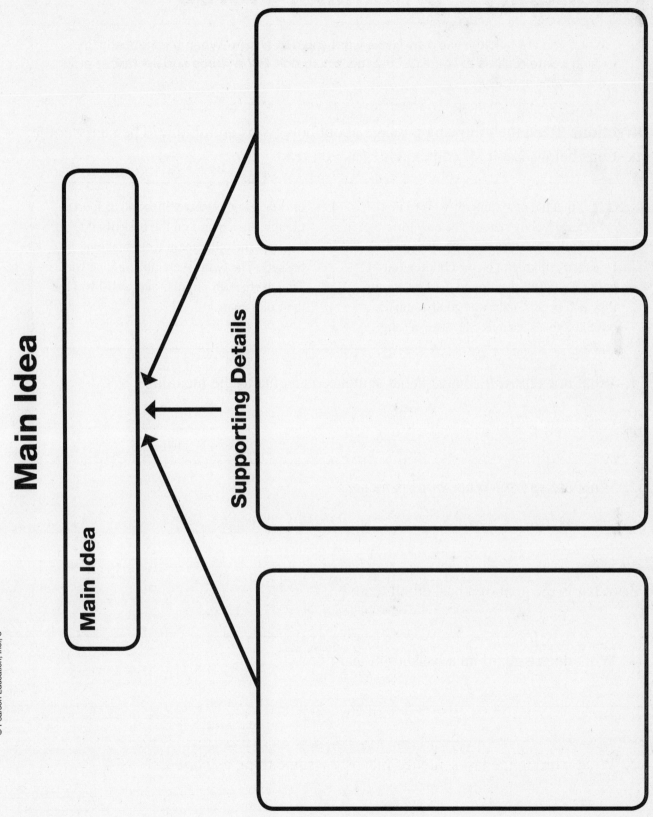

Main Idea

Supporting Details

Vocabulary • Unfamiliar Words

When you are reading, you may find a word you don't know. When this happens, try using **context clues** to figure out the meaning. Look at the words and sentences around the unfamiliar word.

Directions Read the following passage about how twins are unique. Then answer the questions below. Look for context clues as you read.

> When the new students walked in, everybody stared. The new girls were twins! Everyone thought they would be exactly alike. But as the children got to know the twins, they found out how wrong they had been. Cindy was good at music, but Sandy was terrible. She always sang off key. Sandy was really good at sports, though. As a guard on the basketball team, she kept the other team from making baskets. The twins were alike in one way. They were both popular and well-liked by their classmates.

1. What does *terrible* mean? What sentence is a clue to the meaning?

_____

_____

2. What are *sports*? What word is a clue?

_____

_____

3. What is the goal of a basketball team?

_____

_____

4. What does a guard on a basketball team do?

_____

_____

5. What word in the last sentence means the same thing as *popular*?

_____

Home Activity Your child used context clues to figure out the meanings of unfamiliar words. Read a biography or character sketch with your child. Stop when you come to an unfamiliar word and ask your child to use context clues to determine the word's meaning.

3.4.B.1 Use context to determine the relevant meaning of unfamiliar words.

Dictionary

- You can use a **dictionary** to find the meaning of unfamiliar words.
- The words in a dictionary are listed in **alphabetical order.**
- The **guide words** that appear at the top of the page show the first and last entries on that page.

Directions Read the sentences below. One word is underlined. Use the sample dictionary page to write the definition of the underlined word on the line.

gawk • whisper	**swirl** *v.* move along with a twisting motion; whirl
gawk *v.* stare at in a rude way	**wag** *v.* move from side to side or up and down
nag *v.* annoy by complaining about something	**whisper** *v.* to speak very softly and gently
snicker *v.* to laugh in a sly or silly way	

1. I had to <u>whisper</u> so the baby wouldn't wake up.

_____

2. Why did the children <u>gawk</u> at the clown in the supermarket?

_____

3. I watched the snowflakes <u>swirl</u> in the air as they fell.

_____

4. When you see cats <u>wag</u> their tails, you know they are trying to make a decision about something.

_____

5. I put my hand over my mouth so no one would hear me <u>snicker</u>.

_____

6. My sister likes to <u>nag</u> me to put my things away.

_____

Home Activity Your child used a sample dictionary page to define unfamiliar words. Show your child a school dictionary. Play a game in which you cover up the page, showing only the guide words at the top. Have your child list and define five words that appear on the page.

3.4.E.2 Use a dictionary or glossary to determine meanings of unknown words.

Irregular Plurals

Proofread a Report Robbie wrote a report about the class field trip. Circle four misspelled words. Write them correctly. Write the verb Robbie should have used in his second sentence.

> Our class went to the nature center. We seen sheep, gese, and even some wolves.
>
> The two wemen who showed us around said wolves eat everything from big deer to little field mouses—but not children! Still, I wouldn't wunt to get too close to a wolf.

1. _____

2. _____

3. _____

4. _____

5. _____

Proofread Words Fill in a circle to show which word is spelled correctly. Write the word.

6. Two musicians played _____ for the square dance.
   ○ banjoes   ○ banjos   ○ banjoys

6. _____

7. We rolled up our _____ and went to work.
   ○ cuves   ○ cuffes   ○ cuffs

7. _____

8. The _____ helped the shoemaker with his work.
   ○ elves   ○ elfs   ○ elvies

8. _____

9. My mom has some pretty _____ .
   ○ scarves   ○ scarfs   ○ scarvs

9. _____

10. The police officers were _____ .
    ○ herros   ○ heroes   ○ heros

10. _____

Home Activity Your child identified misspelled plurals. Say the singular form of a list word. Ask your child to spell the plural.

3.24.A.1 Use knowledge of letter sounds to spell. 3.24.A.2 Use knowledge of word parts to spell. 3.24.A.3 Use knowledge of word segmentation to spell. 3.24.C.1 Spell high-frequency words from a commonly used list.

© Pearson Education, Inc., 3

Singular and Plural Pronouns

Directions Read the selection. Then read each question that follows the selection. Decide which is the best answer to each question. Mark the space for the answer you have chosen.

Basketball

(1) Basketball is a very popular game. (2) <u>Basketball</u> is played across the country. (3) James Naismith invented it, but <u>James</u> may not even recognize it anymore. (4) Fans fill thousands of seats every night to watch, and <u>the fans</u> love a good show. (5) Michael Jordan was a very popular player. (6) <u>Michael Jordan</u> led his team to 6 championships. (7) The game has female stars too, and many of <u>the female stars</u> are popular, too.

1 What pronoun can replace the noun in sentence 2?

⬭ They

⬭ He

⬭ It

⬭ I

2 What pronoun can replace the noun in sentence 3?

⬭ he

⬭ they

⬭ it

⬭ him

3 What pronoun can replace the noun in sentence 4?

⬭ he

⬭ her

⬭ she

⬭ they

4 What pronoun can replace the noun in sentence 6?

⬭ Him

⬭ He

⬭ They

⬭ It

5 What pronoun can replace the noun in sentence 7?

⬭ her

⬭ she

⬭ we

⬭ them

Home Activity Your child prepared for taking tests on singular and plural pronouns. Read a book with your child. Point out several sentences with pronouns. Have your child identify the pronouns and tell whether they are singular or plural.

★ Understand and use pronouns.

Vowels: *r*-Controlled /ėr/

Directions Circle the words in the box that have the vowel sound /ėr/ as in **bird, her, turn, earn,** and **work.** Then write the words you circled under the word that has the same vowel spelling.

burst	hear	corn	dear	early	there	fern
fire	flare	heart	girl	hurry	learn	pear
perch	skirt	tire	torn	world	worm	

bird

1. _____

2. _____

her

3. _____

4. _____

turn

5. _____

6. _____

earn

7. _____

8. _____

work

9. _____

10. _____

Directions Circle the word that has the same vowel sound as the first word. Then write a sentence that uses the word you circled.

11. farm   frame   dart   rare

_____

12. short   hoot   horn   shot

_____

13. core   cone   to   shore

_____

14. board   boat   proud   roar

_____

Home Activity Your child identified and wrote words with *r*-controlled vowels. With your child, write sentences for the answer words from items 1-10 above. Ask your child to underline the letters that stand for /ėr/.

3.1.B.1.iv Use common syllabication patterns to decode words including *r*-controlled vowels.

Graphic Sources

- A **graphic source** is an image that helps you understand what you read.
- There are many types of graphic sources. They include maps, photos, illustrations, graphs, and diagrams.

Directions Study the following graphic source. Then answer the questions below.

Gulf of Mexico

1. What does this map show? How do you know?

_____

_____

2. Which state is the farthest east on the map?

_____

3. Which state seems to be the largest?

_____

4. Find your home state. Which states border on it?

_____

5. Which state has the fewest border states? How many border states touch this state?

_____

_____

© Pearson Education, Inc., 3

Home Activity Your child looked at a graphic source and answered questions about it. Look at a map of your home town or city with your child. Have your child answer questions about the map.

3.26.A.1.iii Follow the research plan to collect information from multiple sources of written information, including visual sources.

Writing • Imaginative Story

Key Features of an Imaginative Story

- tells a made-up story that did not really happen
- has a plot that builds to a climax
- has characters—people or animals in the story
- has a setting—where and when the story takes place

A Day in the Desert

It was a hot, dry day in the desert that stretches beyond my burrow. Barry and I were building a fort in the sand. Barry is my best friend. We're lizards, more commonly known as Gila monsters. Not only does Barry make great forts, but he can also always make me laugh.

The day became hotter and drier in the midday sun. Barry and I decided to go home. But where was home? We both looked around, but nothing looked familiar. There were stretches of sandy soil in every direction. We had wandered too far into the desert.

"Let's start walking this way," I suggested. Soon we started trotting, our scaly tails tracing paths in the sand behind us. Growing more and more nervous, we began to run.

Suddenly Barry asked, "How far can you run into the desert?"

"I don't know, Barry. How far *can* you run into the desert?"

"You can only run into the desert halfway. After that, you're running *out* of the desert."

I started laughing so hard that I nearly ran into a cactus plant. When I finally looked up, there was a rocky outcrop— the same rocky outcrop that shades the entrance to my burrow—off in the distance.

1. Underline the sentence that is the most exciting part of the plot.

2. Draw a circle around the characters in the story.

3. Draw a box around the words that tell the setting.

Vocabulary

Directions Draw a line from the word to its definition.

Check the Words You Know
___outrun   ___tides
___deserts   ___waterfalls
___peak   ___average
___depth   ___erupted

1. average   violently sent out lava, ash, and gases

2. deserts   the very top of a mountain

3. depth   normal, usual

4. erupted   places with little rainfall

5. peak   having to do with how deep something is

Directions Write the word from the box that best matches each clue.

6. The winners of a race do this.   _____

7. These falling waters are often shown on postcards.   _____

8. Snow is often found on this part of a mountain.   _____

9. Cactus plants grow here.   _____

10. These are related to ocean waters.   _____

Write a Travel Brochure

On a separate sheet of paper, write a travel brochure describing a place and the things people may see there. Use as many vocabulary words as possible.

© Pearson Education, Inc., 3

Home Activity Your child identified and used vocabulary words from *Hottest, Coldest, Highest, Deepest*. With your child, read a story or nonfiction article about Earth science. Talk about landforms. Encourage your child to use vocabulary words in your conversation.

3.4.B.1 Use context to determine the relevant meaning of unfamiliar words.

Subject and Object Pronouns

A pronoun used as the subject of a sentence is called a **subject pronoun.** A pronoun used after an action verb or as the object of a preposition is called an **object pronoun.**

- *I, you, he, she, it, we,* and *they* are subject pronouns.
- *Me, you, him, her, it, us,* and *them* are object pronouns.

Subject Pronouns <u>They</u> visited Mount Rainier. Sam and <u>I</u> went too.
Object Pronouns The mountain amazed <u>them</u>. They took pictures of Sam and <u>me</u>.

Directions Write the pronouns in each sentence.

1. She was on a high mountain, and the wind bothered her. _____

2. In the desert, the sun beats down on you. _____

3. The Mississippi is a long river, and it has many kinds of fish. _____

4. The huge waterfall impressed him. _____

5. He and I watched the tide come into shore. _____

Directions Write *SP* if the underlined pronoun is a subject pronoun. Write *OP* if it is an object pronoun.

6. Lake Superior is the largest of the Great Lakes. <u>It</u> is also the deepest. _____

7. The lake's size interested <u>us</u>. _____

8. Jamal visited Africa. There <u>he</u> saw the Nile River. _____

9. The rains in the tropical forest drenched <u>them</u>. _____

10. The deep snow on the mountain surprised Tina and <u>him</u>. _____

© Pearson Education, Inc., 3

 Home Activity Your child learned about subject and object pronouns. Make up sentences about book and movie characters. Have your child repeat the sentences with pronouns in place of the characters' names.

Vowels: *r*-Controlled

Spelling Words				
third	early	world	certain	dirty
herself	earth	word	perfect	verb
nerve	worm	thirsty	workout	earn

Complete the Sentence Write a list word to complete the sentence.

1. This is really a _____ day!

2. He had a _____ at the gym.

3. I put a _____ on my fishhook.

4. May I have a _____ with you?

5. I'm so _____ I could drink a gallon of water!

6. Don't lose your _____!

7. I'd like to travel around the _____ .

8. This is the _____ time we've won.

1. _____

2. _____

3. _____

4. _____

5. _____

6. _____

7. _____

8. _____

Opposites Write a list word that means the opposite.

9. late

10. unsure

11. noun

12. himself

13. sky

14. clean

15. win

9. _____

10. _____

11. _____

12. _____

13. _____

14. _____

15. _____

earth
certain
early
dirty
herself
verb
earn

Home Activity Your child spelled words with *er, ir, or,* and *ear.* Have your child circle htese letter combinations in the list words.

3.24.A.1 Use knowledge of letter sounds to spell. **3.24.A.2** Use knowledge of word parts to spell.

© Pearson Education, Inc., 3

Story Sequence B

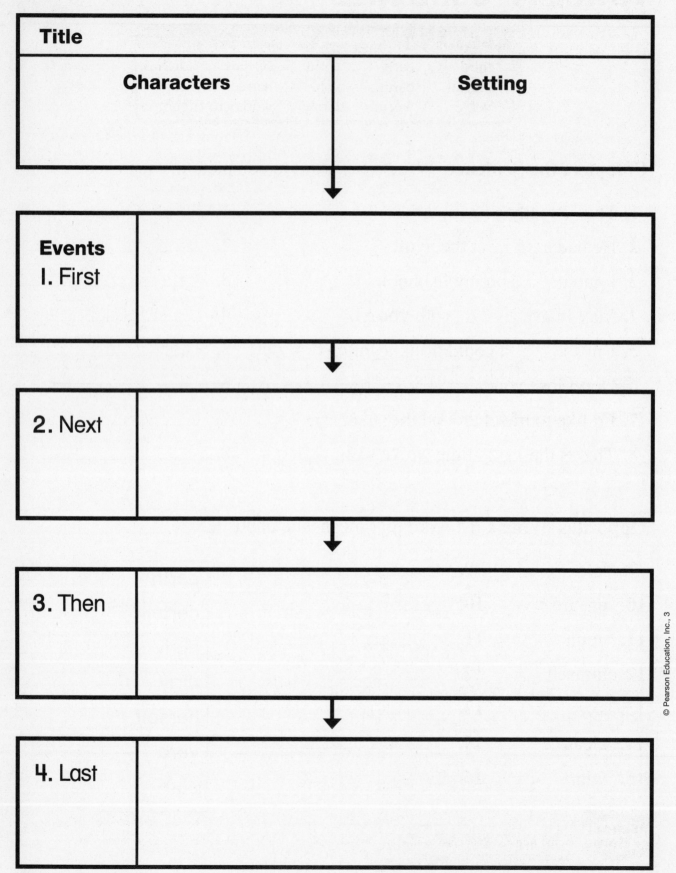

Title	
Characters	**Setting**

Events
1. First

2. Next

3. Then

4. Last

Vocabulary • Unknown Words

- You can use a glossary or a dictionary to find the meaning, syllabication, and pronunciation of **unknown words.**

---

av • er • age (avʹ ər ij) *adj.* normal, usual
depth (depth) *n.* the distance from the top to the bottom
out • run (out runʹ) *v.* to move faster than someone or something

peak (pēk) *n.* the pointed top of a mountain or hill
tide (tīd) *n.* the rise and fall of the ocean about every twelve hours • *PLURAL* **tides**

Directions Read the passage. Use the glossary entries to answer the questions.

On an **average** summer day, some people like to wade far out into the ocean. This can be risky. Incoming **tides** change the **depth** of the water. The water level rises, and the beach disappears. If this happens to you, you can try to **outrun** the tide. Or you may be able to climb to the top of a tall, rocky **peak** in the water and wait until the tide goes out. The best thing to do, though, is to stay out of trouble by learning about tides.

1. How many syllables are in the word *average*?

_____

2. How many syllables are in the word *depth?*

_____

3. What are tides?

_____

4. Does the *e* in *peak* have a long or short sound?

_____

5. Which syllable should you stress when you say *outrun*?

_____

Home Activity Your child used a glossary to understand meanings, syllabication, and pronunciation of words from *Hottest, Coldest, Highest, Deepest*. Read an article about nature with your child. Encourage your child to use a dictionary to find the meanings and pronunciations of unknown words.

3.4.E.2 Use a dictionary or glossary to determine meanings of unknown words.
3.4.E.3 Use a dictionary or glossary to determine syllabication of unknown words.
3.4.E.4 Use a dictionary or glossary to determine pronunciation of unknown words.

Bar Graphs

Bar graphs compare amounts and numbers. The bars can go across or up and down. The words on the graph tell what is being compared. The ends of the bars line up to a number.

Directions The bar graph below shows the five longest distances thrown in a baseball throw event. Use the graph to answer each question.

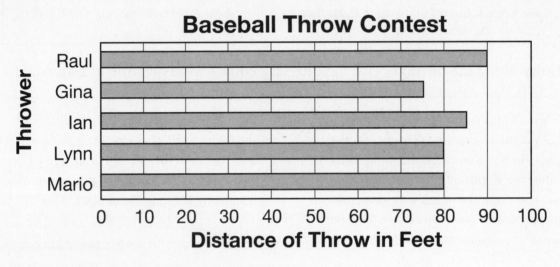

Baseball Throw Contest

Thrower — Raul, Gina, Ian, Lynn, Mario

Distance of Throw in Feet — 0 10 20 30 40 50 60 70 80 90 100

1. What is the distance of the longest throw?

_____

2. Which person threw the shortest distance?

_____

3. What distance did Ian throw the baseball?

_____

4. Which two people threw the same distance?

_____

5. What is the distance between the longest and shortest throws?

_____

Home Activity Your child answered questions by interpreting data in a bar graph. Collect some data about your family, such as height, age, or shoe size. Help your child make a bar graph with this data.

⊕ **3.26.A.1.iii** Follow the research plan to collect information from multiple sources of written information, including visual sources.

Vowels: *r*-Controlled

Proofread Workout Tips Circle four misspelled words. Write them correctly. Cross out the incorrect end mark and write the correct one.

Workout Tips
- Some people plan a workout early in the day, but there's no pirfect time. Just be ceartain you do it!
- Drink extra water—even if you're not thersty.
- Do something you like. Have you herd that jogging is best.

Spelling Words

third
early
world
certain
dirty
herself
earth
word

perfect
verb
nerve
worm
thirsty
workout
earn

Frequently Misspelled Words

another
brother
heard

1. _____   2. _____

3. _____   4. _____

Proofread Words Circle the correctly spelled word. Write it.

5. nurve	nerve	5. _____
6. worm	werm	6. _____
7. ern	earn	7. _____
8. dirty	durty	8. _____
9. third	therd	9. _____
10. hurself	herself	10. _____
11. workout	werkout	11. _____
12. vurb	verb	12. _____

© Pearson Education, Inc., 3

School + Home

Home Activity Your child identified misspelled words with *er*, *ir*, *or*, and *ear*. Pronounce a word. Ask your child to tell which letter combination it contains—*er*, *ir*, *or*, or *ear*.

3.24.A.1 Use knowledge of letter sounds to spell. **3.24.A.2** Use knowledge of word parts to spell. **3.24.C.1** Spell high-frequency words from a commonly used list.

Spelling Vowels: *r*-Controlled   **267**

Subjects and Object Pronouns

Directions Read the selection. Then read each question that follows the selection. Decide which is the best answer to each question. Mark the space for the answer you have chosen.

Mount Everest

(1) <u>Mount Everest</u> is the tallest mountain in the world. (2) Every year, <u>hundreds of people</u> try to climb it. (3) <u>Sir Edmond Hillary</u> was the first man to get to the top of Everest. (4) The mountain was important to <u>Edmond Hillary</u>. (5) But climbing <u>Mount Everest</u> remains very dangerous.

1 What pronoun can replace the noun in sentence 1?

- ⬭ You
- ⬭ He
- ⬭ Them
- ⬭ It

2 What pronoun can replace the noun in sentence 2?

- ⬭ he
- ⬭ they
- ⬭ it
- ⬭ him

3 What pronoun can replace the noun in sentence 3?

- ⬭ He
- ⬭ Him
- ⬭ It
- ⬭ They

4 What pronoun can replace the noun in sentence 4?

- ⬭ he
- ⬭ him
- ⬭ they
- ⬭ it

5 What pronoun can replace the noun in sentence 5?

- ⬭ him
- ⬭ they
- ⬭ it
- ⬭ them

© Pearson Education, Inc., 3

Home Activity Your child prepared for taking tests on subject and object pronouns. Discuss a visit to a farm or zoo with your child. Have your child identify pronouns in the sentences and tell whether they are subject pronouns or object pronouns.

★ Understand and use pronouns.

Prefixes *pre-, mid-, over-, bi-, out-, de-*

Directions Add the prefix **pre-, mid-, over-, out-,** or **de-** to each base word.
Write the new word on the line.

1. over-   +   load   =   _____

2. out-   +   going   =   _____

3. pre-   +   paid   =   _____

4. mid-   +   point   =   _____

5. de-   +   code   =   _____

Directions Choose the word from the box that best fits the definition. Write the word
on the line.

_____   **6.** a word part added to the beginning of a word

_____   **7.** a vehicle with two wheels

_____   **8.** bursting forth

_____   **9.** the middle of the week

_____   **10.** to thaw something that is frozen

> bicycle
> midweek
> outburst
> defrost
> prefix

Directions Add the prefix **pre-, mid-, over-, bi-,** or **out-** to the base word in ( ) to
complete each sentence. Write the word on the line.

_____   **11.** Elena began to collect rocks when she was in (school).

_____   **12.** She thought this hobby would (last) any of her other hobbies.

_____   **13.** It is easy to (look) rocks during the day.

_____   **14.** She found a (color) rock one day.

_____   **15.** Finding them at (night) is nearly impossible.

Home Activity Your child formed and wrote words with the prefixes *pre-, mid-, over-, bi-, out-,* and *de-*.
Work together to list other words with these prefixes, such as *pretest, midway, overhead, bilingual, outgrow,*
and *deflate.* Have your child use each word in a sentence.

3.1.A.1.v Decode multisyllabic words in context by
applying common spelling patterns including using knowledge
of derivational affixes

Fact and Opinion

- A **statement of fact** can be proved true or false.
- A **statement of opinion** gives someone's thoughts or feelings about something.
- Words that express feelings, such as *wise* and *wonderful*, are clues that a statement might be an opinion.

Directions Read the following biographical passage.

> Benjamin Franklin was a man of many interests. Franklin started his career as a printer, but printing was not his only accomplishment. Franklin also organized the first library and the first fire department. Benjamin Franklin was a wise and wonderful citizen. I think we are lucky that he was one of the founders of our country.

Directions Complete the chart by writing one more fact and one more opinion from the passage above. Then answer the question.

Facts	Opinions
Benjamin Franklin was a man of many interests.	Benjamin Franklin was a wise and wonderful citizen.

What facts support the idea the Franklin had many interests?

© Pearson Education, Inc., 3

Home Activity Your child identified facts and opinions in a biographical passage. Together with your child, read an article about a real person. Ask your child to find a statement of fact. Then use the Internet or a reference book to prove the fact is true.

3.13.B.1 Draw conclusions from facts presented in texts.
3.13.B.2 Support assertions with textual evidence.

Writing • Biography

Key Features of a Biography

- tells about the life of a real person

- is usually told in time order

- uses words like he or she

- tells about the person's talents or important achievements

A Tinkering Man's Collection

As a boy, Uncle Stefan loved to tinker. He was good with his hands, and even better with tools. He could fix almost anything around the house, but his passion was working on his bicycle.

Over time Uncle Stefan began to build his own bikes, using spare parts from his workshop. That's how he began his one-of-a-kind bicycle collection. Have you ever seen a bicycle with a round steering wheel for handlebars and a plastic chair cushion for a seat? Uncle Stefan made a bike just like that for me!

Now Uncle Stefan has a shed full of bikes, and do you think they sit around collecting dust? Not on your life! Uncle loans them out to all of us neighborhood kids. And when the bikes start to squeak or show any signs of needing care, a big smile spreads across his face. It is time for Uncle Stefan to grab his toolbox and teach us how to tinker.

1. Find the person this biography tells about and circle his name. Then underline examples of the word *he* that refer to this man.

2. Draw a box around any words or phrases that give clues about when events happen.

Name _____

Vocabulary

Check the Words You Know

___stamps   ___spare
___chores   ___attic
___labeled   ___customer
___board

Directions Write the word from the box that fits the meaning of each sentence.

1. I went to the post office to buy _____ for my letters.

2. The store owner _____ everything with a price.

3. We store things in the _____ at the top of the house.

4. Al had a meeting with the _____ of directors at his company.

5. Taking out trash and washing dishes are my _____ at home.

Directions Circle one word at the end of each sentence that fits the meaning.

6. I had a _____ pencil, so I gave one to my friend to use.
   spare   short

7. The salesman asked each _____ in the store if she needed
   any help.   custom   customer

8. Walking the dog is one of my _____.   chores   chokes

9. We like to play upstairs in the _____.   attention   attic

10. I need two _____ for my mail.
    steps   stamps

Write an Advertisement

On a separate sheet of paper, use vocabulary words to write an advertisement for
something you would like to sell if you owned a store.

Home Activity Your child identified and used vocabulary words from *Rocks in His Head*. Visit a store with
your child and have him or her describe the labels on items. Use as many of this week's vocabulary words
as you can.

3.4.B.1 Use context to determine the relevant meaning of
unfamiliar words.

© Pearson Education, Inc., 3

Possessive Pronouns

Some pronouns show who or what owns, or possesses, something. This kind of pronoun is a **possessive pronoun.**

Possessive Pronouns   *My, mine, your, yours, her, hers, our, ours, his, their, theirs,* and *its* are possessive pronouns.

- This is <u>my</u> gold rock, and that is <u>hers</u>.

Directions Write the possessive pronouns in each sentence.

1. When Tracy visited her granddad, she looked for rocks on his farm.

    _____

2. Her favorite rock was limestone. _____ .

3. Its color was pale gray. _____

4. Her brothers found rocks, and they put them in their granddad's study.

    _____

5. They had a shelf for theirs, and Tracy had a shelf for hers. _____

Directions Choose the possessive pronoun in ( ) that could replace the underlined words in each sentence. Write the sentence.

6. I found a piece of marble, and <u>the marble's</u> color was pink. (their, its)

    _____

7. Your favorite rock is quartz, and <u>my favorite rock</u> is marble. (mine, my)

    _____

8. Is this quartz <u>the quartz you own</u>? (his, yours)

    _____

Home Activity Your child learned about possessive pronouns. With your child, take turns using possessive pronouns in sentences about objects that family members collect. Have your child identify the possessive pronouns in the sentences.

3.22.A.1.vi Use and understand possessive pronouns in the context of reading, writing, and speaking.

Prefixes

Spelling Words				
prepaid	midnight	overflow	outdoors	outline
overgrown	prefix	Midwest	pretest	midpoint
outgoing	overtime	overdue	outside	outfield

Context Clues Write a list word that best completes each sentence.

1. Dad had to work _____ .

2. He stayed up until _____ .

3. The sink began to _____ .

4. My uncle is flying to the _____ .

5. The word *midpoint* has a _____ .

6. My sister is _____ .

7. Before you begin your report, make an _____ .

8. The shrubs look _____ .

9. Our teacher had us take a _____ .

10. My library book is _____ .

Missing Prefixes Write the prefix. Write the list word.

11. _____ doors   **11.** _____

12. _____ point   **12.** _____

13. _____ paid   **13.** _____

14. _____ side   **14.** _____

15. _____ field   **15.** _____

Home Activity Your child spelled words with the prefixes *pre-*, *mid-*, *over-*, and *out-*. Have your child make up sentences using the answers to Exercises 11 to 15 on this page.

✪ **3.24.A.2** Use knowledge of word parts to spell. **3.24.D.1** Spell words with common syllable constructions.

© Pearson Education, Inc., 3

Story Sequence A

Title _____

Beginning

Middle

End

Vocabulary • Multiple-Meaning Words

- A **multiple-meaning** word has more than one meaning.
- If you see a word you know but the meaning does not make sense in the sentence, the word may be a multiple-meaning word. Try another meaning for the word in the sentence.

Directions Read the following passage about one child's special interests. Then answer the questions below. Look for multiple-meaning words as you read.

> My brother has had many hobbies. First he collected stamps. He filled his desk with envelopes full of stamps. Then he started building model airplanes. He hung the models from his ceiling and saved the spare parts in a big box. Now he's started to play chess. He always has a game set up on the floor.
>
> Mom complains about the clutter but she doesn't really mind. "Maybe someday he'll be president of a museum board," she says.

1. Does *stamps* mean "small, sticky papers that stand for postage paid" or "pounds one's foot loudly on the floor"?

_____

_____

2. Does *spare* mean "a bowling score" or "extra"?

_____

3. Does *play* mean "to act the part of a character in a drama" or "to join in on a game"?

_____

4. Does *mind* mean "to obey someone" or "to be bothered by something"?

_____

5. Does *board* mean "a flat piece of wood" or "the group of people in charge of an organization?"

_____

Home Activity Your child chose the correct definitions for multiple-meaning words. See how many meanings of the word *run* you and you child can recall. Make up sentences for several different meanings.

🌐 **3.4.B.2** Use context to distinguish among multiple-meaning words.

Online Information

- You can go **online** to find **information** about almost any topic. You have to follow certain steps. First, you type in the URL. This is like an address. It takes you to the **home page,** or first page, of the Web site you want to use for reference.

- Next, you read the text on the home page and look at the images. Many of the words and images on the home page are **links.** When you click on a link, it takes you to a new page.

Directions Study the Web page and answer the questions that follow.

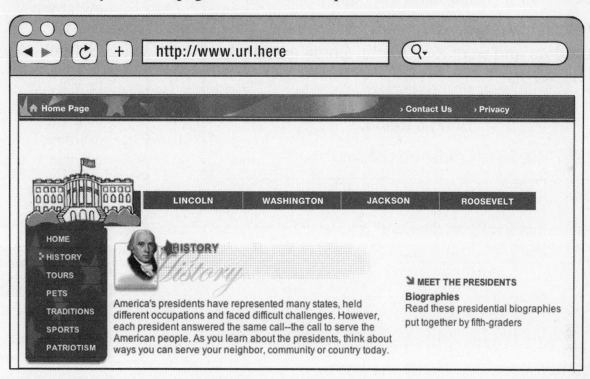

1. What is the URL for this Web site? _____

2. Which link can you click on to read about President Abraham Lincoln?

_____

_____

3. What might you find under the "Pets" link to the left?

_____

_____

4. What is the purpose of this Web site?

_____

_____

© Pearson Education, Inc., 3

School + Home **Home Activity** Your child answered questions about an Internet site. Go online with your child to a United States government Web site. Spend some time looking through the site together. Click on the various links to visit other pages on the site. Help your child understand how to navigate the site.

3.26.A.1.ii.3 Follow the research plan to collect information from multiple sources of oral and written information, including online searches.

Prefixes

Proofread an Announcement Circle four misspelled words. Write them correctly. Rewrite the sentence that has an incorrect verb.

Night Hike

Learn about creatures of the night!

Meet outside the nature center. Dress for outdores and wear long pants. Some areas is overgroan.

    8 P.M. to mid night
    Bring a freind!

Note: The $2 fee must be prepaid.

1. _____   2. _____

3. _____   4. _____

5. _____

Proofread Words Fill in a circle to show which word is spelled correctly. Write the word.

6. ○ middwest   ○ Midwest   ○ midWest   _____

7. ○ overfloe   ○ overflow   ○ ovrflow   _____

8. ○ outgoing   ○ ootgoing   ○ outtgoing   _____

9. ○ midpoin   ○ midpointe   ○ midpoint   _____

10. ○ outfield   ○ outfeild   ○ outfeeled   _____

11. ○ pritest   ○ pretest   ○ preetest   _____

12. ○ ovrtime   ○ overrtime   ○ overtime   _____

© Pearson Education, Inc., 3

Home Activity Your child identified misspelled words with the prefixes *pre-*, *mid-*, *over-*, and *out-*. Pronounce a word. Ask your child to identify the prefix and spell the word.

🌐 **3.24.A.2** Use knowledge of word parts to spell. **3.24.C.1** Spell high-frequency words from a commonly used list. **3.24.D.1** Spell words with common syllable constructions.

Possessive Pronouns

Directions Read the selection. Then read each question that follows the selection. Decide which is the best answer to each question. Mark the space for the answer you have chosen.

Rock Collecting

(1) I have cool rocks in my collection. (2) Dad taught _____ family about rocks. (3) My dad gave me a rock from its collection. (4) The rock is odd, and its color is orange. (5) My sister Tara got down on her knees. (6) She found quartz on her first try. (7) Rock collecting is a good hobby, and it could be our.

1 Which word is the possessive pronoun in sentence 1?

- ⬭ I
- ⬭ rocks
- ⬭ my
- ⬭ in

2 Which pronoun correctly completes sentence 2?

- ⬭ our
- ⬭ mine
- ⬭ hers
- ⬭ its

3 What change, if any, should be made to sentence 3?

- ⬭ Change *its* to **he**
- ⬭ Change *its* to **his**
- ⬭ Change *its* to **mine**
- ⬭ Make no change

4 What change, if any, should be made to sentence 5?

- ⬭ Change *her knees.* to **hers knees.**
- ⬭ Change *her knees.* to **their knees.**
- ⬭ Change *her knees.* to **my knees.**
- ⬭ Make no change

5 What change, if any, should be made to sentence 7?

- ⬭ Change *our.* to **yours.**
- ⬭ Change *our.* to **him.**
- ⬭ Change *our.* to **its.**
- ⬭ Make no change

© Pearson Education, Inc., 3

Home Activity Your child prepared for taking tests on possessive pronouns. Play a board game with your child. Have your child identify possessive pronouns used by any player as you play.

🔄 **3.22.A.1.vi** Use and understand possessive pronouns in the context of reading, writing, and speaking.

Conventions Possessive Pronouns   **279**

Suffixes -er, -or, -ess, -ist

Directions Add the suffix to each base word. Write the new word on the line.

1. edit   +   -or   =   _____

2. art   +   -ist   =   _____

3. conduct   +   -or   =   _____

4. lion   +   -ess   =   _____

5. sell   +   -er   =   _____

Directions Write the word from the box that best fits each definition.

_____ **6.** a doctor who cares for your teeth

_____ **7.** one who ships packages

_____ **8.** one who directs

_____ **9.** a scientist in the field of chemistry

_____ **10.** a woman who greets restaurant guests

> chemist
> dentist
> hostess
> shipper
> director

Directions Add the suffix **-er, -or, -ess,** or **-ist** to the base word in ( ) to complete each sentence. Use the words in the box to help. Write the word on the line.

_____ **11.** Gertrude Ederle was the first woman (swim) to swim across the English Channel.

_____ **12.** Many thought her coach was the greatest swimming (instruct) in the world.

_____ **13.** After she became famous, Ederle was offered work as an (act), but she declined.

_____ **14.** Instead, she traveled as a (tour).

_____ **15.** Later, Ederle became a swimming (teach) for deaf children.

> actress
> instructor
> swimmer
> teacher
> tourist

© Pearson Education, Inc., 3

Home Activity Your child formed and wrote words with the suffixes *-er, -or, -ess,* and *-ist*. Together, think of additional job-related words that end with *-er, -or, -ess,* or *-ist* (such as *doctor, countess, biologist, police officer*). Help your child write a paragraph explaining which jobs sound most interesting to him or her and why.

⬇ **3.1.A.2.iv.2** Decode multisyllabic words independent of context by applying common spelling patterns including using knowledge of common suffixes.

Fact and Opinion

- A statement of **fact** tells something that can be proved true or false. You can prove it by reading or asking an expert.

- A statement of **opinion** tells someone's ideas or feelings. Words that tell feelings, such as *should* or *best,* are clues to opinions.

Directions Read the following passage. Then complete the diagram below.

> Swimming is a sport that helps keep people in good shape. If you have any doubt, just ask Mark Spitz. He held the record for winning the most gold medals in swimming events at the Olympics until 2008.
>
> In Germany, at the Olympics in 1972, Spitz won seven gold medals. He also set new world records in each of the seven events.
>
> During those events, Spitz wore a mustache. The mustache distracted from his great performance. He should have shaved the mustache. That would have been best.

Fact	How to Prove
1.	
2.	

Opinion	Clue words
3.	
4.	

5. How can you find out if Mark Spitz won seven gold medals at the Summer Olympics in 1972? _____

_____

Home Activity Your child identified fact and opinion in a nonfiction passage about swimming. Read another passage or editorial with your child and discuss whether the statements are fact or opinion. Have your child explain how to check to be sure seemingly true statements are really facts.

3.13.B.1 Draw conclusions from facts presented in text.
3.13.B.2 Support assertions with textual evidence.

Writing • Autobiography

Key Features of an Autobiography

- tells the story of a person's own life
- may cover a person's whole life or only part of it
- written in first person

My Autobiography

I was born on August 29th, 2000, in Holland, MI. My mother has told me that when I was born, I cried less than any of the other children on the delivery floor. I guess I was just happy to be here!

A New Sister

My parents are Arthur and Tammy Garza. My father works as a social studies teacher at Brownsville High School. Someday I might even be one of his students! My mother is a lawyer who works for the city government. She helps to make sure that the city's plans will be safe for the environment.

When I was three years old, one of the biggest events in my life happened. My mother had to go away to the hospital for a few days, and my father told me that she'd come back with a big surprise. She came back with my baby sister! Her name is Teresa, and she's just starting school now. Teresa and I have our arguments, like any brother and sister, but I'm glad she's my sister.

Moving to Brownsville

A few years ago, my mother and father gave my sister and me some important news. My mother had gotten a new job in Brownsville, Texas, and so our family would be moving. At first, I couldn't believe what I was hearing. I would have to leave my friends behind, and the neighborhood where I grew up.

The time leading up to the move was full of preparations. Everything we owned was packed in brown boxes. Finally a big yellow truck pulled up outside and our furniture was loaded into it. We drove to Brownsville in my parents' car. When we arrived, our new house was bright and filled with sun.

1. Underline three sentences that tell you that this story is about the author's own life.

2. Circle the three examples of words that show the use of the first person point of view.

Vocabulary

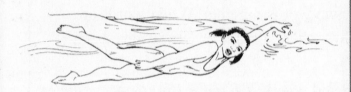

Check the Words You Know

___drowned	___strokes
___medals	___current
___continued	___stirred
___celebrate	

Directions Fill in the blank with a word from the box that fits the meaning of the sentence.

1. He _____ to swim so that he could reach the shore.

2. The more she practiced, the stronger her swimming _____ became.

3. The swimmer won prizes and _____ for every race she won.

4. The ocean _____ was strong, and he worked to swim against it.

5. The waves were high on the day she almost _____.

Directions Draw a line from the word to its meaning.

6. stirred   prizes or ribbons you win

7. celebrate   moved around

8. current   kept on going

9. medals   the movement of ocean water

10. continued   to have a party

Write a Newspaper Article

On a separate sheet of paper, write a newspaper article describing a swimming race. Use as many vocabulary words as possible.

Home Activity Your child identified and used vocabulary words from *America's Champion Swimmer: Gertrude Ederle*. Read a sports article from a newspaper with your child. Encourage your child to discuss the article using this week's vocabulary words.

3.4.B.1 Use context to determine the relevant meaning of unfamiliar words.

Contractions

A **contraction** is a word made by putting two words together. When words are joined in a contraction, an apostrophe shows where a letter or letters have been left out.

- Some contractions combine a pronoun and a verb: *I + am = I'm; he + is = he's; we + are = we're; you + will = you'll; we + will = we'll; they + are = they're.*
- Some contractions combine a verb and *not: can + not = can't; is + not = isn't; do + not = don't; will + not = won't; are + not = aren't.*

Contractions   They're swimming in the lake, but I can't see them.

Directions Read the sentence. Then write the contraction in each sentence.

1. Watch the Olympics, and you'll see some great swimmers. _____

2. The Americans think they'll win many medals. _____

3. I won't miss their big race tonight. _____

4. I can't believe she broke the world record. _____

5. Maybe we'll swim in the Olympics someday. _____

Directions Read the sentence. Write the contraction in each sentence. Then write the word or words that make up the contraction.

6. They're starting the race. _____

7. Jeremy is in this race, and he's in the first lane. _____

8. It's important to get a fast start. _____

9. Isn't a fast turn important also? _____

10. The other swimmers can't beat Jeremy. _____

© Pearson Education, Inc., 3

Home Activity Your child learned about contractions. With your child, read an article in a local newspaper. Have your child identify the contractions and the words that make up each contraction.

⬇ **3.23.C.1.i.1** Recognize punctuation marks including apostrophes in contractions. **3.23.C.1.i.2** Use punctuation marks including apostrophes in contractions. **3.24.F.1** Spell complex contractions.

Suffixes

Spelling Words				
dentist	editor	artist	hostess	actress
swimmer	seller	tutor	tourist	organist
lioness	shipper	chemist	investor	conductor

Definitions Write a list word to name each person.

1. a person who draws and paints   **1.** _____

2. a person who takes care of teeth   **2.** _____

3. a person who moves through water   **3.** _____

4. a person who receives guests   **4.** _____

5. a person who teaches   **5.** _____

6. a person who works on books or magazines   **6.** _____

7. a person who buys and sells stocks   **7.** _____

8. a person who leads an orchestra   **8.** _____

9. a person who plays an organ   **9.** _____

10. a person who works with chemicals   **10.** _____

11. a person who travels to new places   **11.** _____

Rhymes Write the missing word. It rhymes with the underlined word.

12. The _____ sent my sweater in a <u>zipper</u> bag.   **12.** _____

13. He got a <u>propeller</u> from a model plane _____.   **13.** _____

14. Did you see the <u>mess</u> the _____ left backstage?   **14.** _____

15. The _____ eats <u>less</u> food than the lion.   **15.** _____

Home Activity Your child spelled words with the suffixes *-er*, *-or*, *-ess*, and *-ist*. Many of the list words refer to people or occupations. Discuss any unfamiliar words with your child.

3.24.A.2 Use knowledge of word parts to spell. **3.24.D.1** Spell words with common syllable constructions.

Spelling Suffixes   **285**

KWL Chart

Topic _____

What We **K** now	What We **W** ant to Know	What We **L** earned

Suffixes

Spelling Words				
dentist	editor	artist	hostess	actress
swimmer	seller	tutor	tourist	organist
lioness	shipper	chemist	investor	conductor

Proofread a Program Nick wrote the program for the school musical. Circle four misspelled words. Write them correctly. Add the missing punctuation mark.

The Cast

Mad chemist....Don Perlas

The dentest......Julie Blake

The tourist.......Kate Hanson

Music conducter....Steve Carr

Scenery artist....Ann Morgan

We extend special thanks to the editer of the *Daily Press*, Mr Pearson, hoo is our sponsor.

Frequently Misspelled Words

once
who
one

1. _____

2. _____

3. _____

4. _____

Proofread Words Circle the word that is spelled correctly. Write the word.

5. Jake was a ticket **seller   sellor**.   5. _____

6. A **tudor   tutor** helps Don with math.   6. _____

7. Jean is a fast **swimmer   swimer**.   7. _____

8. The **organist   organest** played softly.   8. _____

9. We thanked our **hostes   hostess**.   9. _____

10. The **lioness   liones** paced back and forth. 10. _____

Home Activity Your child identified misspelled words with the suffixes -er, -or, -ess, and -ist. Ask your child to name the four hardest words. Have your child write these words.

3.24.A.2 Use knowledge of word parts to spell. **3.24.C.1** Spell high-frequency words from a commonly used list. **3.24.D.1** Spell words with common syllable constructions.

Spelling Suffixes   **289**

Contractions

Directions Read the selection. Then read each question that follows the selection. Decide which is the best answer to each question. Mark the space for the answer you have chosen.

Learning to Swim

(1) Swimming is not difficult. (2) You will learn some strokes. (3) They are your arm movements. (4) I will show you a kick. (5) It is the most popular kick. (6) Don't forget to breathe correctly. (7) Breathing won't be hard for you.

1 Which contraction is correct for sentence 1?
- ⬭ he's
- ⬭ don't
- ⬭ isn't
- ⬭ we'll

2 Which contraction is correct for sentence 2?
- ⬭ we're
- ⬭ I'm
- ⬭ won't
- ⬭ You'll

3 Which contraction is correct for sentence 3?
- ⬭ They're
- ⬭ Don't
- ⬭ We'll
- ⬭ can't

4 Which two words form the contraction in sentence 6?
- ⬭ I am
- ⬭ Do not
- ⬭ Are not
- ⬭ You will

5 Which two words form the contraction in sentence 7?
- ⬭ will not
- ⬭ can not
- ⬭ you will
- ⬭ are not

School + Home **Home Activity** Your child prepared for taking tests on contractions. Together, sort through the mail and have your child find contractions in advertisements and notices.

3.23.C.1.i.1 Recognize punctuation marks, including apostrophes in contractions. **3.24.F.1** Spell complex contractions.

Syllables VCCCV

Directions Choose the word in ( ) with the VCCCV syllable pattern to finish each sentence. Write the word on the line.

_____ **1.** The third grade (children/students) took a trip to the zoo.

_____ **2.** Their teachers had a (surprise/special) assignment for them.

_____ **3.** The zookeeper gave an (alert/address) to the students.

_____ **4.** He told them to (inspect/watch) each animal's living space.

_____ **5.** He suggested they (compare/contrast) different animals.

_____ **6.** By the end of the day, the students had seen about one (dozen/hundred) animals.

Directions Circle the word that has the VCCCV syllable pattern. Then write a sentence on the line that uses the word you circled.

7. forgive   monster   wonder

_____

8. human   fortress   winner

_____

9. complain   number   writer

_____

10. constant   planet   signal

_____

11. beyond   robin   sample

_____

12. chosen   control   copper

_____

Home Activity Your child wrote words with the VCCCV syllable pattern found in *mon/ster*. Ask your child to read each of the words he or she wrote on the page above. Take turns making up additional sentences using these words. Help your child write the sentences and underline the words with the VCCCV syllable pattern.

⭐ **3.1.B.1.iii** Use common syllabication patterns to decode words including final stable syllable.

Phonics Syllables VCCCV   **291**

Cause and Effect

- A **cause** tells why something happened.
- An **effect** is what happened.
- Words such as *because* and *so* are clues that can help you figure out a cause and its effect. Sometimes a clue word is not used.

Directions Read the following passage.

Camouflage is color or covering that blends with surroundings. Because it is so hard for animals to survive in the wild, some animals use camouflage to keep their enemies from noticing them. A baby deer, or fawn, has a tan coat with light spots. The spots provide camouflage in the sun-dappled forest. Other animals use tricks to protect themselves. The opossum tricks other animals by pretending to be dead. It does this because most other animals will not eat animals they have not killed. Wild animals would not last long if they had no way to hide. They have to be smart so they can find food for themselves and avoid becoming food for other animals.

Directions Fill in the chart to identify cause and effect.

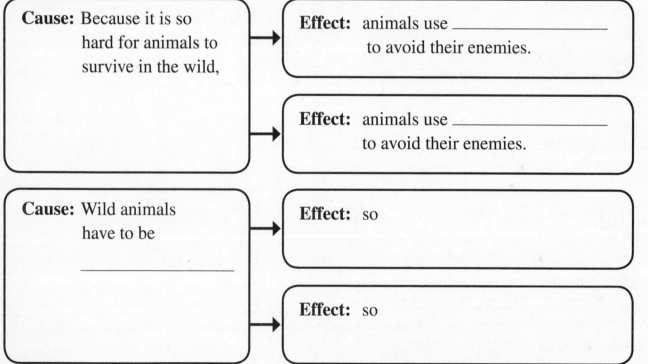

Cause: Because it is so hard for animals to survive in the wild,

→ **Effect:** animals use _____ to avoid their enemies.

→ **Effect:** animals use _____ to avoid their enemies.

Cause: Wild animals have to be _____

→ **Effect:** so

→ **Effect:** so

© Pearson Education, Inc., 3

Home Activity Your child identified cause and effect. Read an article about an animal with your child. Talk about causes and effects.

⊕ **3.13.C.1** Identify explicit cause and effect relationships among ideas in texts.

Writing • Summary

Key Features of a Summary

- retells a piece of writing
- includes only the most important information
- shorter than the original

Summary of Why the Dog Wags His Tail

Long ago, all the animals could speak and understood all the secrets of how things worked in the world. One special animal, Dog, knew all the secrets of the King. One day, Dog told the other animals to follow him because he was going to reveal all the King's secrets. So, many animals followed Dog to the cave.

Dog spoke for a long time telling many incredible secrets. Next, Raven raced to the palace to report to the King what Dog did. After, the King decided to teach Dog a lesson by taking away the Dog's power to speak. Ever since then, when Dog wants to say something he wags his tail—not his tongue.

1. Read the summary. Who are the main characters?

_____

2. What happens at the end of the story?

_____

Vocabulary

Check the Words You Know

___scrambled   ___valley
___echoed   ___clutched
___reeds   ___thatch
___gully

Directions Read each sentence. Write a word from the box to complete each sentence.

1. The boy _____ over the rocks as quickly as he could.

2. The sound of thunder _____ through the night.

3. We walked down the mountain into the _____ below.

4. The bird seemed to disappear in the tall _____ near the lake.

5. We walked up the side of a small _____ to the top of the hill.

Directions Choose the word from the box that best matches each clue. Write the word on the line.

6. held tightly   _____

7. ditch   _____

8. use straw or leaves as a roof   _____

9. repeated, as a sound does   _____

10. tall grasses   _____

Write a Scene from a Play

On a separate sheet of paper, write a scene in which a child finds a baby animal and wants to take care of it. Use as many vocabulary words as possible.

Home Activity Your child identified and used vocabulary words from *Fly, Eagle, Fly!* With your child, read a story or nonfiction article about nature. Discuss the setting. Encourage your child to use vocabulary words in your conversation.

3.4.B.1 Use context to determine the relevant meaning of unfamiliar words.

Prepositions

A **preposition** is the first word in a group of words called a prepositional phrase. A **prepositional phrase** ends with a noun or pronoun called the **object of the preposition.** A prepositional phrase tells more about other words in a sentence.

Preposition	The eagle flew <u>in</u> a circle.
Prepositional Phrase	The eagle flew <u>in a circle</u>.
Object of Preposition	The eagle flew in a <u>circle</u>.

Common Prepositions

Here are some prepositions: *about, above, across, after, against, along, among, around, at, before, behind, below, beneath, beside, between, beyond, by, down, during, except, for, from, in, inside, into, near, of, off, on, onto, out, outside, over, past, since, through, throughout, to, toward, under, underneath, until, up, upon, with, within, without.*

Directions Write the preposition in each sentence.

1. Our class read a book about eagles. _____

2. Bald eagles live in the United States. _____

3. Bald eagles can grab fish from the water. _____

4. The bald eagle population decreased during the 1970s. _____

Directions Write the prepositional phrase in each sentence. Underline the preposition.

5. Another eagle within the United States is the golden eagle.

_____

6. Golden eagles have golden brown feathers on their necks.

_____

© Pearson Education, Inc., 3

Home Activity Your child learned about prepositions. With your child, look at ads. Have your child identify five prepositional phrases.

3.22.A.1.v.1 Use and understand prepositions in the context of reading, writing, and speaking. **3.22.A.1.v.2** Use and understand prepositional phrases in the context of reading, writing, and speaking.

Syllables VCCCV

Spelling Words

monster	surprise	hundred	complete	control
sample	instant	inspect	pilgrim	contrast
explode	district	address	substance	children

Missing Words Write the missing list word to complete each sentence.

1. That was a _____!   1. _____

2. Would you like a _____ of lime yogurt?   2. _____

3. That balloon will _____ if you keep blowing.   3. _____

4. The _____ went on a long journey.   4. _____

5. I couldn't _____ my tears.   5. _____

6. My little sister thinks a _____ lives under   6. _____
   her bed.

7. Many officials _____ the coal mine   7. _____
   every year.

8. My best friend is not in my school _____.   8. _____

Definitions Write the list word that means the same thing
as the word or phrase.

9. one more than ninety-nine   9. _____

10. many boys and girls   10. _____

11. entire   11. _____

12. material   12. _____

13. difference   13. _____

14. moment of time   14. _____

15. numbers that tell where you live 15. _____

© Pearson Education, Inc., 3

Home Activity Your child spelled words with VCCCV (vowel-consonant-consonant-consonant-vowel) syllable patterns. Ask your child to spell the words one syllable at a time.

3.24.A.2 Use knowledge of word parts to spell. **3.24.A.3** Use knowledge of word segmentation to spell. **3.24.A.4** Use knowledge of syllabication to spell.

Scoring Rubric: Writing for Tests: Summary

	4	3	2	1
Focus/Ideas	Strong summary; only uses important information	Good summary; mostly uses important information	Summary has some main ideas and too many details	Does not understand summary form
Organization	Important ideas are in correct sequence	Sequence of events is generally correct	Sequence of events isn't always clear	No clear sequence of events
Voice	Shows understanding of the main ideas	Shows understanding of topic	Lacks understanding of topic	Does not understand topic
Word Choice	Uses strong action verbs and time-order words	Uses some strong action verbs and time-order words	Few or no strong verbs or time-order words	Poor word choice
Sentences	Clear sentences of different lengths and types	Sentences of a few lengths and types	Sentences of similar length and type	No variety of sentence length and type
Conventions	Few, if any, errors; correct use of prepositions	Several small errors; use of prepositions	Many errors; weak use of prepositions	Many serious errors; incorrect or no use of prepositions

Vocabulary • Unknown Words

You can use a glossary or a dictionary to find the meaning, syllabication, and pronunciation of **unknown words.**

---

clutch (kluch) *v.* to grasp something tightly **clutch • es, clutched, clutch • ing**

ech • o (ek′ ō) *v.* to be heard again and again **ech • oes, ech • oed, ech • o • ing**

reed (rēd) *n.* a kind of tall grass that grows in wet places *plural* **reeds**

scram • ble (skram′ bəl) *v.* to make your way, especially by climbing or crawling quickly **scram • bles, scram • bled, scram • bling**

val • ley (val′ ē) *n.* a region of low land that lies between hills or mountains *plural* **val • leys**

Directions Read the passage. Use the glossary entries to answer the questions.

On his first nature hike, Mike stumbled upon an interesting scene. Sloppy looking twig nests perched shakily in the tops of lofty trees. The raspy squawk of a great blue heron echoed around the valley. A few of the tall, gray birds were wading among the reeds in the pond. Mike clutched his binoculars and scrambled down toward the water. He hoped to get a closer look at these strange birds.

1. What does the word *echoed* mean?

_____

2. Would you go up or down to get to a valley?

_____

3. What are reeds?

_____

4. How many syllables are in the word *clutched?*

_____

5. Which syllable should you stress when you say *scrambled?*

_____

Home Activity Your child used a glossary to understand meanings, syllabication, and pronunciation of words from *Fly, Eagle, Fly!* Read an article about nature with your child. Encourage your child to use a dictionary to find the meanings and pronunciations of unknown words.

3.4.E.2 Use a dictionary or glossary to determine meanings of unknown words.
3.4.E.3 Use a dictionary or glossary to determine syllabication of unknown words.
3.4.E.4 Use a dictionary or glossary to determine pronunciation of unknown words.

Outlining and Summarizing

Summarizing refers to finding the most important ideas about a topic or text. You can summarize what you read or what you learn in class. One way to summarize is by making an **outline**. An outline shows a main idea and details, as in the one shown below.

An Endangered Animal—The African Elephant

I. Size
  A. Weight
    1. 7,000 to 15,000 pounds
    2. Males larger
  B. Height and Length
    1. 10 to 13 ft high
    2. 20 to 24 ft long

II. Diet—Vegetation
  A. Grasses
  B. Leaves
  C. Fruit

III. Habitat—Africa
  A. Forest
  B. Grassland

Directions Write the words from the box in the outline. Use the outline above as a guide.

> **Habitat**   **Deer**   **45 to 80 pounds**   **Rabbits**   **Wetlands**

The Red Wolf

I. Size
  A. 4 1/2 to 5 1/2 ft long
  B. Weight
    1. _____
    2. Males larger

II. _____
  A. Forests
  B. Mountains
  C. _____

III. Diet
  A. Mainly small animals
    1. Rodents
    2. _____
  B. Others
    1. Insects
    2. Berries
    3. _____

Home Activity Your child learned how to make an outline to summarize ideas. Give your child information about a familiar topic. Include at least three main ideas and several details about the main ideas. Help him or her organize these ideas in an outline.

3.26.C.2 Sort evidence into provided categories.

Syllables VCCCV

Spelling Words				
monster	surprise	hundred	complete	control
sample	instant	inspect	pilgrim	contrast
explode	district	address	substance	children

Proofread a Paragraph James wrote about stamp collecting. Circle four words that are spelled incorrectly. Cross out the extra word in the first sentence.

Some childrn try to collect a sample of each stamp pictured over in a stamp album. I tried that, but I thought I'd never get a complete collection. Most of my pages were empty. Now I collect only Chrismas stamps. I have almost two hunderd stamps. Does that surpris you?

Frequently Misspelled Words

Christmas
went

1. _____   2. _____

3. _____   4. _____

Proofread Words Fill in a circle to show which word is spelled correctly. Write the word.

5. In the dark, the tree looked like a _____ .
○ monstor   ○ monster   ○ montser

5. _____

6. They gave me a free _____ at the grocery store.
○ sample   ○ saple   ○ slampe

6. _____

7. What is your _____ ?
○ adress   ○ addres   ○ address

7. _____

8. I ate so much, I thought I would _____ !
○ explod   ○ esplode   ○ explode

8. _____

Home Activity Your child spelled words with VCCCV (vowel-consonant-consonant-consonant-vowel) syllable patterns. Have your child circle the three consecutive consonants in a list word and underline the vowels on either side.

3.24.A.2 Use knowledge of word parts to spell. **3.24.A.3** Use knowledge of word segmentation to spell. **3.24.A.4** Use knowledge of syllabication to spell. **3.24.C.1** Spell high-frequency words from a commonly used list.

Prepositions

Directions Read the selection. Then read each question that follows the selection. Decide which is the best answer to each question. Mark the space for the answer you have chosen.

Eagles

(1) Eagles live throughout the world. (2) They build their nests on treetops. (3) Eagles hunt during the day. (4) They spot prey from the air. (5) Eagles rest at night.

1 What is the preposition in sentence 1?
- ⬭ throughout
- ⬭ eagles
- ⬭ world
- ⬭ live

2 What is the preposition in sentence 2?
- ⬭ their
- ⬭ they
- ⬭ on
- ⬭ nests

3 What is the preposition in sentence 3?
- ⬭ hunt
- ⬭ during
- ⬭ the
- ⬭ day

4 What is the prepositional phrase in sentence 4?
- ⬭ the air
- ⬭ They spot
- ⬭ They spot prey
- ⬭ from the air

5 What is the prepositional phrase in sentence 5?
- ⬭ at night
- ⬭ Eagles rest
- ⬭ rest at night
- ⬭ Eagles rest at

School + Home **Home Activity** Your child prepared for taking tests on prepositions. Look through a cookbook with your child. Ask him or her to find three prepositional phrases in a recipe and identify the preposition in each one.

3.22.A.1.v.1 Use and understand prepositions in the context of reading, writing, and speaking. **3.22.A.1.v.2** Use and understand prepositional phrases in the context of reading, writing, and speaking.

Irregular Plurals

Spelling Words				
wolves	knives	feet	men	children
women	sheep	heroes	scarves	mice
geese	cuffs	elves	banjos	halves

Word Meanings Write the list word for each meaning clue.

1. animals that give wool

2. more than one mouse

3. stringed instruments

4. brave people

5. two equal parts of a whole

6. more than one man

7. small make-believe people

Complete the Sentence Write the letters from the shaded boxes to finish the sentence.

8. People wear _____ around their necks.

Proofreading Draw a line through the misspelled word in each sentence. Write the word correctly.

9. The childrun learned spelling words. _____

10. The wolfs howled at the moon. _____

11. A baby has small foots. _____

12. A flock of gooses flew over us. _____

13. I got mustard on my shirt cuffes. _____

14. These knifes are very sharp. _____

15. Three womin painted the room. _____

 Home Activity Your child is learning to spell irregular plurals. Say the singular form of a list word (*mouse*). Ask your child to spell the plural (*mice*). Continue until all the words have been spelled.

3.24.A.1 Use knowledge of letter sounds to spell. **3.24.A.2** Use knowledge of word parts to spell. **3.24.A.3** Use knowledge of word segmentation to spell.

Singular and Plural Pronouns

Directions Write the pronoun in each sentence.

1. Have you seen people play basketball? _____

2. They can have a lot of fun. _____

3. We have a basketball team. _____

4. Troy can dribble the ball and shoot it. _____

5. He is the best player on this team. _____

6. Maya is not tall, but she is fast. _____

7. We were watching another team. _____

8. They were a very talented bunch. _____

9. Maya wanted to challenge them. _____

10. Thanks to Maya, we won the game. _____

Directions Write *S* if the underlined pronoun is singular. Write *P* if it is plural.

11. Some people like sports, and <u>they</u> join a team. _____

12. Fans watch <u>them</u> from the bleachers. _____

13. Janet jumps, and <u>she</u> glides through the air. _____

14. All of <u>us</u> watch Janet play basketball. _____

15. <u>I</u> guess people will invent even more games to play. _____

16. Maybe <u>we</u> can think of a new game. _____

17. Dan has an idea, and I like <u>it</u>. _____

18. <u>He</u> plays on several sports teams. _____

19. Janet asked me to play ball with <u>her</u>. _____

20. Dan wants me to play a game with <u>him</u>. _____

© Pearson Education, Inc., 3

★ Understand and use pronouns.

Vowels: *r*-Controlled

Spelling Words				
third	early	world	certain	dirty
herself	earth	word	perfect	verb
nerve	worm	thirsty	workout	earn

Classifying Write the list word that belongs in each group.

1. first, second, ___   **1.** _____

2. yourself, himself, ___   **2.** _____

3. letter, syllable, ___   **3.** _____

4. unclean, messy, ___   **4.** _____

5. positive, sure, ___   **5.** _____

6. correct, all right, ___   **6.** _____

7. noun, adjective, ___   **7.** _____

Scrambled Words Unscramble the list words. Write them correctly.

8. lyear   **8.** __ __ __ __ __

9. enrve   **9.** __ __ __ __ __

10. hirstyt   **10.** __ __ __ __ __ __ __

11. touwkor   **11.** __ __ __ __ __ __ __

12. nrea   **12.** __ __ __ __

13. threa   **13.** __ __ __ __ __

14. rowld   **14.** __ __ __ __ __

15. rowm   **15.** __ __ __ __

Proverb Write the words you wrote for number 8 and for number 15. You will read some famous words of wisdom.

The _____ bird catches the _____.
    8   15

Home Activity Your child practiced spelling words with *er*, *ir*, *or*, and *ear*. Ask your child to write the words and to circle the letters for the *r*-vowel sounds. Then read the words together. When you come to circled letters, exaggerate the vowel sound by stretching it out.

3.24.A.1 Use knowledge of letter sounds to spell.
3.24.A.2 Use knowledge of word parts to spell.

Subject and Object Pronouns

Directions Write *SP* if the underlined pronoun is a subject pronoun. Write *OP* if it is an object pronoun.

1. <u>I</u> visited one of the hottest places in the world. _____

2. <u>We</u> went to Death Valley in the summer. _____

3. The hot sun dazzled <u>us</u>. _____

4. We took plenty of water for Robert and <u>them</u>. _____

5. <u>They</u> took pictures of the desert plants. _____

Directions Choose the correct pronoun to complete each sentence. Write the sentence.

6. My family and (me, I) visited the Grand Canyon.

_____

_____

7. (We, Us) looked down one mile at the canyon's bottom.

_____

_____

8. The canyon's colors surprised Jack and (me, I).

_____

_____

9. Dad and (he, him) rafted on the river at the bottom of the canyon.

_____

_____

10. Later (they, them) hiked in the park.

_____

_____

Prefixes

Opposites Write the list word that is opposite in meaning to the given word or phrase.

1. indoors _____
2. suffix _____
3. noon _____
4. on time _____
5. posttest _____
6. infield _____
7. Mideast _____
8. inside _____

Spelling Words

prepaid
midnight
overflow
outdoors
outline
overgrown
prefix
Midwest

pretest
midpoint
outgoing
overtime
overdue
outside
outfield

Word Search Circle the list words in the puzzle. Look across and down. Write the words you find.

m	o	u	t	g	o	i	n	g	a	c
i	v	o	v	e	r	g	r	o	w	n
d	e	v	f	g	m	s	w	u	g	l
p	r	e	p	a	i	d	t	t	p	s
o	f	v	m	u	n	y	r	l	w	a
i	l	t	o	v	e	r	t	i	m	e
n	o	q	b	f	v	p	c	n	l	b
t	w	s	k	i	z	g	v	e	u	m

9. _____ 12. _____ 14. _____

10. _____ 13. _____ 15. _____

11. _____

Home Activity Your child learned to spell words with the prefixes *pre-*, *mid-*, *over-*, and *out-*. Make two sets of cards with list words on them. Play Concentration. When a match is made, the person must spell the word correctly to keep the cards.

306 Spelling

3.24.A.2 Use knowledge of word parts to spell. **3.24.D.1** Spell words with common syllable constructions.

Possessive Pronouns

Directions Write the possessive pronouns in the sentences.

1. Uncle Rick has valuable rocks on his ranch. _____

2. Aunt Julie makes her jewelry with the stones. _____

3. She likes their blue color. _____

4. Our gifts were made from her purple stones. _____

5. Mine is a necklace, and hers is a pin. _____

Directions Choose the possessive pronoun in ( ) that could replace the underlined words in each sentence. Write the sentence.

6. I bought a ring, and the ring's stones are green. (their, its)

_____

_____

7. The artists showed us the artists' best jewelry. (his, their)

_____

_____

8. The green stones are the color of Laura's eyes. (hers, her)

_____

_____

9. Are these earrings the earrings you own? (his, yours)

_____

_____

10. My necklace is ruby, and Jen's necklace is turquoise. (hers, yours)

_____

_____

3.22.A.1.vi Use and understand possessive
pronouns in the context of reading, writing, and speaking.

Conventions 307

Suffixes

Spelling Words				
dentist	editor	artist	hostess	actress
swimmer	seller	tutor	tourist	organist
lioness	shipper	chemist	investor	conductor

Adding Suffixes Add a suffix to the base word. Write the list word you make in the chart.

base	-er	-or	-ess	-ist
1. invest				
2. tour				
3. sell				
4. lion				
5. art				
6. edit				
7. host				
8. organ				
9. conduct				

Proofreading Circle the correctly spelled word. Write the word.

10. dentalist   dentist   **11.** _____

11. actess   actress   **11.** _____

12. shipper   shiper   **12.** _____

13. tutor   tuter   **13.** _____

14. swimer   swimmer   **14.** _____

15. chemist   chemest   **15.** _____

Home Activity Your child practiced spelling words with the suffixes *-er*, *-or*, *-ess*, and *-ist*. To practice together, choose a word. Draw blanks for each letter, then write in the suffix. Let your child guess the word and fill in the remaining blanks. Then have him or her write the whole word.

3.24.A.2 Use knowledge of word parts to spell. **3.24.D.1** Spell words with common syllable constructions.

Contractions

Directions Write the contraction in each sentence. Then write the word or words that make up the contraction.

1. You can't win the race without training.

   _____

2. These are Olympic athletes, and they're training many hours each week.

   _____

3. She's a great swimmer.

   _____

4. She didn't know swimming was so challenging.

   _____

5. Maybe you'll become a swimmer too.

   _____

Directions Write the contraction for the underlined words.

6. You <u>will not</u> believe Gertrude Ederle's strength and will power.

   _____

7. She <u>could not</u> have crossed the English Channel without them.

   _____

8. The Channel is wide, and <u>it is</u> stormy.

   _____

9. Many swimmers have tried to swim the Channel, and <u>they have</u> given up.

   _____

10. Gertrude Ederle was a great swimmer, and <u>she is</u> my role model.

   _____

3.23.C.1.i.2 Use punctuation marks including apostrophes in contractions. **3.24.F.1** Spell complex contractions.

Syllables VCCCV

Spelling Words				
monster	surprise	hundred	complete	control
sample	instant	inspect	pilgrim	contrast
explode	district	address	substance	children

Analogies Write the list word that completes each comparison.

1. **Adult** is to **adults** as **child** is to _____.

2. **Begin** is to **end** as **unfinished** is to _____.

3. **1,000** is to **thousand** as **100** is to _____.

4. **Check** is to **examine** as **examine** is to _____.

5. **Light** is to **dark** as **compare** is to _____.

6. **Quick** is to **fast** as **immediate** is to _____.

7. **Explorer** is to **pioneer** as **traveler** is to _____.

8. **Real** is to **person** as **make-believe** is to _____.

Finding Syllables Decide where to divide each word into syllables. Write each syllable. Remember that for VCCCV words, you divide after the first consonant.

hundred = hun dred

9. surprise _____ _____

10. control _____ _____

11. sample _____ _____

12. substance _____ _____

13. address _____ _____

14. district _____ _____

15. explode _____ _____

Home Activity Your child is learning spelling words with the VCCCV (vowel-consonant-consonant-consonant-vowel) syllable pattern. Ask your child to write each word and to circle in crayon the three consonants that come together.

3.24.A.2 Use knowledge of word parts to spell. **3.24.A.3** Use knowledge of word segmentation to spell. **3.24.A.4** Use knowledge of syllabication to spell.

© Pearson Education, Inc., 3

Prepositions

Directions Write the preposition in each sentence.

1. The eagle held a fish in its feet. _____

2. The fish was for the baby eagles. _____

3. The eagle's nest was high above the lake. _____

4. The baby eagles' cries filled the air of the forest. _____

5. The mother eagle landed on the big nest. _____

Directions Write the prepositional phrase in each sentence. Underline the preposition.

6. These eagles live in Florida.

_____

7. They make their homes along the marshes.

_____

8. They lay their eggs during the winter.

_____

9. The mother bird stays with the eggs.

_____

10. The father bird gets food from the water.

_____

11. He drops it into the babies' mouths.

_____

12. The babies will leave the nest before summer.

_____

3.22.A.1.v.1 Use and understand prepositions in the context of
reading, writing, and speaking. **3.22.A.1.v.2** Use and understand
prepositional phrases in the context of reading, writing, and speaking.

Conventions 311

Problem-Solution Chart

Directions Fill in the chart with notes on the problem and solution you are going to write about in your essay. Include the facts and details you will use to support your ideas. Write a topic sentence and concluding statement for your essay.

Topic Sentence

Notes on Problem

Notes on Solution

Concluding Statement

3.17.A.2 Plan a first draft by generating ideas through a range of strategies. **3.17.B.2** Develop drafts by organizing ideas into paragraphs.

Concluding Statements

Directions Underline the sentence that is the best concluding statement for each paragraph.

1. There's a dog that talks and a man whose wig keeps falling off. Sometimes I laugh so hard that I begin to cry.

   Concluding Statements

   In one episode, a car drove into a garage and out the other side.

   This is by far the funniest show on television.

   Sometimes my dad watches the show with me.

2. By the end of the day, we had walked thirteen miles. We had climbed three mountains and crossed two rivers. All I'd had to eat was a peanut butter sandwich.

   Concluding Statements

   There wasn't even any jelly for the sandwich.

   The views from the mountain tops were beautiful.

   I slept very, very well that night.

Directions Write a concluding statement for each paragraph.

3. Cape Cod has long, sandy beaches. There are miles of bike trails and beautiful lakes and forests. The nights are cool, and the days are warm and sunny.

   _____

   _____

4. My brother Bob helps me with my homework and makes sure I'm ready for school each morning. He takes me fishing, plays ball with me, and reads to me at night.

   _____

   _____

⊕ **3.17.B.2** Develop drafts by organizing ideas into paragraphs. **3.20.A.1.iii** Create brief compositions that contain a concluding statement.

Unit 4 Writing Process **313**

Prepositional Phrases

> Make your writing more specific by using prepositional phrases to add details.
>
> **General**   We swept up trash.
> **More Specific** We swept up trash on the playground.

Directions Read each sentence and the three prepositional phrases below it. Circle the prepositional phrase that can be used to add specific details to the sentence. Add the prepositional phrase and write the new sentence.

1. Parents and kids can help clean up DeSoto Park.

Prepositional Phrases   in the trash   from the community   through the river

_____

_____

2. We hauled away a pile.

Prepositional Phrases   of old newspapers   at our meeting   into the woods

_____

_____

3. Students met in the park.

Prepositional Phrases   under the water   for my mom   at ten in the morning

_____

_____

4. We threw all the litter.

Prepositional Phrases   for a safe park   into a dumpster   by hard work

_____

_____

3.17.C.1 Revise drafts for coherence. **3.17.C.5** Revise drafts for audience. **3.22.A.1.v.2** Use and understand prepositional phrases in the context of reading, writing, and speaking.

Peer and Teacher Conferencing
Problem-Solution Essay

Directions Read your partner's essay. Refer to the Revising Checklist as you write your comments or questions. Offer compliments as well as revision suggestions. Then take turns talking about each other's draft. Give your partner your notes. After you and your teacher talk about your essay, add your teacher's comments to the notes.

Revising Checklist

Focus/Ideas

☐ Is the problem-solution essay focused on one problem in the school or community?

☐ Does the writer offer a logical method of solving the problem?

Organization

☐ Is there a clear topic sentence and concluding statement?

☐ Are details of the problem and solution organized in separate paragraphs?

Voice

☐ Does the writer show care and understanding of the problem?

Word Choice

☐ Are time-order words used effectively in the solution?

Sentences

☐ Do prepositional phrases add details to the essay?

☐ Are sentences clear, varied, and logical?

Things I Thought Were Good _____

_____

Things I Thought Could Be Improved _____

_____

Teacher's Comments _____

_____

★ Revise final drafts in response to feedback from peers. ★ Revise final drafts in response to feedback from teacher.

Syllable Pattern CV/VC

Directions Circle the word with two vowels together where each vowel has a separate vowel sound. Then underline the letters that stand for the two different vowel sounds.

1. clean   paint   patio

2. audio   faith   search

3. greed   journal   rodeo

4. either   medium   southern

5. beach   pound   pioneer

6. duo   poison   waiter

7. grain   group   stadium

8. mean   freeze   video

Directions Read the paragraph. Circle all the underlined words with two vowels together where each vowel has a separate vowel sound. Write the words on the lines below.

> Marie was <u>eager</u> to <u>create</u> a new song. She <u>thought</u> she had an <u>idea</u> for a tune. She <u>tried</u> it on the <u>piano</u>. Then she wrote a part for the <u>violin</u>. She liked the way it <u>sounded</u>. Marie invited three <u>friends</u> to go to the <u>studio</u> with her. Her <u>friends</u> were singers. Marie <u>explained</u> the music. The <u>trio</u> made a <u>stereo</u> recording. Someday you might even hear it on the <u>radio</u>.

9. _____   10. _____

11. _____   12. _____

13. _____   14. _____

15. _____   16. _____

Home Activity Your child identified and wrote words in which two vowels together each stand for a separate vowel sound, as in *stereo* and *stadium*. Ask your child to read the words aloud from the page above. Have your child name the long vowel sounds in each word.

3.1.B.1.ii Use common syllabication patterns to decode words including open syllable (CV).

Compare and Contrast

- When you **compare and contrast** two or more things, you tell how they are alike and different.
- Some clue words that signal that things might be the same are *like, same, both, also,* and *as well as.*
- Some clue words that signal that things might be different are *but, however, different,* and *instead.*

Directions Read the following passage.

> Fong and his family traveled to Senegal for the summer. On their first night, they ate dinner at a friend's house. Instead of tables and chairs, everyone sat on the floor around a big blanket. Out came a large bowl of food.
>
> Fong watched as the dinner guests ate from the bowl of food with their hands. Rather than taking food onto a plate as they did at home, the guests ate from the part of the bowl that faced them. Just like at home, the food was delicious.

Directions Fill in the Venn diagram to compare and contrast two styles of dining.

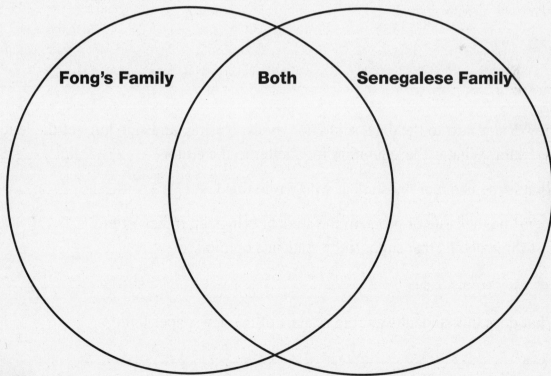

Fong's Family   Both   Senegalese Family

Home Activity Your child compared and contrasted dining customs in two different cultures. Talk with your child about customs you grew up with and compare and contrast them with customs today.

★ Compare and contrast ideas and information.

© Pearson Education, Inc., 3

Writing • Letter to the Editor

Key Features of a Letter to the Editor

- includes the features of a letter: date, salutation, body, closing, and signature
- is written to bring attention to an issue or problem
- often tries to be persuasive

January 5, 2009

Dear Editor,

At Smith School, we have a terrible playground. We have rusty monkey bars and a slide that is not slippery. We don't have a jungle gym or a merry-go-round like Jones School. The ground is cement. If people fall, they might get hurt. This playground is no fun. It's also dangerous.

Students need a good playground. I sit all day in my classroom. I work hard learning and taking tests, so recess is important to me. I want to have fun at recess. The students at Smith School have voted for a new playground. It will have a jungle gym and a merry-go-round. It will have a floor made of recycled tires, so if people fall, they won't get hurt.

We will pay for the new playground by raising money. We are holding a bake sale in the school gym on January 17 and 18. On February 7 and 8, we will collect glass and aluminum in the school parking lot to recycle. We hope people will come to these events to help us earn our new playground.

Sincerely,
Cassie Taff

1. Draw a star next to the date, salutation, body, closing, and signature of the letter to the editor. What is the salutation for a letter to the editor? _____

   What is the name of the student who wrote this letter? _____

2. Underline the issue or problem the student brings up in her letter. List three details that support the student's opinion.

   _____

3. What does this student want the readers of the newspaper to do?

   _____

   Draw a box around three words or phrases that persuade the reader to help.

   _____

Vocabulary

Directions Write the word on the line that fits the meaning of the sentence.

> ### Check the Words You Know
> ___festival ___rhythm
> ___paces ___graceful
> ___pale ___cotton
> ___handkerchief ___snug

1. Every New Year, my neighborhood has a _____ with fireworks.

2. One song had a great _____, so everyone danced.

3. The dancer moved her arms in _____ curves.

4. I pull the covers up to my chin, and then I feel _____ in bed.

5. In summer, I wear cool _____ T-shirts.

Directions Match the word with its meaning. Draw a line from the word to its definition.

6. paces   piece of cloth for wiping one's nose or face

7. pale   wrapped up; warm and cozy

8. handkerchief   walks; steps

9. cotton   having very little color

10. snug   material made from a plant

Write a Description

On a separate sheet of paper, describe a costume that you would like to wear on a special occasion. Use as many vocabulary words as possible.

Home Activity Your child identified and used words from *Suki's Kimono.* Read a story about Japan together. Encourage your child to discuss the article or story using this week's vocabulary words.

© Pearson Education, Inc., 3

3.4.B.1 Use context to determine the relevant meaning of unfamiliar words.

Name _____

Adjectives and Articles

An **adjective** is a word that describes a person, place, or thing. Adjectives tell more about nouns. *A, an,* and *the* are special kinds of adjectives called **articles.**

> **Adjectives**   <u>Some</u> girls wore <u>long</u>, <u>bright</u> skirts.
> **Articles**   <u>A</u> boy wore <u>an</u> awesome shirt to <u>the</u> party.

- The articles *a* and *an* are used only with singular nouns. *A* is used before a word that begins with a consonant sound: *a jacket, a full cup. An* is used before a word that begins with a vowel sound: *an eagle, an orange jacket, an empty cup.*
- Use *the* before singular or plural nouns: *the shoe, the shoes.*

Directions Write the adjective that describes each underlined noun.

1. Many countries have colorful <u>clothing</u> for celebrations. _____

2. Indian women wear silk <u>dresses</u>. _____

3. Many Scottish men have plaid <u>kilts</u> for special occasions. _____

4. In Russia, men put on long <u>coats</u>. _____

5. Japanese kimonos are made in many <u>colors</u>. _____

Directions Circle the article in ( ) that correctly completes each sentence.

6. The American Indian wore (a, an) jacket with colorful beads.

7. (A, The) short pants that that man is wearing are German.

8. The African man wore (a, an) orange robe.

9. (The, A) Mexican musicians had big hats.

10. The woman from Chile wore (a, an) outfit with a long, white skirt.

Home Activity Your child learned about adjectives and articles. On a walk, ask your child to use adjectives to describe various objects, such as a house, a tree, and a dog.

⭐ **3.22.A.1.iii.1** Use descriptive adjectives in the context of reading, writing, and speaking. **3.22.A.1.iii.2** Use and understand limiting adjectives in the context of reading, writing, and speaking. **Also 3.22.A.1.iii.3.**

© Pearson Education, Inc., 3

Syllable Pattern CV/VC

Spelling Words				
create	medium	piano	idea	radio
video	studio	violin	duo	patio
rodeo	pioneer	trio	stadium	audio

Connections Connect the first and last parts of the word. Write the word.

vide-   -oneer   **1.** _____

vi-   -o   **2.** _____

pi-   -um   **3.** _____

stadi-   -a   **4.** _____

ide-   -olin   **5.** _____

Seeing Relationships Read the first word pair. Write a list word to complete the second word pair.

6. see and television, hear and _____   **6.** _____

7. farmer and field, artist and _____   **7.** _____

8. huge and large, middle-sized and _____   **8.** _____

9. ceiling and dining room, sky and _____   **9.** _____

10. three and trio, two and _____   **10.** _____

11. wreck and fix, destroy and _____   **11.** _____

12. sight and video, sound and _____   **12.** _____

13. clang and bell, music and _____   **13.** _____

14. twin and duo, triplet and _____   **14.** _____

15. clown and circus, cowboy and _____   **15.** _____

© Pearson Education, Inc., 3

Home Activity Your child spelled words with CV/VC (consonant-vowel-vowel-consonant) syllable pattern. Discuss any list words that may be unfamiliar to your child.

3.24.A.2 Use knowledge of word parts to spell. **3.24.A.3** Use knowledge of word segmentation to spell. **3.24.A.4** Use knowledge of syllabication to spell.

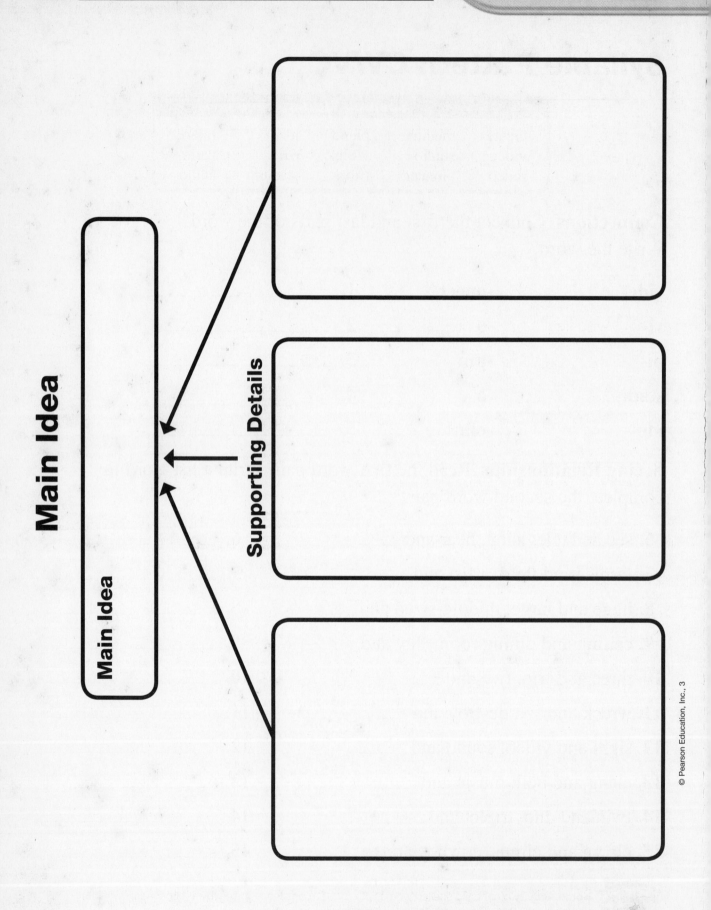

Main Idea

Main Idea

Supporting Details

Vocabulary • Synonyms

- Sometimes you may come across a word you don't know. There may be another word in the sentence that has the same meaning. These words are called **synonyms**, and they can help you figure out the meaning of a word.
- Look for **synonyms** to help you figure out the meaning of unfamiliar words.

Directions Circle the synonym for the underlined word. Then write the meaning of the underlined word on the line.

1. The <u>festival</u> was held as a celebration of the city's anniversary.

_____

2. You grab the baseball, and I'll <u>snatch</u> the glove from my locker.

_____

3. José walked three <u>paces</u> in front of me, but Jim walked several steps behind.

_____

4. I feel so warm and <u>snug</u> inside my sleeping bag.

_____

5. I am happy to tell you that I'm <u>pleased</u> with your schoolwork.

_____

6. The flag <u>flutters</u> and waves in the wind.

_____

7. It is not kind to laugh at people, so please stop <u>giggling</u>.

_____

8. If it is <u>chilly</u> outside, wear a hat so you won't get cold.

_____

Home Activity Your child used synonyms and context clues to find the meaning of unfamiliar words. Read a story or folktale with your child. Encourage your child to identify unfamiliar words by looking for kynonyms within the text.

🌀 **3.4.C.2** Identify synonyms.

Newsletter

- A **newsletter** is just what its name sounds like. It is a letter that contains news. Many groups publish newsletters. These groups include clubs, associations, labor unions, and political parties. Newsletters usually contain announcements of upcoming events, information about membership, articles about recent events, and descriptions of the group's goals.

- Newsletters are usually published weekly or monthly. They are usually only a few pages long.

Directions Read the newsletter and answer the questions that follow.

✥ Li'l Theater Alliance Rag ✥

Fall Issue

AUDITIONS	ON STAGE THIS FALL
September 1, 9 A.M.—5 P.M. Walnut Street Theater, Studio 5	*A Little Night Music.* September 12–October 31. Barrymore Theater.
The Sound of Music. We need two boys and five girls, ages 5–16. Singing and some dancing.	*Macbeth.* September 19–October 10. The Little Shakespeare Company That Could.
Miss Saigon. We need two boys, ages 3–5, to play Tam. Asian Americans encouraged to audition. Tam is a silent role; acting experience a plus.	*The Cherry Orchard.* September 1–30. Chekhov Repertory Theater.
Edwin Booth Awards	**BENEFIT**
This year the Booth Awards for Excellence in Theater, sponsored by the Li'l Theater Alliance, will be presented in the Verdi Theater. The November 1 award ceremony will begin promptly at 7 P.M. For the list of nominees, see page 6.	The local theater community was shocked to hear of the fire that destroyed the Phoenix Theater. We are pleased to announce that several Alliance theaters have agreed to donate a portion of the ticket sales for the week of October 1–7 to the Phoenix.

---

1. Who might be interested in reading this newsletter?

_____

2. What are the Edwin Booth Awards?

_____

3. When can you see a performance of *The Cherry Orchard?*

_____

4. How often is the newsletter issued? _____

Home Activity Your child read a newsletter and answered questions about the information. Share with your child a newsletter that you receive at home. Discuss the different kinds of listings and articles in the newsletter with your child.

★ Understand the organization of newspapers and newsletters and how to use those print materials.

Syllable Pattern CV/VC

Proofread a Menu Circle four misspelled words in the menu specials. Write them correctly. Write an adjective that could have been used instead of *nice*.

Pioneer Cáfe

Specials
Lunch duo.......1/2 sandwich, soup of the day
Lunch treo.......1/2 sandwich, soup of the day,
       salad

Our favorite float: a meduim cola with berry
       ice cream
You won't beleive how good it is!
Or, creat your own nice float flavor.

Spelling Words

create
medium
piano
idea
radio
video
studio
violin

duo
patio
rodeo
pioneer
trio
stadium
audio

1. _____   2. _____

3. _____   4. _____

5. _____

Frequently Misspelled Words

cousin
believe

Proofread Words Circle the word that is spelled correctly. Write it on the line.

6. Did you see the new **stadium staduim**?   6. _____

7. We watched a **vidio video** last night.   7. _____

8. Tara plays the **paino piano**.   8. _____

9. Your **idia idea** is fantastic!   9. _____

10. I like that **radio radioe** station!   10. _____

Home Activity Your child spelled words with CVVC (consonant-vowel-vowel-consonant) and CVV (consonant-vowel-vowel) syllable patterns. Have your child divide the list words into syllables.

3.24.A.2 Use knowledge of word parts to spell. 3.24.A.3 Use knowledge of word segmentation to spell. 3.24.A.4 Use knowledge of syllabication to spell. 3.24.C.1 Spell high-frequency words from a commonly used list.

Spelling Syllable Pattern CV/VC   **325**

Adjectives and Articles

Directions Read the selection. Then read each question that follows the selection. Decide which is the best answer to each question. Mark the space for the answer you have chosen.

American Clothing Traditions

(1) America is not known for its clothing traditions. (2) However, many Americans dress up for special occasions or events. (3) _____ wedding is sure to have tuxedos and fancy dresses. (4) Sports fans wear colorful clothes at games. (5) Some fans even paint their faces bright colors. (6) Another place to see different clothes is at a costume party. (7) You may see scary monsters or a big star.

1 What adjective describes *occasions* in sentence 2?

- ⬭ dress
- ⬭ up
- ⬭ special
- ⬭ events

2 What article could you use at the beginning of sentence 3?

- ⬭ An
- ⬭ The
- ⬭ A
- ⬭ Big

3 What adjective is used in sentence 5?

- ⬭ bright
- ⬭ paint
- ⬭ faces
- ⬭ colors

4 What article is used in sentence 6?

- ⬭ at
- ⬭ a
- ⬭ Another
- ⬭ to

5 What two adjectives are used in sentence 7?

- ⬭ monsters, star
- ⬭ You, see
- ⬭ scary, star
- ⬭ scary, big

Home Activity Your child prepared for taking tests on adjectives and articles. Circle a paragraph in a newspaper or magazine article. Ask your child to count the articles in the paragraph.

🌐 **3.22.A.1.iii.1** Use descriptive adjectives in the context of reading, writing, and speaking. **3.22.A.1.iii.2** Use and understand limiting adjectives in the context of reading, writing, and speaking. **Also 3.22.A.1.iii.3.**

Homophones

Directions Choose the word that best matches each definition. Write the word
on the line.

_____ 1. a small room in a prison   sell   cell

_____ 2. to record on paper   right   write

_____ 3. 60 minutes   hour   our

_____ 4. not strong   weak   week

_____ 5. a period of darkness   knight   night

_____ 6. swallowed   ate   eight

_____ 7. a story   tail   tale

_____ 8. also   to   too

Directions Choose the best word to complete each sentence. Write the word
on the line.

_____ 9. My aunt (cent/sent) us a letter.

_____ 10. I did not (hear/here) you.

_____ 11. The letter said my aunt would (meat/meet) us at
the airport.

_____ 12. Our (plain/plane) arrived late.

_____ 13. We looked everywhere and did not (sea/see) my aunt.

_____ 14. Finally (eye/I) spotted her near the baggage claim area.

_____ 15. Then we (knew/new) everything would be fine in our
new country.

Home Activity Your child identified and wrote homophones—words that sound the same but have
different meanings and spellings. Work with your child to make a list of other homophones, such as *for/four*,
heard/herd, *sail/sale*, and *one/won*. Take turns writing sentences that correctly use each homophone.

⊕ **3.4.C.4** Identify homophones. **3.4.C.8** Use homophones.   **Phonics** Homophones   **327**

© Pearson Education, Inc., 3

Main Idea and Details

- The **topic** is what a piece of writing is about.
- The **main idea** is the most important idea about a topic.
- **Supporting details** are small pieces of information that tell more about the main idea.

Directions Read the following passage.

If you're going to eat cookies, you should eat homemade cookies. When you make your own cookies, you can make cookies that are as good for you as possible. My grandmother and I often make cookies together. We always use the freshest ingredients. We look for recipes that don't use much sugar. We put in healthy foods, such as nuts and raisins, to give our cookies their special flavor. Nothing tastes better than a warm cookie right out of the oven!

Directions Fill in the graphic organizer to show the topic, main idea, and details of the passage.

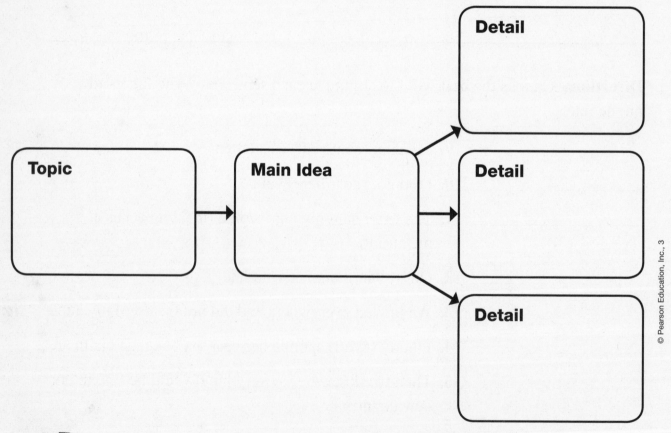

Home Activity Your child identified the main idea and supporting details in a passage. Read a realistic story with your child. Then ask him or her to identify the topic, main idea, and the supporting details.

🌀 **3.13.A.1** Identify details or facts that support the main idea.

Writing • Personal Narrative

Key Feature of a Personal Narrative

- tells about a personal experience
- written in the first person
- usually written in the order in which the events happened

Costume Party

My name is Tony. I'm the odd person in my family. That's because I'm the only boy. I have two older sisters and two younger ones. I'm right in the middle.

Last year, a friend of ours was having a costume party. We all wanted to go. Mom said we had to clean our bedrooms before we went to the party.

I made a deal with my sisters. If they would clean my room, I would let them choose my costume. After we made the deal, my sisters cleaned my room. I thought that was pretty cool.

When it was time to get dressed for the party, my sisters decided on a costume for me. They dressed me up like a rabbit and painted my face! I was kind of mad at first. Then Mom said it was the funniest thing she had seen in a long time. I had to smile. I did look pretty funny. We all had a good laugh.

1. How can you tell this narrative is written in first person?

_____

2. What words does the author use to tell you how long ago the events in this narrative happened?

_____

3. What words does the author use to show the order of events in the narrative?

_____

Vocabulary

Directions Choose a vocabulary word from the box and write it next to its meaning.

_____ 1. flies at a great height

_____ 2. bunch of flowers

_____ 3. hard to do or understand

_____ 4. eating with short, quick bites

_____ 5. walk or dock built out over water

Check the Words You Know
___bouquet
___circus
___difficult
___nibbling
___pier
___soars
___swallow

Directions Choose a word from the box that fits the meaning of the sentence and write it on the line.

6. The _____ performers included clowns, tumblers, trapeze artists, and trained lions and tigers.

7. My throat hurt too much to _____ anything except ice-cold drinks.

8. I like to watch the squirrels _____ the scraps of food we toss into the garden.

9. Abuelito's kite _____ high above the others because he has great skill.

10. I would not have found the exam so _____ if I'd only studied harder.

Write a Story

On a separate sheet of paper, write a short story about a fun day you once spent with a parent or grandparent. Use as many vocabulary words as you can in your writing.

Home Activity Your child identified and used vocabulary words from *I Love Saturdays y domingos*. Read an article about circus animals with your child. Use this week's vocabulary words to talk about the article.

3.4.B.1 Use context to determine the relevant meaning of unfamiliar words.

© Pearson Education, Inc., 3

Comparative and Superlative Adjectives

Adjectives are often used to make comparisons. To compare two people, places, or things, you usually add *-er* to an adjective to make a comparative adjective. To compare three or more people, places, or things, you usually add *-est* to an adjective to make a superlative adjective.

Sometimes you must change the spelling of an adjective when you write the *-er* or *-est* form.

Drop final *e*	fine	finer	finest
Change *y* to *i*	easy	easier	easiest
Double final consonant	big	bigger	biggest

Chicago is a <u>bigger</u> city than Baltimore.
New York is the <u>biggest</u> city in the United States.

Directions Underline the adjective that compares in each sentence.

1. Abuelito goes to the seashore on the sunniest day of the week.

2. This fish is smaller than that one.

3. Abuelito makes the prettiest kite of all.

4. Abuelito has the cleanest aquarium in town.

5. Some fish in the aquarium are bigger than others.

Directions Write *C* if the underlined adjective is a comparative adjective. Write *S* if it is a superlative adjective.

6. Grandpa had a <u>harder</u> childhood than his granddaughter. _____

7. Grandma's grandmother had the <u>longest</u> trip to California. _____

8. The <u>roughest</u> ride was in a covered wagon. _____

9. Was Grandpa's trip from Europe <u>easier</u>? _____

10. Abuelita is the <u>proudest</u> grandparent. _____

Home Activity Your child learned about adjectives that compare. Ask your child to describe some television programs using adjectives that compare.

3.22.A.1.iii.1 Use descriptive adjectives in the context of reading, writing, and speaking.

Conventions Comparative and Superlative Adjectives **331**

© Pearson Education, Inc., 3

Homophones

Spelling Words

to	too	two	week	weak
road	rode	stair	stare	bear
bare	write	right	new	knew

Context Clues Write the missing words. Use all the words in each homophone group in one sentence.

Do you (1) _____ with your (2) _____ hand?

1. _____ **2.** _____

The (3) _____ dogs want (4) _____ eat (5) _____ .

3. _____ **4.** _____ **5.** _____

Sam (6) _____ he'd get a (7) _____ bike.

6. _____ **7.** _____

We (8) _____ on the bumpy (9) _____.

8. _____ **9.** _____

He's felt (10) _____ all (11) _____ .

10. _____ **11.** _____

The dancing (12) _____ danced in its (13) _____ feet.

12. _____ **13.** _____

The cats just (14) _____ at the (15) _____ .

14. _____ **15.** _____ .

Home Activity Your child wrote homophones. Point to a list word. Have your child use the word in a sentence.

3.24.A.1 Use knowledge of letter sounds to spell. **3.24.A.2** Use knowledge of word parts to spell. **3.24.E.1** Spell single syllable homophones.

Name _____

Scoring Rubric: Writing for Tests: Personal Narrative

	4	3	2	1
Focus/Ideas	Focuses on specific, real memory; told from writer's point of view	Includes events from writer's memory; told from writer's point of view	Includes some events from writer's memory; mostly told from writer's point of view	Narrative does not focus on real events from writer's memory
Organization	Clear order of events	Can follow order of events	Unclear order of events	No order of events
Voice	Writer shows personal emotions, thoughts, and opinions	Writer shows some personal emotions, thoughts, and opinions	Writer shows few personal emotions, thoughts, and opinions	Writer shows no personal emotions, thoughts, and opinions
Word Choice	Strong use of verbs and adjectives to bring the story to life	Good try at using verbs and adjectives	Poor use of verbs and adjectives; story lacks description	No effort made to use verbs and adjectives
Sentences	Clear sentences of different lengths and types	Sentences of a few lengths and types	Sentences of similar length and type	No variety of sentence length and type
Conventions	Few, if any, errors; correct use of verbs and adjectives	Several small errors; use of verbs and adjectives	Many errors; weak use of verbs and adjectives	Many serious errors; incorrect or no use of verbs and adjectives

Vocabulary • Homophones

- A **cygnet** is a baby swan and a **signet** is a heavy gold ring. The two words sound exactly alike, but they look different and they mean different things. Words that sound alike but look different and have different meanings are called **homophones**.
- You can use **context clues** to figure out the correct homophone to use in a sentence.

Directions Next to each word below, write its homophone.

1. brake _____

2. waist _____

3. pane _____

4. pause _____

5. soar _____

6. rap _____

7. suite _____

8. reed _____

Directions Each sentence below has a pair of homophones in ( ). Use context clues to choose the correct homophone and underline it.

9. The bald eagle and the stars and stripes are (cymbals, symbols) of the U.S.A.

10. The driver slammed his foot on the (brake, break) when he saw the deer.

11. Someday I hope to (right, write) a play as famous as *Macbeth*.

12. The squirrel (hoards, hordes) acorns all fall so she can eat during the winter.

13. The crowds cheered for the speaker until they were (hoarse, horse).

14. Don't forget to (ring, wring) out the dishcloth after you clean the sink.

15. The streets of San Francisco are often hidden in the morning (missed, mist).

16. The long, hot August afternoon had left me feeling (board, bored) and restless.

17. A (bare, bear) got into our kitchen and ate all our food while we were on vacation.

18. It would take two weeks for the catcher's injured shoulder to (heal, heel).

© Pearson Education, Inc., 3

Home Activity Your child identified and compared homophones. Read a short story with your child. Point to words that have homophones, such as *stare*. Take turns with your child defining the word in the story, then spelling and defining its homophone (i.e., *stair*).

⭐ **3.4.C.4** Identify homophones. **3.4.C.8** Use homophones.

Maps

Maps are drawings of places that show cities, states, and countries. Some maps show roads. Other maps show hills, mountains, and bodies of water. **Symbols** show the location of different places.

Directions Look at the map of Florida. Then answer the questions.

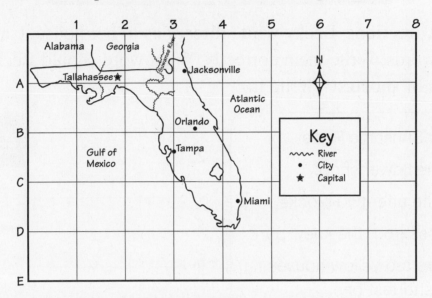

1. Florida is located between which two bodies of water?

_____

2. What is the state capital of Florida? What number and letter tell the location of the capital?

_____

3. Which two states border Florida?

_____

4. What river is shown on the map?

_____

5. Would you use this map to find the road routes you would follow to drive from Tampa to Orlando? Explain.

_____

© Pearson Education, Inc., 3

School + Home **Home Activity** Your child answered questions about a simple state map. Look at a map of your own state with your child. Locate places you have visited. Point out major rivers, lakes, mountains, or any appropriate landform. If possible, identify the bordering states.

3.26.A.1.iii Follow the research plan to collect information from multiple sources of written information, including visual sources.

Research 335

Homophones

Spelling Words				
to	too	two	week	weak
road	rode	stair	stare	bear
bare	write	right	new	knew

Proofread Directions Becky wrote directions to her house. Circle four misspelled words. Write them correctly. What word should Becky have used instead of **shortest**? Write it.

- Start on Sunshine Rode
- Go to the flower shop.
- Turn write after two blocks.
- It's across from the knew park.
- There are too yellow houses. It's the shortest one.

1. _____

2. _____

3. _____

4. _____

5. _____

Frequently
Misspelled
Words

too
two

Meaning Connections Write a list word to complete the sentence.

6. I'm the art helper this _____ .

7. It's a grizzly _____ !

8. Mom _____ the train to work.

9. We just _____ the boat would sink.

10. The box is on the top _____ .

11. Tie the leash _____ the post.

12. Don't use _____ much flour in the cake.

6. _____

7. _____

8. _____

9. _____

10. _____

11. _____

12. _____

© Pearson Education, Inc., 3

School + Home **Home Activity** Your child identified misspelled homophones. Ask your child to spell and define three groups of homophones.

★ **3.24.A.1** Use knowledge of letter sounds to spell. **3.24.A.2** Use knowledge of word parts to spell. **3.24.C.1** Spell high-frequency words from a commonly used list. **3.24.E.1** Spell single syllable homophones.

Comparative and Superlative Adjectives

Directions Read the selection. Then read each question that follows the selection. Decide which is the best answer to each question. Mark the space for the answer you have chosen.

A Fun Day with Grandparents

(1) Of all the people in her family, Ana's grandparents are more happy about her visit. (2) At breakfast, Grandma makes a bigger breakfast than Ana's mother usually makes. (3) Her pancakes with honey are sweeter than eggs. (4) They have a party that is lively than a regular day. (5) A piñata is the most great part of the party. (6) Grandma gives Ana a necklace as a gift. (7) Her grandparents are the nicest grandparents in the world.

1 What change, if any, should be made to sentence 1?

- ⬭ Change *more happy* to **more happier**
- ⬭ Change *more happy* to **happiest**
- ⬭ Change *more happy* to **most happy**
- ⬭ Make no change

2 What change, if any, should be made to sentence 3?

- ⬭ Change *sweeter* to **sweetest**
- ⬭ Change *sweeter* to **more sweet**
- ⬭ Change *sweeter* to **most sweeter**
- ⬭ Make no change

3 What change, if any, should be made to sentence 4?

- ⬭ Change *lively* to **livelier**
- ⬭ Change *lively* to **most lively**
- ⬭ Change *lively* to **more liveliest**
- ⬭ Make no change

4 What change, if any, should be made to sentence 5?

- ⬭ Change *most great* to **greater**
- ⬭ Change *most great* to **most greatest**
- ⬭ Change *most great* to **greatest**
- ⬭ Make no change

5 What change, if any, should be made to sentence 6?

- ⬭ Change *large* to **larger**
- ⬭ Change *large* to **largest**
- ⬭ Change *large* to **more larger**
- ⬭ Make no change

Home Activity Your child prepared for taking tests on adjectives that compare. Have your child find two adjectives that compare in a letter or an e-mail from a friend or family member.

�',' **3.22.A.1.iii.1** Use descriptive adjectives in the context of reading, writing, and speaking.

Conventions Comparative and Superlative Adjectives **337**

Vowel Patterns *a, au, aw, al, augh, ough*

Directions Choose the word with the vowel sound in **ball**. Write the word on the line.

_____ **1.** We moved (because/when) we wanted to live near family.

_____ **2.** Now we live in a (little/small) apartment.

_____ **3.** Mom works hard so that someday we can buy a house with a (lawn/yard).

_____ **4.** Sometimes we (speak/talk) about our old home.

_____ **5.** We think about the beautiful land and the (banana/palm) trees that grew everywhere.

_____ **6.** We (caught/found) fish in the ocean every day.

_____ **7.** We miss some things, but we (always/still) agree that we are glad we came to this country.

_____ **8.** In this country, we found what we (needed/sought).

Directions Write **a, au, aw, al, augh** or **ough** to complete each word. Use the word box to help you. Write the whole word on the line before the sentence.

| cough | automobile | sausage | shawl | taught | walk | walnut |

_____ **9.** I picture my grandmother in her rocker, wearing a purple sh_____ l around her shoulders.

_____ **10.** I remember the scent of warm w_____ lnut rolls.

_____ **11.** I miss the s_____ sage she cooked for our dinner.

_____ **12.** It was so good and spicy that it made me c_____.

_____ **13.** But it was my grandmother who t_____ t us to enjoy what we have now.

_____ **14.** We can w_____ k around freely wherever we want.

_____ **15.** We even have our own _____ tomobile.

Home Activity Your child identified and wrote words with the vowel sound in *ball* as in *small, because, lawn, talk, taught,* and *cough*. Work together to write a list of words that rhyme with these words. Then have your child write sentences that include words on the list.

3.1.B.1.v.2 Use common syllabication patterns to decode words including diphthongs.

© Pearson Education, Inc., 3

Sequence

- To tell the **sequence** in a story, tell the important events in the order in which they happened.
- Clue words such as *first, next, then,* and *finally* are often used to sequence in a story. Dates, days, and times can also be clues.

Directions Read the following passage.

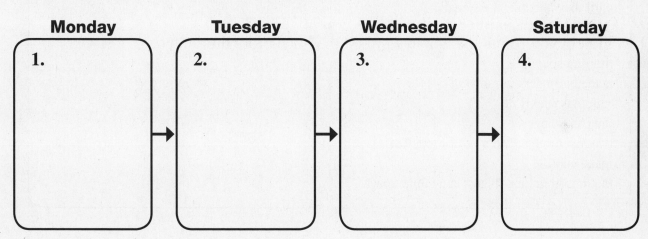

The first clue that a big change was coming happened at dinner on Monday. Mom and Dad started talking about travel. They said travel would be a good experience for my sister and me. On Tuesday, Dad told us he would be working overseas for a year and the whole family would go along. From Wednesday to Friday we packed. Finally, the big day came. We flew for hours and hours on Saturday. We stepped out of the plane and into a new adventure.

Directions Fill in the graphic organizer to show the important story events in the correct sequence. Then answer the question.

Monday	**Tuesday**	**Wednesday**	**Saturday**
1.	2.	3.	4.

5. How did clue words help you fill in the organizer above?

_____

_____

Home Activity Your child identified the sequence in a realistic story. Talk with your child about a day or activity you shared. Then ask your child to use clue words to tell the events in sequence.

3.8.A.1 Sequence the plot's main events. **3.22.A.1.viii.2** Use and understand transitions that indicate a conclusion in the context of reading, writing, and speaking.

Comprehension 339

© Pearson Education, Inc., 3

Writing • Free Verse Poetry

Key Features of Free Verse Poetry

- words arranged in lines
- no fixed rhyme schemes
- may or may not have stanzas
- may include little or no punctuation

---

music class

steady *thump thump thump* CLASH
drums and cymbals
make me jerk stiffly
on the hard seat
where I was told to sit

a long screech
like a mad barn cat
I press my hands hard against my ears
until they hurt like the sound
made by that violin

tinkling sounds
made by fingers running up
running quickly down
the piano keys
two and three and four struck together
make chords
that my stretching fingers can't quite reach

then the soothing flow
of a mellow tone
like melting dark chocolate
sending warm waves down my back
filling my middle with comfort

my first day of music class
and I chose
the cello.

---

1. Circle the last word of each line in the first stanza. Do these words rhyme?

_____

2. How are the line lengths in the second stanza different?

_____

3. Write the words in the third stanza that create a mental picture of hands playing the piano.

_____

Vocabulary

Check the Words You Know

___homesick   ___described   ___curious
___raindrops   ___airport   ___delicious
___farewell   ___memories   ___cellar

Directions Draw a line from the word to its definition.

1. homesick   parting

2. farewell   told what something looked like

3. memories   longing for home

4. delicious   things you remember

5. described   tasting very good

6. cellar   an underground room

Directions Write a word from the box that fits the meaning of the sentence.

7. I opened my umbrella when I felt _____ falling on my head.

8. At the _____ I wait to board the plane.

9. I enjoy social studies because I am _____ about the world.

10. I have many happy _____ of my summer vacation.

11. This Chinese restaurant has _____ food.

Write a Journal Entry

On a separate sheet of paper, write a journal entry about a happy memory you have. Use as many vocabulary words as possible.

Home Activity Your child identified and used words from *Good-Bye, 382 Shin Dang Dong*. Read a story or poem that tells about feelings. Discuss the story or poem using this week's vocabulary words.

3.4.B.1 Use context to determine the relevant meaning of unfamiliar words.

Adverbs

An **adverb** is a word that can tell when, where, or how something happens.

Now the movers pack the furniture. (when)
They carry the furniture outside. (where)
They carefully load the van. (how)

- Adverbs can come before or after the verbs they describe.
- Adverbs that tell how something happens often end in *-ly.*

Directions Underline the adverbs in the sentences.

1. Kim's mother often cooks Korean dishes.

2. She chops cabbage carefully.

3. She gently mixes more vegetables.

4. She quickly cooks the mixture on the stove.

Directions Choose the correct word in ( ) to write each new sentence.

5. Everyone (usual, usually) wears costumes to the school party.

_____

_____

6. Kim (happily, happy) wears her Korean outfit.

_____

7. The jacket fits (tight, tightly) around her shoulders.

_____

8. The skirt falls (loosely, loose) around her feet.

_____

© Pearson Education, Inc., 3

Home Activity Your child learned about adverbs. Ask your child to describe something he or she did today using one or more adverbs.

3.22.A.1.iv.1 Use and understand adverbs about time in the context of reading, writing, and speaking. **Also, 3.22.A.1.iv.2, 3.22.A.1.viii.1, 3.22.A.1.viii.2.**

Vowel Patterns *au, augh, ou, ough*

Spelling Words				
because	though	taught	bought	touch
would	author	could	enough	sausage
fought	should	faucet	daughter	brought

Definitions Write the list word that fits the clue.

1. gave instructions   1. _____

2. battled for something   2. _____

3. writer of articles or stories   3. _____

4. opposite of the word *son*   4. _____

5. paid for something   5. _____

Word Meanings Write the missing list word to complete each sentence.

6. Anjay likes cheese and _____ on his crackers.   6. _____

7. We _____ not swim after eating.   7. _____

8. My mom made _____ salad for ten people.   8. _____

9. We won the game _____ of good defense.   9. _____

10. Andrea got water from the _____.   10. _____

11. On Fitness Day, I _____ a jump rope to school.   11. _____

12. The blanket is soft to _____.   12. _____

13. If we practice, we _____ be great.   13. _____

14. We need the key to get inside, _____.   14. _____

15. I _____ love to watch that program!   15. _____

© Pearson Education, Inc., 3

Home Activity Your child wrote words with *au, augh, ou,* and *ough* that make different vowel sounds. Have your child pronounce each word to make sure they are saying the vowel sound correctly.

3.24.A.1 Use knowledge of letter sounds to spell. **3.24.A.2** Use knowledge of word parts to spell.

Spelling Vowel Patterns *au, augh, ou, ough*   343

Web A

Vocabulary • Word Structure

- A **compound word** is a word made up of two or more smaller words.
- You can often figure out the meaning of an unfamiliar compound word if you know the meanings of the smaller words. Sometimes the meanings of the smaller words do not help with meaning but do help you recognize the compound word.

Directions Read the following passage about a boy who returned to his birthplace. Then answer the questions below. Look for compound words as you read.

> Haresh had moved away from India when he was a baby. He couldn't remember his birthplace at all, so he was glad when his grandparents asked him to visit them in India. Haresh had a great time. He ran through the raindrops with cousins he had just met. He saw many new sights. But Haresh was a little homesick. When it was time to say farewell and report to the airport, he was ready. Haresh looked forward to returning to India next summer, though.

1. What are the two parts of *birthplace*?

_____

2. How do the two parts of *raindrops* help you figure out the word's meaning?

_____

_____

3. If you are homesick, what do you want to do?

_____

4. What two smaller words make up the compound word *farewell*?

_____

5. Which word is compound—*report* or *airport*? How do you know?

_____

_____

Home Activity Your child identified and used compound words. With your child, see how many compound words you can think of that include the word *over*. Make a list of the words.

★ Recognize compound words and their word parts.

Atlas

An **atlas** is a book of maps. **CD-ROM atlases** contain maps too. CD-ROMs can store a large amount of information on a small disk. On one CD-ROM, you can find a collection of maps of countries, states, cities, as well as road maps.

Directions Look at the map of Massachusetts. Then answer the questions below.

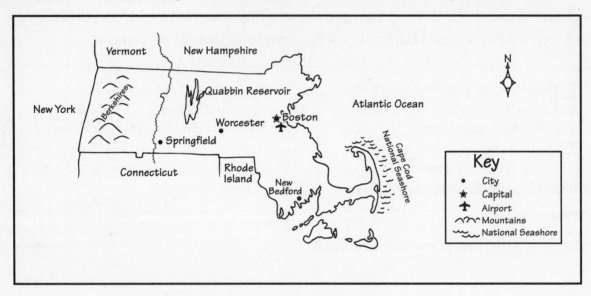

1. What are the names of two cities in Massachusetts?

_____

2. The airport is located near which city and which body of water?

_____

3. Which two states border Massachusetts on the north?

_____

4. What are the Berkshires?

_____

5. How would you describe the location of the Quabbin Reservoir in the state?

_____

Home Activity Your child answered questions about a map. Look at an atlas with your child. Look through the different maps and discuss all of the different features that are shown.

3.26.A.1.iii Follow the research plan to collect information from multiple sources of written information, including visual sources.

Vowel Patterns *au, augh, ou, ough*

Spelling Words				
because	though	taught	bought	touch
would	author	could	enough	sausage
fought	should	faucet	daughter	brought

Proofread a List Ella wrote about her day in class. Circle the four spelling mistakes. Write the words correctly. Write the word Ella should have used in the last sentence instead of better.

Class was very interesting becauze we had a guest speaker. She was an author. She brout her book with her. The book was about goals. She said we shoold always have goals. She tawt us to aim high and be the better we can be.

1. _____

2. _____

3. _____

4. _____

5. _____

Frequently Misspelled Words

because
caught
thought

Proofread Words Fill in a circle to show which word is spelled correctly. Write the word.

6. ○ fout   ○ fawt   ○ fought   _____

7. ○ faucet   ○ fawcet   ○ foucet   _____

8. ○ tuch   ○ touch   ○ toucgh   _____

9. ○ enuff   ○ enouh   ○ enough   _____

10. ○ woud   ○ would   ○ woughd   _____

11. ○ could   ○ cood   ○ coud   _____

12. ○ thogh   ○ thow   ○ though   _____

School + Home

Home Activity Your child wrote words with *au, augh, ou,* and *ough* that make different vowel sounds. Ask your child to circle the four hardest words for him or her to spell and then write them.

3.24.A.1 Use knowledge of letter sounds to spell. **3.24.A.2** Use knowledge of word parts to spell. **3.24.C.1** Spell high-frequency words from a commonly used list.

Spelling Vowel Patterns *au, augh, ou, ough*   **347**

© Pearson Education, Inc., 3

Adverbs

Directions Read the selection. Then read each question that follows the selection. Decide which is the best answer to each question. Mark the space for the answer you have chosen.

Korea

(1) It rains heavily in Korea in winter. (2) After the rains, the rice grows quickly in the wet fields. (3) Farmers soon plant some vegetables. (4) Fishermen work there on the coasts. (5) They catch many kinds of fish easily. (6) Some farmers grow oranges yearly. (7) Today Korea produces much food.

1 Which word is an adverb in sentence 1?
- ⬭ rains
- ⬭ in
- ⬭ heavily
- ⬭ winter

2 Which word is an adverb in sentence 3?
- ⬭ plant
- ⬭ some
- ⬭ Farmers
- ⬭ soon

3 Which word is an adverb in sentence 4?
- ⬭ on
- ⬭ the
- ⬭ there
- ⬭ They

4 Which word is an adverb in sentence 5?
- ⬭ easily
- ⬭ many
- ⬭ catch
- ⬭ They

5 Which word is an adverb in sentence 7?
- ⬭ Korea
- ⬭ Today
- ⬭ much
- ⬭ produces

© Pearson Education, Inc., 3

Home Activity Your child prepared for taking tests on adverbs. While reading a book with your child, have him or her describe the actions in a picture using two adverbs in the description. Then have your child explain what might happen next.

🌐 **3.22.A.1.iv.1** Use and understand adverbs about time in the context of reading, writing, and speaking. **Also, 3.22.A.1.iv.2, 3.22.A.1.viii.1.**

Name _____

Vowel Patterns *ei, eigh*

Directions Read each sentence. Underline the word that has *ei* or *eigh*. Write *long a,* *long e,* or *long i* on the line to tell what sound the vowel pattern stands for.

_____ 1. We enjoy shopping at our neighborhood bakery.

_____ 2. We always go on either Friday or Saturday.

_____ 3. Shelves of baked goods reach from floor to ceiling.

_____ 4. I'm not the right height yet to reach the top shelf.

_____ 5. That shelf must be eight feet high!

_____ 6. We weigh all our choices and make up our minds.

_____ 7. We smile when we receive our package from the salesclerk.

Directions Choose a word from the box to match each clue. Write the word on the line.

_____ 8. a strap used to control a horse

_____ 9. to grab an object

_____ 10. free time

_____ 11. a person who lives nearby

_____ 12. the space between something's lowest and highest point

_____ 13. cargo carried from one place to another by truck, ship, or other vehicle

_____ 14. not tell the truth

_____ 15. a blood vessel in a living creature's body

deceive
freight
height
leisure
neighbor
rein
seize
vein

Home Activity Your child identified and used words with the long *a, e,* or *i* sound spelled *ei* or *eigh.* Work together to make a crossword puzzle, beginning with words and definitions from this page.

3.1.B.1.v.1 Use common syllabication patterns to decode words including vowel digraphs. **3.1.C.1** Decode words applying knowledge of common spelling patterns.

Phonics Vowel Patterns *ei, eigh* **349**

Draw Conclusions

- A **conclusion** is a decision or opinion that makes sense based on facts and details.
- You can also use what you **already know** to draw a conclusion.

Directions Read the following passage and use the information to complete the chart below.

My dad is a baker. He works right around the corner from our house. He leaves our house in the morning, when it is still very, very dark out. He has to start early so people can have fresh baked goods when the bakery opens.

Dad doesn't mind getting up so early. He says it's really quiet outside when he goes to work. And he especially likes the smiles on people's faces when they bite into something good that he has made.

Directions Write a fact from the story in boxes 1–3. Write something you know about that relates to the story in box 4. Then write a conclusion in box 5.

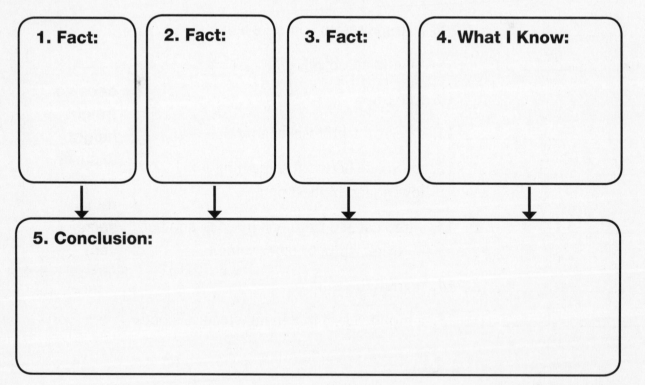

1. Fact:

2. Fact:

3. Fact:

4. What I Know:

5. Conclusion:

© Pearson Education, Inc., 3

Home Activity Your child learned about drawing conclusions. Tell your child about something that you did today. Ask him or her to draw a conclusion based on what you've said and what he or she already knows about you or the thing you did.

★ Draw and support logical conclusions about text.

Writing • Invitation

Key Features of an Invitation

- gives the reason for the invitation
- provides a date, time, and location
- includes contact information if a reply is needed
- often uses creative pictures or drawings

Monday Night Party!

What: You are warmly invited to join my family for a night of pizza, pasta, and football. Help us cheer on our favorite team as they fearlessly clash with their opponents. It is shaping up to be the most thrilling game of the season! We will have plenty of pizza, pasta, and snacks to munch on as football history is made.

When: Monday, January 6, at 5:30 PM

Where: Lila's apartment
        2846 N. Marina St., #304
        Seattle, WA 98000

R.S.V.P. Please call Lila at 200-525-5543 to let me know if you can make it!

---

1. Underline the words that tell why Lila is having a pizza party.

2. Draw a circle around each of the following: date, time, and location.

3. Draw a box around the contact information.

Vocabulary

Directions Write the word from the box that fits the meaning of each sentence.

> **Check the Words You Know**
>
> ___bakery ___dough
> ___batch ___braided
> ___mixture ___boils
> ___ingredients

1. I walked to the _____ to buy bread.

2. Mom and I made a _____ of 24 muffins for the bake sale.

3. Flour is one of the main _____ in baking.

4. My father _____ water when he makes tea.

Directions Read the definition. Write **true** next to the word with that meaning. Write **false** next to the word that does not have that meaning.

5. several things blended together

   _____ mixture   _____ braided

6. a place where breads are made and sold.

   _____ batch   _____ bakery

7. made into a twisted shape

   _____ braided   _____ boiled

8. a mix of flour and other ingredients that you bake

   _____ bakery   _____ dough

Write a Menu

On a separate sheet of paper, create a menu for a restaurant. Your menu may include foods for breakfast, lunch, or dinner. Use as many vocabulary words as possible.

Home Activity Your child identified and used words from *Jalapeño Bagels*. Read a recipe or magazine article about food. Discuss the recipe or article using the vocabulary words.

3.4.B.1 Use context to determine the relevant meaning of unfamiliar words.

Name _____

Comparative and Superlative Adverbs

> You can use **adverbs** to compare actions. The *-er* form of an adverb compares two actions. This is a **comparative adverb.** The *-est* form of an adverb compares three or more actions. This is a **superlative adverb.**
>   Jeremy works <u>hard</u>.
>   Jeremy works <u>harder</u> than Tom does.
>   Jeremy works <u>hardest</u> of all the students.
> Most adverbs that end in *-ly* use *more* and *most* to make comparisons.
>   The truck moved <u>slowly</u>.
>   The truck moved <u>more slowly</u> than the car.
>   The truck moved <u>most slowly</u> of all.

Directions Underline the adverb that compares in each sentence.

1. Mrs. Alvarez sings the loudest of all the employees at the bakery.

2. She bakes faster than Mr. Lane does.

3. The bread dough rises most quickly of all.

4. You must knead bread dough more carefully than other kinds of dough.

5. Mrs. Alvarez has been baking longer than you have.

Directions Circle the correct word in ( ) to complete each sentence.

6. The muffins bake (slower, slowest) than the cinnamon rolls.

7. Mr. Costa works the (faster, fastest) of all the bakers.

8. Of all the workers, Tony sings (more cheerfully, most cheerfully).

9. Mr. Costa mixes sweet roll dough (most rapidly, more rapidly) than Tony.

10. The sweet rolls are done (sooner, soonest) of all.

Home Activity Your child learned about adverbs that compare. Ask your child to compare how he or she rides a bicycle to the way a friend rides, using an adverb that compares.

3.22.A.1.iv.1 Use and understand adverbs about time in the context of reading, writing, and speaking. **3.22.A.1.iv.2** Use and understand adverbs about manner in the context of reading, writing, and speaking.

Conventions Comparative and Superlative Adverbs **353**

Vowel Patterns *ei, eigh*

> **Spelling Words**
>
> | ceiling | neighbor | either | eighteen | height |
> | neither | weight | leisure | protein | freight |
> | receive | weigh | deceive | sleigh | conceited |

Finish the Sentence Write a list word to complete the sentence.

1. How much does the bag _____?   1. _____
2. I want to go for a _____ ride.   2. _____
3. My _____ is moving soon.   3. _____
4. Meat is a good source of _____.   4. _____
5. I want _____ soup or salad.   5. _____
6. My cousin is _____ years old.   6. _____
7. The _____ of the bridge is 150 feet.   7. _____
8. The train was loaded with _____.   8. _____
9. The _____ was too heavy for me to lift.   9. _____

Definitions Write the list word that fits the clue.

10. time to rest and play   10. _____
11. opposite of the word *give*   11. _____
12. rhymes with the word *greeted*   12. _____
13. to try to trick   13. _____
14. rhymes with the word *either*   14. _____
15. opposite of the word *floor*   15. _____

> neither
> leisure
> ceiling
> receive
> deceive
> conceited

© Pearson Education, Inc., 3

School + Home **Home Activity** Your child wrote words with the vowel pattern *ei* and *eigh*. Read a sentence on this page. Ask your child to spell the list word.

3.24.A.1 Use knowledge of letter sounds to spell. **3.24.A.2** Use knowledge of word parts to spell.

Name _____

Four-Column Chart

© Pearson Education, Inc., 3

Vocabulary • Unfamiliar Words

- Sometimes you come across words you don't know. You can use the words and sentences around the **unfamiliar word** to help you figure out its meaning.
- Look for context clues around unfamiliar words to help you figure out what they mean.

Directions Read each sentence. Use context clues to figure out the meaning of the underlined word. Write the meaning on the line.

1. After dinner my brother likes ice cream, but I like cake for <u>dessert</u>.

_____

2. Our cat likes milk, but he <u>especially</u> loves cream.

_____

3. This cake is made with only four <u>ingredients</u>, but it still tastes delicious.

_____

4. My mom cooks many <u>international</u> foods, such as those from China and Spain.

_____

5. Would you like to work in a <u>bakery</u>, where they make cakes and cookies?

_____

6. If you follow this <u>recipe</u>, you will make a delicious cornbread.

_____

7. Pancakes are a <u>mixture</u> of flour, eggs, and milk.

_____

8. I would like a <u>piece</u> of cherry pie.

_____

© Pearson Education, Inc., 3

Home Activity Your child used context clues to find the meaning of unfamiliar words. Read a story or advertisement about a bakery. Encourage your child to look for context clues to figure out the meaning of unfamiliar words.

🌐 **3.4.B.1** Use context to determine the relevant meaning of unfamiliar words.

Outlining

Summarizing is finding the most important ideas about a topic. You can summarize when you read sources during research. One way to summarize is by making an outline. An **outline** shows a main idea and details, like the one shown below.

Favorite Mexican Dishes

I. Meat
   A. Beef
      1. Dried beef
      2. Grilled beef steak
   B. Poultry
      1. Chicken
      2. Chicken enchiladas

II. Vegetables
   A. Beet salad
   B. Zucchini with corn

III. Fruit
   A. Grapefruit salad
   B. Mango salsa

Directions Write the words from the box in the outline. Use the outline above as a guide.

> Shrimp   Peppers   Spaghetti   Parmesan   Vegetables

Common Italian Ingredients

I. Cheese
   A. Mozzarella
   B. _____

II. _____
   A. Mushrooms
   B. Onions
   C. _____

III. Pasta
   A. Rigatoni
   B. _____

IV. Fish
   A. Salmon
   B. Sea bass
   C. _____

© Pearson Education, Inc., 3

Home Activity Your child learned how to make an outline to summarize ideas. Write the names of several different foods. Ask your child to organize the food names in an outline by food groups.

3.26.C.2 Sort evidence into provided categories.

Vowel Patterns *ei, eigh*

Spelling Words				
ceiling	neighbor	either	eighteen	height
neither	weight	leisure	protein	freight
receive	weigh	deceive	sleigh	conceited

Proofread a Paragraph Jay wrote his opinion about the best breed of dog. Circle the four misspelled words. Write them correctly. Then rewrite the run-on sentence as two separate sentences.

> I think the labrador is the best dog. They are eether black, chocolate, or yellow. They are very friendly with family, naybors, and even the mailman! They wiegh a lot, so you have to make sure they don't sit on you, if they do you might get licked. There is allmost nothing you can't do with a labrador!

Frequently Misspelled Words

believe
friend

1. _____ 2. _____

3. _____ 4. _____

5. _____

Proofread Words Circle the word that is spelled correctly. Write it.

6. ceiling   cieling   6. _____

7. neether   neither   7. _____

8. eightteen   eighteen   8. _____

9. height   hight   9. _____

10. protein   proteine   10. _____

11. sleigh   sleiy   11. _____

12. decieve   deceive   12. _____

Home Activity Your child identified misspelled words with the vowel pattern *ei* and *eigh*. Have your child pronounce each spelling word and underline the vowel patterns.

3.24.A.1 Use knowledge of letter sounds to spell. 3.24.A.2 Use knowledge of word parts to spell. 3.24.C.1 Spell high-frequency words from a commonly used list.

© Pearson Education, Inc., 3

Comparative and Superlative Adverbs

Directions Read the selection. Then read each question that follows the selection. Decide which is the best answer to each question. Mark the space for the answer you have chosen.

International Day at My School

(1) Tomorrow is International Day at my school. (2) My class works _____ of all the classes. (3) We prepare _____ than anyone. (4) My group is in charge of the food fair. (5) Allison, a girl in my group, said she will get there the _____. (6) The food fair will last _____ this year than last year. (7) But we are ready to work hard. (8) Our teacher said if we do, this year will go _____ than ever.

1 What superlative adverb can you use in sentence 2?

- ☐ hard
- ☐ harder
- ☐ hardest
- ☐ most hard

2 What comparative adverb can you use in sentence 3?

- ☐ frequentest
- ☐ frequenter
- ☐ most frequently
- ☐ more frequently

3 What superlative adverb can you use in sentence 5?

- ☐ earlier
- ☐ more early
- ☐ earliest
- ☐ most earliest

4 What comparative adverb can you use in sentence 6?

- ☐ longest
- ☐ longer
- ☐ more long
- ☐ most long

5 What comparative adverb can you use in sentence 8?

- ☐ more smoothly
- ☐ most smoothly
- ☐ smoothest
- ☐ most smooth

© Pearson Education, Inc., 3

School + Home **Home Activity** Your child prepared for taking tests on adverbs that compare. While working in the kitchen with your child, ask him or her to make up a sentence about cooking that includes an adverb that compares.

🌐 **3.22.A.1.iv.1** Use and understand adverbs about time in the context of reading, writing, and speaking. **3.22.A.1.iv.2** Use and understand adverbs about manner in the context of reading, writing, and speaking.

Conventions Comparative and Superlative Adverbs **359**

Name_____

Suffixes -y, -ish, -hood, -ment

Directions Combine the base word and suffix. Write the new word on the line.

1. pay   +   -ment   =   _____

2. cloud   +   -y   =   _____

3. self   +   -ish   =   _____

4. boy   +   -hood   =   _____

5. storm   +   -y   =   _____

6. excite   +   -ment   =   _____

7. false   +   -hood   =   _____

8. baby   +   -ish   =   _____

Directions Add **-y, -ish, -hood,** or **-ment** to the base word in ( ) to best complete each sentence. Use the word box for help. Write the new word on the line.

> **childhood**   **entertainment**   **foolish**   **frosty**
> **movement**   **neighborhood**   **snowy**

_____ **9.** During my (child) we moved often.

_____ **10.** We moved to a (neighbor) with woods and a pond nearby.

_____ **11.** Playing outdoors provided plenty of (entertain).

_____ **12.** One (snow) day, my brother and I decided to go skating.

_____ **13.** We were scared by (move) along the edge of the pond.

_____ **14.** How (fool) we felt when we saw it was Ben, our new neighbor.

_____ **15.** We thought it was a (frost) snowman come to life.

Home Activity Your child added the suffixes -y, -ish, -hood, and -ment to base words to form new words. Work together to form other words with these suffixes, such as *thirsty, childish,* and *shipment.* Have your child write sentences using the new words.

✪ **3.1.A.1.iv.2** Decode multisyllabic words in context by applying common spelling patterns including using knowledge of common suffixes. **3.4.A.3** Identify the meaning of common suffixes.

Author's Purpose

- The **author's purpose** is the author's reason for writing.
- An author usually writes to inform, to persuade, to entertain, or to express an opinion.

Directions Read the following passage.

Philadelphia is a wonderful place to visit. It is a beautiful city with lots of history. The Declaration of Independence and the U.S. Constitution were signed in Philadelphia. You can tour Independence Hall, where these documents were written.

The downtown area has several beautiful parks. You can sit in a park and hear live music while you eat ice cream and watch people.

Philadelphia has theaters, concert halls, great restaurants, and stores. You can always find something interesting to do in Philadelphia.

Directions Fill in the graphic organizer to tell the author's purpose and support your response. Then answer the question.

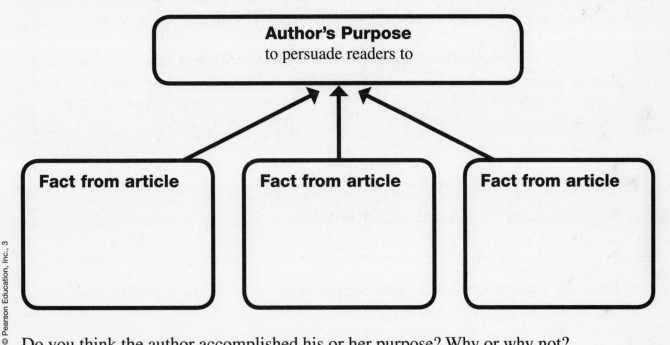

Do you think the author accomplished his or her purpose? Why or why not?

_____

_____

© Pearson Education, Inc., 3

Home Activity Your child identified an author's purpose for writing. Read a story or article together. Talk about why the author might have written it.

3.14.A.1 Identify what the author is trying to persuade the reader to think or do.

Comprehension 361

Writing • Book Review

Key Features of a Book Review

- tells the name of the book and what the book is about
- gives an opinion about the story or subject
- often urges others to read, or avoid, the book
- demonstrates an understanding of the text

Name: Rita Pein

Book Review: <u>My Colors, My World/Mis colores, mi mundo</u>

Everyone will love the amazing colors in <u>My Colors, My World/Mis colores, mi mundo.</u> The book is about a young girl who lives in a desert area. When people think about deserts, they usually think of different shades of brown. The desert can seem very plain. But the desert in this book is filled with beautiful pinks, oranges, and greens.

This book is fun to read for many reasons. The illustrations are lively and beautiful to behold. The colors seem to jump off the pages. The narrator tells how the colors relate to the world around her. She shows examples of where they each appear.

The best part about this book is that it's written in both English and Spanish. If you can read Spanish, you can read the Spanish side. If you can read English, you can read the English side. If you want to learn one of these languages, you can read both sides to learn new words. In conclusion, this book has so much to offer—vibrant colors and beautiful words. You will love it!

---

1. Circle the title of the book that appears in the review.

2. Write one sentence summarizing the book.

_____

3. Does the writer think readers will like the book? How do you know?

_____

3.22.A.1.viii.2 Use and understand transitions that indicate a conclusion in the context of reading, writing, and speaking.

Name _____

Vocabulary

Directions Underline the word that completes each sentence. Write the word on the line.

Check the Words You Know
___flights   ___fierce   ___stoops   ___treasure
___pitcher   ___feast   ___ruined   ___cardboard

1. Our team's _____ struck everyone out.

    pitcher   treasure

2. My neighbors' _____ needed repairs to the broken stairs.

    fierce   stoops

3. After my aunt discovered the chest in the attic, she found a _____.

    feast   treasure

4. My grandmother made us a special _____ for the holiday.

    flights   feast

5. I walked up three _____ of stairs.

    treasure   flights

Directions Write the word from the box that completes each sentence.

6. The lion looked very _____ when it growled.

7. We packed the books in a _____ box.

8. I ate so much at the _____ that I'm not hungry now.

9. The cake was _____ when she dropped it on the floor.

10. The ring from my grandfather is something to keep as a _____.

Write a Thank-You Note

On a separate sheet of paper, write a thank-you note that James might write to Uncle Romie after his visit. Use as many vocabulary words as possible.

Home Activity Your child has identified and used the vocabulary words from *Me and Uncle Romie*. Read a story about a family together. Have a conversation with your child about your family, using some of the vocabulary words in this lesson.

3.4.B.1 Use context to determine the relevant meaning of unfamiliar words.

© Pearson Education, Inc., 3

Conjunctions

A **conjunction** is a word that connects words or groups of words.

- To add information, use the conjunction *and*. To show a choice, use the conjunction *or*. To show a difference, use the conjunction *but*.

  James went to the park <u>and</u> a ball game.
  James had never been to New York City, <u>but</u> he liked it.
  James could stay in the city <u>or</u> go back home.

- You can use a conjunction to combine two sentences into a compound sentence. Add a comma before the conjunction in a compound sentence.

  James went to a ball game. Then he went home.
  James went to a ball game, and then he went home.

Directions Write the conjunction in each sentence.

1. Railroads were built in the 1800s, and Americans soon depended on them. _____

2. Americans could travel by stagecoach, but trains were much faster. _____

3. People could go 20 miles or all the way across country. _____

4. Today Americans travel by airplanes, cars, and trains. _____

5. You can take a train within a city or between cities. _____

Directions Circle the conjunction in ( ) that best completes each sentence.

6. Daniel saw the Statue of Liberty (but, and) the Empire State Building.

7. Was the Statue of Liberty dedicated in 1884 (or, but) 1886?

8. It was sent to the United States in 1884, (or, but) it was dedicated in 1886.

9. Is the statue made of copper (but, or) marble?

10. The statue was cleaned (but, and) restored in the 1980s.

© Pearson Education, Inc., 3

Home Activity Your child learned about conjunctions. Ask your child to name his or her favorite things to do after school, using one or more conjunctions.

🔖 **3.22.A.1.vii** Use and understand coordinating conjunctions in the context of reading, writing, and speaking.

Suffixes

Spelling Words				
rocky	foolish	rainy	childhood	selfish
treatment	movement	neighborhood	childish	parenthood
crunchy	bumpy	payment	sleepy	shipment

Opposites Write the missing list word. It will be the **opposite** of the underlined word.

1. This lizard's skin is <u>smooth</u>.   **1.** _____

2. Do you think tomorrow will be <u>sunny</u>?   **2.** _____

3. I was <u>alert</u> the entire trip.   **3.** _____

4. The salesman was <u>generous</u> with his time.   **4.** _____

5. There's a lot of <u>stillness</u> in the wasp nest.   **5.** _____

6. Our guide seemed <u>wise</u> to me.   **6.** _____

7. My brother acts pretty <u>grown up</u>.   **7.** _____

8. Dad collected coins throughout his <u>adulthood</u>.   **8.** _____

Context Clues A word is missing from each of the opinions below. Write the missing word.

9. Jelly with _____ peanut butter tastes best.

10. Anyone would like to get a _____ of gifts.

11. I should get a _____ for washing dishes.

12. My _____ is the friendliest.

13. A _____ beach is not much fun.

14. There's nothing easy about _____ .

15. The best _____ for a cold is to rest.

Home Activity Your child spelled words with the suffixes *-y, -ish, -hood,* and *-ment.* Have your child try spelling the base word and the suffix separately.

🌀 **3.24.A.2** Use knowledge of word parts to spell. **3.24.D.1** Spell words with common syllable constructions.

Spelling Suffixes   **365**

Critique/Book Review

Title _____

Author _____

Illustrator _____

Plot or Nonfiction Topic _____

My Opinion _____

Additional Notes:

Vocabulary • Context Clues

- Homonyms are words that are spelled and pronounced the same way but have different meanings.
- Use **context clues,** or the words around a homonym, to figure out what the word means.

Directions Read the following passage. Then answer the questions below. Look for context clues that show the meanings of homonyms as you read.

> In the city, I go to big league baseball games. When I visited the country, I went to a minor league game. I didn't think I'd like that kind of baseball, but I was wrong. In the city, we have to climb several flights to get to our seats. At the small, minor league stadium, we sat down close to the field and saw the pitcher clearly. It was easy to see everything on the field. The food was good, too. We gobbled up as much as we could. I didn't miss my big league team at all.

1. In this passage, does *kind* mean "nice and generous" or "type or sort"?

   _____

2. What are *flights*? What word is a clue to the meaning?

   _____

3. How do you know that *pitcher* means "the player who throws the ball to a batter"?

   _____

4. Does *gobbled* mean "made a sound like a turkey" or "ate quickly"? How do you know?

   _____

   _____

5. Does *miss* mean "to feel the absence of" or "a title for a girl"?

   _____

Home Activity Your child used context clues to understand homonyms. Say sentences with homonyms such as *squash* (to crush/a vegetable) or *mine* (belonging to me/to take coal or other minerals from the ground). Ask your child to use context clues to determine the meaning of each word.

✪ **3.4.B.1** Use context to determine the relevant meaning of unfamiliar words.

Vocabulary 367

Electronic Text

- A **search engine** can help you find online resources on a topic. To use a search engine, type in a **keyword** or phrase. In a few seconds, the search engine will pull up a list of Internet sites that contain the word or phrase.

- Sometimes the list contains hundreds or thousands of results. You can narrow your search by using the "Advanced Search" feature. This feature allows you to describe your topic more specifically.

Directions To complete this worksheet, you need a computer. Follow the instructions below and fill in the answers as you go.

1. Choose a topic for a class presentation. Write the topic here.

_____

2. Type in the URL www.kidsclick.org and hit Enter/Return.

3. Click on the major category where you think you will find information on your topic. Write the name of the category here.

_____

4. Now you see a list of narrower topics. Click on a narrower category. Write its name here.

_____

5. Now you see a list of Web sites with descriptions of the information you can find there. Choose a Web site that may have information for your presentation. Explain why you chose this resource.

_____

_____

_____

6. Click on the link (the underlined word or phrase) to explore the Web site you chose. Discuss the experience of doing online research with a partner.

Home Activity Your child read about search engines and used a child-appropriate search engine to research a topic. Try another online search with your child. Work together to choose a topic, narrow it, and find appropriate Web sites with information on your topic.

3.13.D.1 Use text features to locate information.

Name _____

Suffixes

Spelling Words				
rocky	foolish	rainy	childhood	selfish
treatment	movement	neighborhood	childish	parenthood
crunchy	bumpy	payment	sleepy	shipment

Proofread an Order Form Greg is selling snack bars for his team. Circle four spelling errors and one capitalization error. Write the words correctly.

Order Form		
Item	**How Many?**	**Cost**
rocky road bars	3	$ 3.00
crunchie bars	2	$ 2.00
	Total:	$ 5.00

Deliver to: 1413 Sleepy Hollow Road

Notes: Deliver on saturday.
Leave the box on the vary top step unless it is rainey.
The paymant has been made.

Frequently Misspelled Words
different
very

1. _____ 2. _____ 3. _____

4. _____ 5. _____

Proofread Words Circle the word that is spelled correctly.

6. The **shipmint   shipment** should arrive soon.

7. This ride is **bumpy   bumpie**.

8. Don't be **selfist   selfish** with the markers.

9. We are having a **nieghborhood   neighborhood** picnic.

10. He spent his **childhood   childood** in Cleveland.

Home Activity Your child identified misspelled words with the suffixes *-y*, *-ish*, *-hood*, and *-ment*. Have your child underline the suffixes in the list words.

3.24.A.2 Use knowledge of word parts to spell. **3.24.C.1** Spell high-frequency words from a commonly used list. **3.24.D.1** Spell words with common syllable constructions.

© Pearson Education, Inc., 3

Conjunctions

Directions Read the selection. Then read each question that follows the selection. Decide which is the best answer to each question. Mark the space for the answer you have chosen.

My Birthday Party

(1) I had a big birthday party this year, with lots of friends _____ family. (2) Aunt Laurie did not make it, _____ Uncle Hal did. (3) I got both books _____ games for presents. (4) My mother set up a net in the backyard. (5) People could either play volleyball _____ badminton. (6) Some people stayed late. (7) We played board games.

1 What conjunction can you use to complete sentence 1?

- ⬭ but
- ⬭ and
- ⬭ or
- ⬭ to

2 What conjunction can you use to complete sentence 2?

- ⬭ but
- ⬭ and
- ⬭ or
- ⬭ from

3 What conjunction can you use to complete sentence 3?

- ⬭ but
- ⬭ to
- ⬭ and
- ⬭ or

4 What conjunction can you use to complete sentence 5?

- ⬭ but
- ⬭ and
- ⬭ some
- ⬭ or

5 Which answer best combines sentences 6 and 7 using a conjunction?

- ⬭ Some people stayed late, but we played board games.
- ⬭ Some people stayed late, and we played board games.
- ⬭ Some people stayed, late but we played board games.
- ⬭ Some people stayed, late and we played board games.

© Pearson Education, Inc., 3

Home Activity Your child prepared for taking tests on conjunctions. Read a short newspaper article with your child and have him or her point out conjunctions.

✪ **3.22.A.1.vii** Use and understand coordinating conjunctions in the context of reading, writing, and speaking.

Syllable Pattern CV/VC

Spelling Words				
create	medium	piano	idea	radio
video	studio	violin	duo	patio
rodeo	pioneer	trio	stadium	audio

Hidden Words Circle the list word hidden in each puzzle. Write the word.

1. m b c r e a t e t c   _____

2. c p i o n e e r d g   _____

3. b n k m e d i u m   _____

4. f o i d e a j d c a   _____

5. o l s t a d i u m   _____

6. u v i o l i n l m p   _____

Meaning Clues Circle the word that fits the meaning clue. Write it.

7. moving pictures   video or audio   _____

8. outdoor space   piano or patio   _____

9. pair   duo or radio   _____

10. artist's workplace   rodeo or studio   _____

11. sound   audio or duo   _____

12. group of three   trio or duo   _____

13. hear music and news here   patio or radio   _____

14. instrument with keys   piano or radio   _____

15. place where cowboys   radio or rodeo   _____
compete

Summarizing Look at the words you wrote for numbers 7–15. Write a sentence that tells how they are all alike.

_____

Home Activity Your child spelled words with the CVVC (consonant-vowel-vowel-consonant) and CVV (consonant-vowel-vowel) syllable patterns. Together, write the words on a calendar page. Fill the calendar. Take turns choosing a date and spelling the word on that date.

3.24.A.2 Use knowledge of word parts to spell. **3.24.A.3** Use knowledge of word segmentation to spell. **3.24.A.4** Use knowledge of syllabication to spell. **3.24.C.1** Spell high-frequency words from a commonly used list.

Spelling 371

© Pearson Education, Inc., 3

Name _____

Adjectives and Articles

Directions Circle each article. Underline each adjective.

1. Once, the word *kimono* referred to all clothes in Japan.

2. Then a new piece of clothing was invented.

3. People called the loose outfit a kimono.

4. They loved the bright, colorful kimonos.

5. A kimono was an outfit for both men and women.

Directions Choose the article in ( ) that correctly completes each sentence. Write the sentence.

6. Kimonos had (a, an) advantage over other clothes.

_____

_____

7. On (a, an) winter day, people could wear many layers of kimonos.

_____

_____

8. Around 1900, (a, the) people of Japan began wearing styles from Europe and America.

_____

_____

9. Now, people might wear kimonos for (a, the) wedding.

_____

_____

10. Kimonos are (a, an) enchanting sight at parties and festivals.

_____

_____

© Pearson Education, Inc., 3

3.22.A.1.iii.1 Use descriptive adjectives in the context of reading, writing, and speaking. **3.22.A.1.iii.2** Use and understand limiting adjectives in the context of reading, writing, and speaking. **Also 3.22.A.1.iii.3.**

Homophones

Spelling Words				
to	too	two	week	weak
road	rode	stair	stare	bear
bare	write	right	new	knew

Complete the Sentences Write the list word that completes each sentence.

1. Jason has (to, two) bikes.   _____

2. Next (week, weak) is my eighth birthday.   _____

3. Can you (write, right) neatly with a pen?   _____

4. Do not (stair, stare) at people on the street.   _____

5. Maya wants to go to the party (two, too).   _____

6. Which (road, rode) goes to the park?   _____

7. Maya had no shoes, so her feet were (bear, bare). _____

8. Who (new, knew) the answer to the problem?   _____

9. I tripped on a (stair, stare) and fell.   _____

Mixed-up Homophones Cross out two incorrectly used list words in each sentence. Write the correct words.

A knew baby kitten is very week.

10. _____   **11.** _____

We road too the show in a big car.

12. _____   **13.** _____

Is the bare in the write cage?

14. _____   **15.** _____

Home Activity Your child is learning to spell homophones—words with the same pronunciation but different spellings and meanings. Ask your child to point to a list word, spell it, and use it in a sentence. Continue until all words have been used.

3.24.A.1 Use knowledge of letter sounds to spell. **3.24.A.2** Use knowledge of word parts to spell. **3.24.C.1** Spell high-frequency words from a commonly used list. **3.24.E.1** Spell single syllable homophones.

Spelling   373

Comparative and Superlative Adjectives

Directions Underline the adjectives that compare in the sentences.

1. I have the friendliest grandparents in the world.

2. Grandpa is the busiest man in town.

3. He is older than many of his neighbors.

4. No one is nicer than Grandma.

5. I have the tastiest meals at her house.

Directions Choose the adjective in ( ) that correctly completes each sentence. Write the sentence.

6. Abuelito's life was (easier, easiest) in Texas than in Mexico.

_____

_____

7. Grandpa's stories are (longer, longest) than Abuelito's.

_____

_____

8. The family sailed on the (bigger, biggest) ship in Europe.

_____

_____

9. It was (safer, safest) than a trip in a covered wagon.

_____

_____

10. My grandparents tell the (finer, finest) stories in the world.

_____

_____

© Pearson Education, Inc., 3

✪ **3.22.A.1.iii.1** Use descriptive adjectives in the context of reading, writing, and speaking.

Vowel Patterns *au, augh, ou, ough*

Spelling Words				
because	though	taught	bought	touch
would	author	could	enough	sausage
fought	should	faucet	daughter	brought

Synonyms Write the list word for each synonym or synonym phrase. The answer to the riddle will be in the shaded boxes.

What is a skunk worth?

1. writer

2. meat

3. able to

4. female child

5. all that was needed

6. water tap

Before and After Write the list word that begins and ends with the same letters as each word shown.

7. bright _____

8. bone _____

9. world _____

10. said _____

11. trench _____

12. alter _____

Home Activity Your child is learning to spell words with *au, augh, ou,* and *ough.* Ask your child to circle these letters in each word and say the vowel sound that each makes.

3.24.A.1 Use knowledge of letter sounds to spell. **3.24.A.2** Use knowledge of word parts to spell.

Adverbs

Directions Underline the adverbs in the sentences.

1. Luis's family recently moved to a new place.

2. Luis excitedly moved his things into his new room.

3. Next he went to meet his new neighbors.

4. Yesterday Luis saw his new school.

5. He soon got to know the new neighborhood.

Directions Choose the correct word in ( ) to complete each new sentence. Write the new sentence.

6. Maria (sudden, suddenly) felt homesick for her old school.

_____

_____

7. (Usual, Usually), Maria enjoyed meeting new people.

_____

_____

8. She sat (quietly, quiet) in class all day.

_____

_____

9. Some girls (cheerful, cheerfully) asked Maria to play.

_____

_____

10. She (quick, quickly) felt better.

_____

_____

3.22.A.1.iv.1 Use and understand adverbs about time in the context of reading, writing, and speaking. 3.22.A.1.iv.2 Use and understand adverbs about manner in the context of reading, writing, and speaking.

Vowel Patterns *ei, eigh*

Spelling Words				
ceiling	neighbor	either	eighteen	height
neither	weight	leisure	protein	freight
receive	weigh	deceive	sleigh	conceited

Crossword Puzzle Write the list word that could be used in an answer to each question.

Across

2. the top of a room

5. how tall something is

6. cargo

7. trick

Down

1. to get

2. overly proud

3. not either

4. carriage used on snow

Alphabetizing Write each group of words in ABC order.

neighbor	9. _____	weight	12. _____
protein	10. _____	leisure	13. _____
either	11. _____	eighteen	14. _____

© Pearson Education, Inc., 3

School + Home **Home Activity** Your child learned spelling words with the vowel pattern *ei* and *eigh*. Together, divide the words into two groups based on their vowel pattern. Ask your child to choose words from each group to spell to you.

🌟 **3.24.A.1** Use knowledge of letter sounds to spell. **3.24.A.2** Use knowledge of word parts to spell.

Comparative and Superlative Adverbs

Directions Underline the adverb that compares in each sentence.

1. Bread bakes longer than biscuits do.

2. The big oven heats more quickly than the other ovens.

3. Of all the breads, the banana bread will be done soonest.

4. Mrs. Stone kneads dough harder than Kelly does.

5. Of all the neighbors, Mrs. Lopez works most slowly.

Directions Choose the correct word in ( ) to complete each sentence. Write the new sentence.

6. Of all the girls, Jo learned (more quickly, most quickly) how to bake breads.

_____

_____

7. She worked (hard, hardest) of all on her tomato bread.

_____

_____

8. Everyone eats her pumpkin bread (faster, fastest) than any other bread.

_____

_____

9. Uncle Dan compliments Jo (more frequently, most frequently) than I do.

_____

_____

10. Jo stays in the kitchen (longer, longest) than Mom.

_____

_____

© Pearson Education, Inc., 3

3.22.A.1.iv.1 Use and understand adverbs about time in the context of reading, writing, and speaking. **3.22.A.1.iv.2** Use and understand adverbs about manner in the context of reading, writing, and speaking.

Suffixes

Spelling Words				
rocky	foolish	rainy	childhood	selfish
treatment	movement	neighborhood	childish	parenthood
crunchy	bumpy	payment	sleepy	shipment

Suffix Story Read the story. Circle each list word where the writer forgot to use a suffix. Write the word with its suffix.

One rain day a fool king went for a ride.

1. _____   2. _____

The road was bump and rock.

3. _____   4. _____

The king wanted to get a ship of crunch cereal.

5. _____   6. _____

The move of the coach made the king feel sleep.

7. _____   8. _____

In the right neighbor, the king made a pay for the cereal.

9. _____   10. _____

The self king was very child and gobbled up all the cereal with both hands.

11. _____   12. _____

This was his treat of cereal ever since child.

13. _____   14. _____

Parent should help him know better.

15. _____

 Home Activity Your child spelled words with the suffixes -*y*, -*ish*, -*hood*, and -*ment*. Have your child read the story on the page, using the words he or she wrote as answers.

3.24.A.2 Use knowledge of word parts to spell. **3.24.C.1** Spell high-frequency words from a commonly used list. **3.24.D.1** Spell words with common syllable constructions.

Conjunctions

Directions Write the conjunction in each sentence.

1. Would you rather visit the city or the country on your trip? _____

2. You can ride horses and have picnics in the country. _____

3. The country is quiet, but it is interesting. _____

4. In the city, you can go to museums and cafés. _____

5. You can ride in buses, trains, or taxis. _____

Directions Choose the conjunction in ( ) that best completes each sentence. Write the sentence.

6. We went to the museum (but, and) saw all kinds of art.

_____

_____

7. We saw paintings of people (and, but) buildings.

_____

_____

8. Most sculptures stand on the floor, (or, but) some hang from the ceiling.

_____

_____

9. Did you like the paintings (but, or) the sculptures better?

_____

_____

10. My trip to the museum was educational (but, or) tiring.

_____

_____

3.22.A.1.vii Use and understand coordinating conjunctions in the context of reading, writing, and speaking.

Name _____

Persuasion Chart

Directions Fill in the graphic organizer with ideas for the introduction, supporting reasons, and conclusion in your persuasive essay.

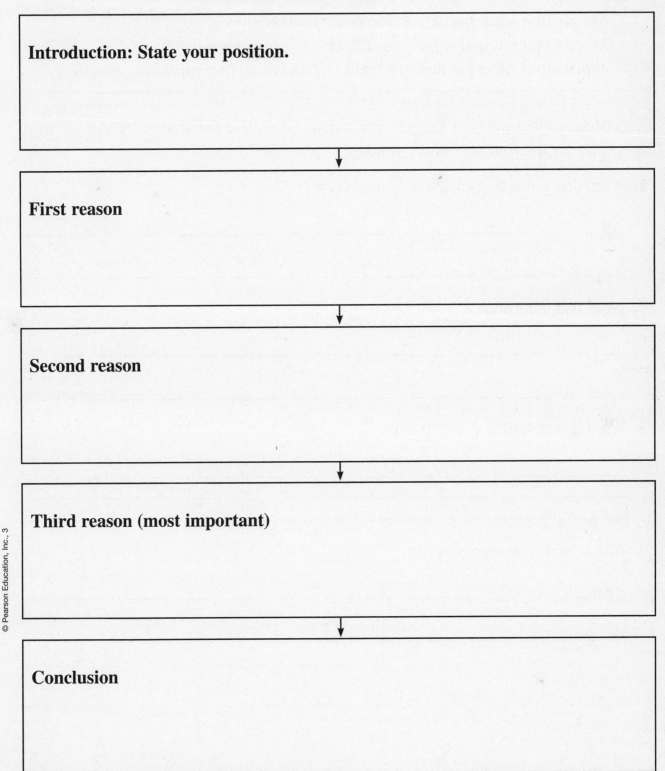

Introduction: State your position.

↓

First reason

↓

Second reason

↓

Third reason (most important)

↓

Conclusion

© Pearson Education, Inc., 3

3.17.B.1 Develop drafts by categorizing ideas. **3.17.B.2** Develop drafts by organizing ideas into paragraphs. **3.22.A.1.viii.2** Use and understand transitions that indicate a conclusion of the context of reading, writing, and speaking.

Use Persuasive Words

Persuasive words convince readers to take an action or agree with the writer's position. Here are some different kinds of persuasive words:

    Words that state that an action is necessary: *should, must, important*

    Words that compare: *best, most delicious, most important*

    Words that describe positive traits: *educational, healthful, safe, effective*

Directions Write sentences for your persuasive essay. Use the kind of persuasive word shown. Underline your persuasive words.

1. Word that states that an action is necessary

   _____

   _____

2. Word that compares

   _____

   _____

3. Word that describes positive traits

   _____

   _____

4. Any kind of persuasive word

   _____

   _____

★ Develop drafts using persuasive words.

Name _____

Add Adverbs

You have learned that adverbs tell about verbs. They can tell **when** (*soon, often*), **where** (*outside, here*), or **how** (*excitedly, carefully, hungrily*) something happens. You can use adverbs to make your essay more specific and persuasive.

General   She looked at the photographs of Puerto Rico.

More Specific   She looked closely at the photographs of Puerto Rico.

Directions Add an adverb to each sentence to make it more specific. Write the new sentence.

1. Japanese people ___ wear kimonos for special occasions.

_____

_____

2. Sam ate the big plate of spaghetti ___.

_____

_____

3. Tourists in China ___ walk on the Great Wall.

_____

_____

4. You must wrap those Mexican vases ___.

_____

_____

Editing 3

Directions This is part of a persuasive essay. Edit the paragraph. Look for errors in spelling, grammar, and mechanics. Use proofreading marks to show the corrections.

Proofreading Marks	
Delete (Take out)	⌐ℛ
Add	∧
Spelling	⬭
Uppercase letter	≡
Lowercase letter	/

After learned about the culture of Japan I want to make a Japanese meal This will be a interesting way to experence Japans customs and recipes right at home. I really wants to make Japanese noodles sushi, and green tea cake. Ill find these delicious recipe in a japanese cookbook and help shop for the engredients. I will assist in preparing the meal and cleaned up the kitchen when we are throu. The meal will be a tasty treat for our entire family. we may even like these recipes so much that we wanted to try more foods from Japan or other countries. Best of all the food's we will be preparing are nutritious because we will be cooking with vegtables, rice meat, and noodles.

Now you'll edit the draft of your persuasive essay. Next you'll use your revised and edited draft to make a final copy of your essay. Finally, you'll share your written work with your audience.

🟤 **3.17.D** Edit drafts for grammar, mechanics, and spelling, using a teacher-developed rubric. **3.17.E.1** Publish written work for a specific audience.

Vowel Sounds in *moon* and *foot*

Directions Circle each word with the vowel sound in **moon** or the vowel sound in **foot**. Then write each word in the correct column.

1. Our school took us on a field trip to an art museum.

2. We spent a full day studying famous paintings and statues.

3. We looked at works by some of the art world's true masters.

4. After we returned to class, our teacher asked us to make a new drawing in our notebooks.

5. I sketched a picture of President Lincoln wearing a black wool suit and a very tall hat.

vowel sound in moon

6. _____

7. _____

8. _____

9. _____

10. _____

vowel sound in foot

11. _____

12. _____

13. _____

14. _____

15. _____

Directions Cross out the one word in each line that does **not** have the vowel sound in **moon** or the vowel sound in **foot**.

16. build   cushion   glue

17. bushel   rocket   smooth

18. button   bookstore   juice

19. football   stew   story

20. balloon   pudding   throat

Home Activity Your child identified and wrote words with the vowel sounds in *moon* (as in *school, new, glue,* and *fruit*) and *foot* (as in *cookie* and *cushion*). Have your child write riddles using words with the vowel sounds in *moon* and *foot*. Try to guess the answer after your child reads each riddle to you.

© Pearson Education, Inc., 3

3.1.B.1.v.1 Use common syllabication patterns to decode words including vowel digraphs. **3.1.B.1.v.2** Use common syllabication patterns to decode words including diphthongs.

Phonics Vowel Sounds in *moon* and *foot*   **385**

Fact and Opinion

- A **statement of fact** tells something that can be proved true or false. You can prove it by reading or asking an expert.

- A **statement of opinion** tells someone's ideas or feelings. Words that tell feelings, such as *should* or *best,* are clues to opinions.

Directions Read the following passage.

A symbol is something that stands for something else. There are many symbols that stand for the United States. The bald eagle is the national bird of the United States. The cartoon-like character, Uncle Sam, also stands for our country. But the best symbol of all is the red, white, and blue United States flag. We should always show respect for our country's flag.

Directions Complete each chart by writing one more fact and one more opinion from the passage above. Then answer the question.

Fact	How to Prove
A symbol is something that stands for something else.	Look up the word *symbol* in the dictionary.
1.	2.

Opinion	Clue Words
But the best symbol of all is the red, white, and blue United States flag.	best
3.	4.

5. What supports the statement, *There are many symbols that stand for the United States.*

Home Activity Your child identified facts and opinions in a passage. Read an article about the United States. Find a statement of fact. Then find a statement of opinion. Have your child explain the difference.

★ Distinguish between fact and opinion.

© Pearson Education, Inc., 3

Writing • Notes

Key Features of Notes

- used to capture important ideas
- often help with a future writing task
- may include abbreviations, short sentences, and sentence fragments

Notes on *The Story of the Statue of Liberty*
(pages 378 and 379)

- Bartholdi wanted the S. of L. to be so large people could climb up inside it
- Other people gave him ideas about how to build it
- First—a large steel skeleton
- People worked on the head and crown
- others worked on the torch—held in right hand
- In left hand—tablet with July 4, 1776, Declaration of Independence
- Torch arm sent to Philadelphia in 1876, then to NYC
- Head shown in Paris to raise money

1. Circle all the proper nouns that are capitalized, including abbreviations.

2. What does the abbreviation "S. of L." stand for in these notes?

_____

_____

3. Why was the statue's head shown in Paris?

_____

_____

Vocabulary

Directions Solve each riddle with a word from the box. Write the word on the line.

1. I describe something that you will always remember.

What am I? _____

2. People who live in a free country have me.

What am I? _____

3. Kings and queens wear me on their heads.

What am I? _____

4. I am another word for uncovered.

What am I? _____

5. I am a light that helps people see in dark caves.

What am I? _____

> ### Check the Words You Know
> ___liberty
> ___crown
> ___tablet
> ___symbol
> ___unveiled
> ___torch
> ___models
> ___unforgettable

Directions Write the word from the box that best completes each sentence below.

6. The wood carver made two _____ of an airplane.   _____

7. At night we lit a _____ to help us see our campsite.   _____

8. A flag is a _____ of a country.   _____

9. A _____ is a stone that has writing cut into it.   _____

Write an Editorial

On a separate sheet of paper, write an editorial about the first time the Statue of Liberty was seen in New York. Write as if you worked for a newspaper. Tell readers how you felt when you first saw the new statue. Use as many vocabulary words as possible.

Home Activity Your child has identified and used vocabulary from *The Story of the Statue of Liberty*. Read a story together about this or another historical monument. Have a conversation about the monument and its meaning. Encourage your child to use vocabulary words.

3.4.B.1 Use context to determine the relevant meaning of unfamiliar words.

Capital Letters

Use **capital letters** for proper nouns. Proper nouns include days of the week, months of the year, and holidays. Titles for people should be capitalized when they are used with a person's name. Do not capitalize titles when they are used by themselves.

Incorrect	Last october aunt Rosie and my Uncle gave a party for halloween.
Correct	Last October Aunt Rosie and my uncle gave a party for Halloween.
Incorrect	Does mother's day come earlier than memorial day?
Correct	Does Mother's Day come earlier than Memorial Day?

Directions Write the words that should have capital letters correctly.

1. Last may Mara saw some wonderful sights.

_____

2. Mara's mom and aunt lucy took her to the Statue of Liberty.

_____

3. They saw the Liberty Bell in philadelphia on memorial day.

_____

Directions Write the sentences. Use capital letters correctly.

4. Bartholdi hoped the statue would be finished by july 4, 1876.

_____

_____

5. Only the statue's arm and torch were ready by the fourth of july.

_____

_____

Home Activity Your child learned about capital letters. While looking at a magazine, ask your child to point out three capital letters used for days of the week, months of the year, or holidays.

3.23.B.1.i Use capitalization for geographical names and places. **3.23.B.1.ii** Use capitalization for historical periods. **3.23.B.1.iii** Use capitalization for official titles of people.

Vowel Sounds in *moon* and *foot*

Spelling Words				
few	school	true	goose	fruit
cookie	cushion	noodle	bookmark	balloon
suit	chew	glue	Tuesday	bushel

Names Write list words to name the pictures.

1. _____   **2.** _____   **3.** _____

Categorizing Add a list word to each group.

4. duck, chicken, ___   **4.** _____

5. cake, pie, ___   **5.** _____

6. paste, tape, ___   **6.** _____

7. Sunday, Thursday, ___   **7.** _____

8. pillow, pad, ___   **8.** _____

9. liter, quart, ___   **9.** _____

Rhyming Words Complete each sentence with a list word that rhymes with the underlined word.

10. We <u>grew</u> a _____ different kinds of vegetables.

11. It's _____ that <u>blue</u> is my favorite color.

12. I will blow up your _____ <u>soon</u>.

13. The meat in this <u>stew</u> is hard to _____ .

14. That <u>doodle</u> you drew looks like a _____ .

15. The _____ building seems <u>cool</u> today.

© Pearson Education, Inc., 3

Home Activity Your child wrote words with the vowel sound in *moon* (spelled *oo, ew, ue, ui*) and the vowel sound in *foot* (spelled *oo, u*). Have your child pronounce and spell the words with *oo*.

🌐 **3.24.A.1** Use knowledge of letter sounds to spell.
3.24.A.2 Use knowledge of word parts to spell.

Main Idea

Main Idea

Supporting Details

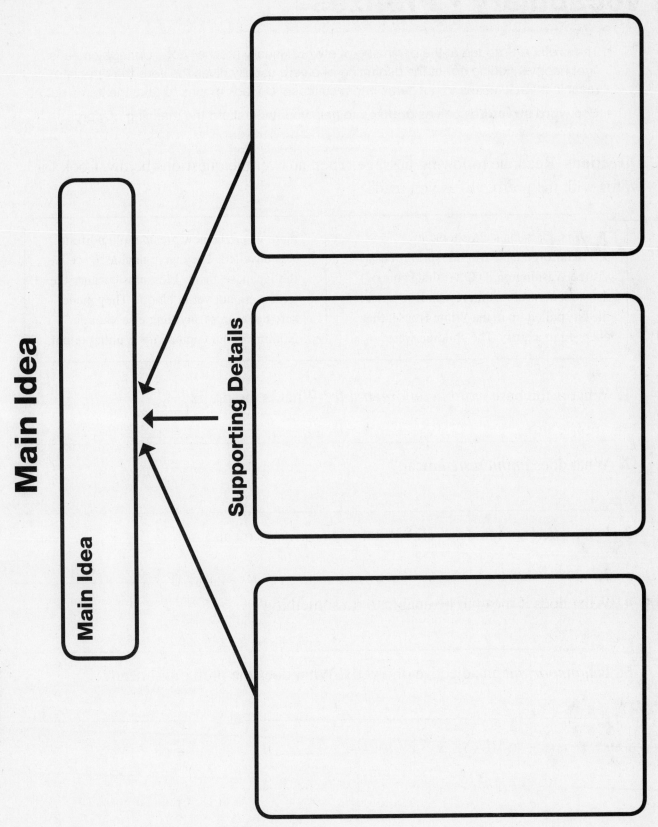

Vocabulary • Prefixes

- The **prefix *un-*** added at the beginning of a word usually means "not." *Unhappy* means "not happy." Adding *un-* at the beginning of a verb usually gives the verb the opposite meaning. *Pack* means to put items into a suitcase. *Unpack* means to take the items out.

- Use **word structure** such as **prefixes** to help you understand the meaning of words.

Directions Read the following passage. Then answer the questions below. Look for words with the prefix *un-* as you read.

> Mrs. Camden's class took an unforgettable trip last spring. They visited Washington, D.C. At first some of the students were uninterested. But when the bus pulled up to the White House, that changed in a hurry. The children were there when the new presidential portrait was unveiled. They were unable to see the Japanese cherry blossoms because the trees were not yet in bloom. They made sure not to miss anything else, though. Nothing in our capital city is unimportant.

1. What is the base word in *unforgettable*? What is the prefix?

_____

2. What does *uninterested* mean?

_____

3. Is *unveiled* a noun or a verb? What does *unveiled* mean?

_____

4. What does it mean to be unable to do something?

_____

5. Is *unimportant* an adjective or a verb? What does the prefix *un-* mean?

_____

Home Activity Your child read words that begin with the prefix un-. Play an opposites game with your child. Say the opposite of what you mean by adding a un- to a word in the sentence. Have your child remove the prefix to figure out what you really mean. For example, say, "Always unlock the door when you're home alone." Your child should tell you that you really mean, "Always lock the door."

⭐ **3.4.A.1** Identify the meaning of common prefixes. **3.4.A.2** Know how prefixes change the meaning of roots.

Time Line

A **time line** shows events in the order that they happened or will happen. It can show days, weeks, months, and years.

Directions Look at the time line. Use the time line to answer the questions.

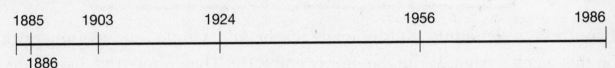

1885 Statue parts arrive in New York in June.
1886 President Grover Cleveland officially accepts statue on October 28.
1903 Poem by Emma Lazarus is added to the base.
1924 Statue becomes a national monument.
1956 Island is renamed Liberty Island.
1986 Centennial celebration honors statue's 100th year.

1. What is the first year shown on the time line?

_____

2. In which year was a poem added to the statue?

_____

3. When did the statue parts arrive in New York? When did President Cleveland accept the statue? About how much time passed between these two events?

_____

4. What major events happened between 1920 and 1960?

_____

5. Why was 1986 an important year for the Statue of Liberty?

_____

Home Activity Your child read information on a time line and answered questions about it. Help your child list the dates of some important family events. Ask him or her to make a time line with these events.

🌐 **3.26.A.1.iii** Follow the research plan to collect information from multiple sources of written information, including visual sources.

Vowel Sounds in *moon* and *foot*

Spelling Words				
few	school	true	goose	fruit
cookie	cushion	noodle	bookmark	balloon
suit	chew	glue	Tuesday	bushel

Proofread a Schedule Kelsey made a schedule. Circle four spelling errors on this week's page. Write the words correctly. Then circle five words that need capital letters.

monday	no school—cuold go to Gym for Kids
tuesday	fruit and cooky sale
wednesday	blow up ballons for party
thursday	Jena's birthday party
friday	Jena's tru birthday

Frequently Misspelled Words

through
took
would
could

1. _____ 2. _____

3. _____ 4. _____

Proofread Words Fill in a circle to show which word is spelled correctly. Write it.

5. ○ noddle ○ noodle ○ noodel 5. _____
6. ○ bookmark ○ bukmark ○ book mark 6. _____
7. ○ cushon ○ cushion ○ cooshion 7. _____
8. ○ ballewn ○ ballon ○ balloon 8. _____
9. ○ glew ○ gleu ○ glue 9. _____
10. ○ friut ○ fruit ○ froot 10. _____

© Pearson Education, Inc., 3

Home Activity Your child identified misspelled words with the vowel sound in *moon* (spelled *oo, ew, ue, ui*) and the vowel sound in *foot* (spelled *oo, u*). Ask your child to write a sentence containing two or more list words.

3.24.A.1 Use knowledge of letter sounds to spell. **3.24.A.2** Use knowledge of word parts to spell. **3.24.C.1** Spell high-frequency words from a commonly used list.

Capital Letters

Directions Read the selection. Then read each question that follows the selection. Decide which is the best answer to each question. Mark the space for the answer you have chosen.

A New Home

(1) The family sailed across the ocean in february. (2) On friday, the ship arrived in a new country. (3) The next day Aunt Sue took her guests to the city.

(4) Their aunt told the family about holidays in america. (5) She said people enjoy fireworks on Independence Day. (6) Americans remember explorers on columbus day. (7) I hope Grandpa visits us at Hanukkah.

1 What change, if any, should be made to sentence 1?

 ⬭ Change *february* to **February**

 ⬭ Change *family* to **Family**

 ⬭ Change *ocean* to **Ocean**

 ⬭ Make no change

2 What change, if any, should be made to sentence 2?

 ⬭ Change *country* to **Country**

 ⬭ Change *ship* to **Ship**

 ⬭ Change *friday* to **Friday**

 ⬭ Make no change

3 What change, if any, should be made to sentence 3?

 ⬭ Change *took* to **Took**

 ⬭ Change *guests* to **Guests**

 ⬭ Change *city* to **City**

 ⬭ Make no change

4 What change, if any, should be made to sentence 4?

 ⬭ Change *holidays* to **Holidays**

 ⬭ Change *america* to **America**

 ⬭ Change *aunt* to **Aunt**

 ⬭ Make no change

5 What change, if any, should be made to sentence 6?

 ⬭ Change *explorers* to **Explorers**

 ⬭ Change *columbus day* to **Columbus Day**

 ⬭ Change *remember* to **Remember**

 ⬭ Make no change

© Pearson Education, Inc., 3

Home Activity Your child prepared for taking tests on capital letters. Look at a calendar with your child and have him or her point out capital letters and explain the reasons for their use.

🏠 **3.23.B.1.i** Use capitalization for geographical names and places. **3.23.B.1.ii** Use capitalization for historical periods. **3.23.B.1.iii** Use capitalization for official titles of people.

Schwa spelled with an *a, e, i, o, u,* and *y*

Directions Choose the word with a vowel that has the same sound as the underlined vowels in **ab̲out, tak̲en, penc̲il, lem̲on, circ̲us,** and **Siby̲l** to complete each sentence. Write the word on the line to the left.

_____ **1.** Susan was (afraid/scared) to walk her dog without a leash.

_____ **2.** Every time she opened the front door, the little (pooch/rascal) ran off.

_____ **3.** One time she took her dog to a (local/nearby) park.

_____ **4.** All the (animals/doggies) were fetching or chasing.

_____ **5.** Susan removed her puppy's (vinyl/nylon) leash and let the dog run freely.

_____ **6.** When her dog ran off, Susan opened a (paper/plastic) bag and pulled out a treat.

_____ **7.** Susan's dog quickly (traveled/bounded) back.

_____ **8.** Now anytime Susan offers her dog a tasty (biscuit/morsel), it comes racing to her.

Directions Circle the letter in each word that stands for the same sound as the underlined vowels in **ab̲out, tak̲en, penc̲il, lem̲on, circ̲us,** and **Siby̲l.**

9. kitchen   **12.** family   **15.** vinyl   **18.** ago

10. river   **13.** melon   **16.** dollar   **19.** open

11. surprise   **14.** sugar   **17.** nickel   **20.** canyon

© Pearson Education, Inc., 3

© Pearson Education, Inc., 3

School + Home

Home Activity Your child identified and wrote words that contain the vowel sound called schwa, heard in words with unaccented syllables such as *about, taken, pencil, lemon, circus,* and *Sibyl.* Help your child write sentences with words that have this sound. Ask your child to read each sentence and identify the letter that stands for the schwa sound.

★ Decode multisyllabic words in context and independent of context by applying common letter-sound correspondences including single letters (consonants and vowels).

Cause and Effect

- An **effect** is something that happens.
- A **cause** tells why that thing happens.
- An effect may have more than one cause.

Directions: Read the following passage.

No matter where you live, English sparrows probably live nearby. Like most of us, the ancestors of today's English sparrows were immigrants. The first family members came from England. They were set free in New York in the 1800s. Over the years, sparrows have moved to all parts of our country.

Americans have a love-hate relationship with sparrows. Some people dislike them because, they say, the sparrows push aside native birds and because they are messy.

Many people enjoy sparrows. They like them because they think they're cute and because sparrows eat harmful worms and insects.

Directions: Fill in the chart to identify cause and effect.

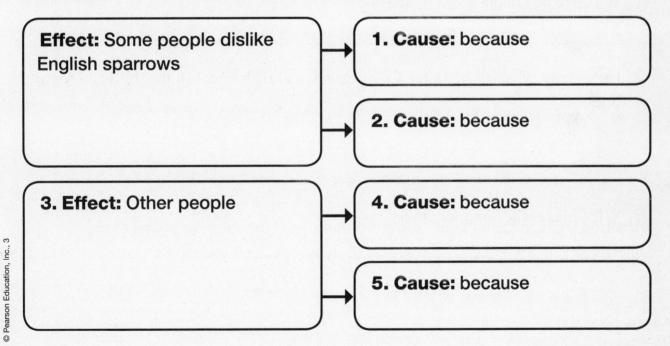

Effect: Some people dislike English sparrows

1. Cause: because

2. Cause: because

3. Effect: Other people

4. Cause: because

5. Cause: because

© Pearson Education, Inc., 3

Home Activity Your child identified cause and effect. With your child, talk about a wild bird or animal that lives near your home. Talk about causes and effects related to having the bird or animal nearby.

3.13.C.1 Identify explicit cause and effect relationships among ideas in texts.

Comprehension 397

Writing • Limerick

Key Features of Limericks

- a form of poetry
- made up of five lines and a specific rhyme scheme (*aabba*)
- sometimes humorous or witty

The Toad in the Shoe

1   A hungry toad lived in a shoe;

2   alone, he was always so blue.

3   A friend would fly in,

4   the toad, he would grin,

5   and then he would eat his lunch, too.

1. Which words in the poem rhyme?

_____

2. How many syllables are in the first, second, and fifth lines? In the third and fourth lines?

_____

_____

3. What makes this limerick funny?

_____

Vocabulary

Directions Match each word with its meaning. Draw a line to connect them.

Check the Words You Know
___narrow   ___foolish
___perches   ___bows
___recipe   ___chilly
___foreign

1. foolish   cool

2. recipe   from a different country

3. narrow   silly

4. chilly   directions for cooking food

5. foreign   skinny

Directions Write the word from the box that best completes each sentence below.

6. Watch the red bird as it _____ on the branch.   _____

7. After he sings, he _____ to the audience.   _____

8. The gap was too _____ for me to squeeze through.   _____

9. He moved here from a _____ country called Sudan.   _____

10. My stepmother wrote that _____ for beef stew.   _____

Write a Recipe

On a separate sheet of paper, write a recipe for something you like to eat or drink. It can be something simple, like chocolate milk or a sandwich. Use as many vocabulary words as possible.

Home Activity Your child identified and used vocabulary words from *Happy Birthday Mr. Kang.* Have your child plan a menu for dinner or help you prepare food from a written recipe. Encourage your child to use vocabulary words in conversations.

3.4.B.1 Use context to determine the relevant meaning of unfamiliar words.

Abbreviations

An **abbreviation** is a shortened form of a word. Many abbreviations begin with a capital letter and end with a period.

- Some titles used for names of people are abbreviations. For example, *Dr.* is the abbreviation for *Doctor*. The title *Miss* is not abbreviated.

  Mr. Don Lee Chang   Ms. Lucy Ruiz   Mrs. Maya Levin

- An **initial** is the first letter of a name. It is written with a capital letter and is followed by a period.

  Mr. Don L. Chang   L. T. Ruiz   M. E. Levin

- The names of days and months can be abbreviated. *May, June,* and *July* are not abbreviated.

  Days of the Week
  Sun.   Mon.   Tues.   Wed.   Thurs.   Fri.   Sat.
  Months of the Year
  Jan.   Feb.   Mar.   Apr.   Aug.   Sept.   Oct.   Nov.   Dec.

Directions Write each abbreviation. Be sure to capitalize letters and use periods correctly.

1. Mrs W. Wenders   _____

2. j r Burton   _____

3. sat, aug 4   _____

4. ms T j. Matthews   _____

Directions Some abbreviations can be used in sentences. Find the word that can be abbreviated in the sentence below. Write the sentence with the abbreviation.

5. Mister Alexis got a pet bird when he moved to this country.

_____

_____

© Pearson Education, Inc., 3

Home Activity Your child learned about abbreviations. Look through the mail with your child. Have him or her identify abbreviations used for people's names and titles.

Schwa

Spelling Words				
above	another	upon	animal	paper
open	family	travel	afraid	nickel
sugar	circus	item	gallon	melon

Context Clues Write the missing spelling word.

1. May I have _____ piece of pizza?   1. _____

2. I have three dimes and one _____ in my bank.   2. _____

3. He was eating a slice of _____.   3. _____

4. I wrote a letter on a sheet of green _____.   4. _____

5. My _____ likes to watch football Sunday afternoons.   5. _____

6. Please get a _____ of milk.   6. _____

7. The _____ had clowns and acrobats.   7. _____

8. Is the _____ bowl empty?   8. _____

9. Each _____ on the list must be done by noon.   9. _____

10. Once _____ a time, there was a handsome prince.   10. _____

11. My favorite _____ is the giraffe.   11. _____

Opposites Write the spelling word that means the opposite.

12. shut   _____

13. brave   _____

14. stay home   _____

15. below   _____

afraid
travel
above
open

Home Activity Your child spelled words with the schwa sound (an unstressed vowel sound such as the *a* in *above*). Have your child pick a number between 1 and 15. Read the list word with that number and ask your child to spell it.

© Pearson Education, Inc., 3

3.24.A.1 Use knowledge of letter sounds to spell. **3.24.A.2** Use knowledge of word parts to spell. **3.24.B.1.vi** Spell words with abstract vowels.

Spelling Schwa **401**

T-Chart

Vocabulary • Antonyms

- Sometimes when you read you see unfamiliar words. The **context**, or words around it, may help you figure out the meaning.
- Look to see if the author used an **antonym**, a word with the opposite meaning, and use that word to help you with the meaning of the unfamiliar word.

Directions Read the paragraph. Then answer the questions below.

My family wanted to eat at a Chinese food restaurant instead of the usual burger place. We had never been to a Chinese restaurant before and were excited to learn about a different culture. We walked in through a narrow hallway that didn't seem wide enough for us to fit.

We drank hot tea with dinner, which was perfect because I was chilly. I tried to eat with chopsticks, but felt foolish because I seemed clumsy with them. I thought it was sensible to ask for a fork! After this restaurant becomes an old favorite, maybe my family will again try something new—maybe Brazilian food!

1. What does the word *usual* mean in the passage? What context clue helps?

_____

2. What does the word *narrow* mean in the passage? What context clue helps?

_____

3. What does the word *chilly* mean in the passage? What context clue helps?

_____

4. What does the word *foolish* mean in the passage? What context clue helps?

_____

5. What does the word *old* mean in the passage? What context clue helps?

_____

© Pearson Education, Inc., 3

Home Activity Your child has identified and used context clues to understand new words. Read a story with your child and encourage looking for context clues to help her or him understand the meaning of unfamiliar words.

🐢 **3.4.C.5** Use antonyms.

Maps

Maps are drawings of places that show cities, states, and countries. Maps can show the location of landforms, bodies of water, and other important places.

Directions Look at the map of China. Then answer the questions.

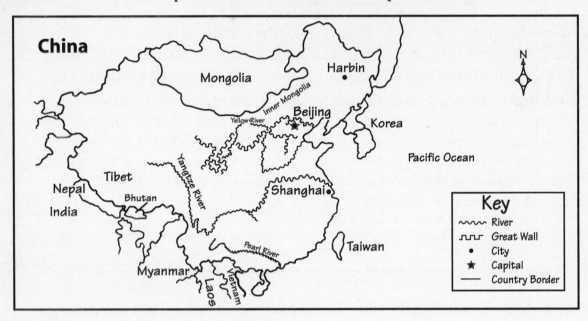

1. What are two countries that border China?

_____

2. Which river is located in southern China?

_____

3. The Great Wall runs along the border of which region?

_____

4. The capital of China is located close to which body of water?

_____

5. Is Mongolia a country, or is it part of China? How can you tell?

_____

Home Activity Your child answered questions about a map of China. Together, look at maps of different countries. Find countries that are divided into states, provinces, regions, and so on. Look for each country's landforms, bodies of water, cities, and the capital.

3.26.A.1.iii Follow the research plan to collect information from multiple sources of written information, including visual sources.

Schwa

Spelling Words				
above	another	upon	animal	paper
open	family	travel	afraid	nickel
sugar	circus	item	gallon	melon

Proofread a Description Jake wrote about an imaginary animal. Circle four words that are spelled incorrectly and two words that should be combined into one compound word. Write the words correctly.

My anamal looks like a lizard with opun wings. It has beutiful colors. It lives above the tree tops. For food it breaks open a mellon. It is not afraid of any thing.

Frequently Misspelled Words

upon
again
beautiful

1. _____   2. _____   3. _____

4. _____   5. _____   6. _____

Proofread Words Fill in a circle to show which word is spelled correctly. Write the word.

7. There was an _____ in the paper about our class.   7. _____

   ○ itam   ○ itum   ○ item

8. Are you _____ you might get lost on the subway?   8. _____

   ○ afraid   ○ ifraid   ○ afriad

9. There are five people in my _____ .   9. _____

   ○ family   ○ famaly   ○ familie

10. The candy cost a _____ each.   10. _____

   ○ nicle   ○ nickle   ○ nickel

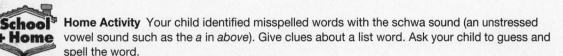

Home Activity Your child identified misspelled words with the schwa sound (an unstressed vowel sound such as the *a* in *above*). Give clues about a list word. Ask your child to guess and spell the word.

© Pearson Education, Inc., 3

3.24.A.1 Use knowledge of letter sounds to spell. **3.24.A.2** Use knowledge of word parts to spell. **3.24.B.1.vi** Spell words with abstract vowels. **3.24.C.1** Spell high-frequency words from a commonly used list.

Abbreviations

Directions Read the selection. Then read each question that follows the selection. Decide which is the best answer to each question. Mark the space for the answer you have chosen.

A Birthday Party

(1) I went to a friend's birthday party last April. (2) The party was on a Monday. (3) It was held at Mister Edwards' house. (4) On the Wednesday before the party, I got a present for my friend. (5) My friend's name is Richard James Edwards. (6) I will have a party for my own birthday in October.

1 How would you abbreviate the word "April" in sentence 1?

◯ Ap.

◯ Apr.

◯ App.

◯ Apar.

2 How would you abbreviate the word "Monday" in sentence 2?

◯ Moon.

◯ Nov.

◯ Mo.

◯ Mon.

3 Which word can you abbreviate in sentence 3?

◯ Edwards'

◯ held

◯ Mister

◯ house

4 How could you abbreviate "Richard James Edwards" in sentence 5?

◯ R. J. Edwards

◯ Richard J. E.

◯ Richard James E.

◯ R. James E.

5 Which word can you abbreviate in sentence 6?

◯ party

◯ October

◯ birthday

◯ own

Home Activity Your child prepared for taking tests on abbreviations. Have your child write the days of the week, using abbreviations correctly.

★ Recognize and use abbreviations.

Final Syllables *-tion, -ion, -ture, -ive, -ize*

Directions Circle the correctly spelled word in each pair.

1. commosion   commotion

2. invasion   invation

3. generasion   generation

4. posision   position

5. relaxasion   relaxation

6. division   divition

7. vacasion   vacation

8. explotion   explosion

Directions Add **-ture, -ive,** or **-ize** to complete each word below. Write the complete word on the line. (HINT: there is only one correct choice for each word.)

9. pas _____

10. act _____

11. rup _____

12. mass _____

13. maxim _____

14. real _____

15. cap _____

16. adven _____

Directions Choose four words from the above list and write a sentence for each word.

17. _____

18. _____

19. _____

20. _____

© Pearson Education, Inc., 3

Home Activity Your child identified and wrote words that end with the syllables *-tion, -ion, -ture, -ive,* and *-ize.* Work together to write sentences using the words from the page above. Ask your child to underline the final syllable in the words used from this page.

3.1.B.1.iii Use common syllabication patterns to decode words including final stable syllable.

Name _____

Graphic Sources

- **Graphic sources** are ways of showing information visually, or in a way you can see.
- Charts, diagrams, maps, and graphs are examples of graphic sources.

Directions Read the following passage.

The principal made an exciting announcement. Students would be allowed to draw on the walls! But they couldn't just scribble any old thing. Each class would submit a plan for a mural that would express school pride.

Mrs. Maki's students held a meeting to decide what to show on their mural. The students suggested a school sports team in action, students working in the media center, or students participating in activities such as drama, choir, or band. After listing the possibilities, the class took a vote. Which idea do you think won?

Directions: Use information from the passage to create a graphic source that shows the information in a visual way. Then use the information in your graphic source to help explain the passage.

Home Activity Your child created a graphic source to show information from a passage visually. Read a newspaper or magazine article with your child. Ask your child to make a graphic source that shows information from the passage at a glance.

408 Comprehension

★ Create a graphic source to explain information in a text.

© Pearson Education, Inc., 3

Writing • Description

Key Features of a Description

- explanation of something using sensory details
- is a written "picture" for the reader
- includes careful word choice

Description of "Girl with a Pearl Earring"

At a museum, I saw the painting "Girl with a Pearl Earring" by Johannes Vermeer. The painting is so ancient that when I studied it closely, I could see many tiny cracks in the canvas. In the painting, a girl looks over her left shoulder. Her skin is pale. Her dark eyes seemed to follow me when I moved. Over her hair she wears a soft blue scarf. The only other bright color in the painting is the girl's mouth, which is red like an apple. A lot of the painting is dark as night. It has a black background, and the girl's back and the side of her face are in shadow. A white earring gleams in her left ear like a star.

The painting makes me wonder what it was like to live a long time ago. It also makes me feel kind of gloomy, because the girl looks a little sad. Her mouth is open a little, as if she wants to say something. I wonder what she would say if she could talk?

1. Find the topic of this description and circle it.

2. Underline the sensory details that help you imagine what this painting looks like. Remember, sensory details appeal to taste, touch, sound, smell, and sight.

3. Draw a box around other strong details that show careful word choice.

Name _____

Vocabulary

Directions Match each word with its meaning. Draw a line to connect them.

1. support   someone born in a place

2. native   a statement of an idea

3. social   provide help

4. encourages   having to do with other people

5. expression   urges

Directions Write the word from the box that best completes each sentence below.

6. We moved to the United States and _____ in Houston.   _____

7. My father always _____ me to study hard.   _____

8. My parents are active in _____ neighborhood sports.   _____

9. My cousin was born in Madrid, so she is a _____ of Spain.   _____

10. My parents _____ my team by cheering at all of my games.   _____

Write a Description

On a separate sheet of paper describe a painting that you think would look good on the wall of a building in your neighborhood. Use as many vocabulary words as possible.

Home Activity Your child has identified and used vocabulary words from *Talking Walls: Art for the People.* Take a walking tour of your neighborhood. Encourage your child to use this week's vocabulary words as you talk about what you see.

3.4.B.1. Use context to determine the relevant meaning of unfamiliar words.

Combining Sentences

When you **combine sentences,** you join two sentences that are about the same topic. You make them into one sentence.

- You can join two simple sentences and make a compound sentence. Add a comma and a conjunction such as *and, but,* or *or.*

  Jen drew a tree. I drew a bird. Jen drew a tree, and I drew a bird.

- You can combine two sentences that have the same subject.

  Jen got blue paint. Jen painted the sky. Jen got blue paint and painted the sky.

- You can combine two sentences that have the same predicate.

  Jen painted. I painted. Jen and I painted.

- You can combine two sentences by using an appositive.

  We made a mural. A mural is a wall painting. We made a mural, a wall painting.

- You can combine two sentences by using adjectives or adverbs.

  That mural is big. Our mural is bigger. Our mural is bigger than that mural.
  We painted the mural. We painted it quickly. We painted the mural quickly.

- You can combine two sentences by using prepositional phrases.

  They saw the mural. It was on Main Street. They saw the mural on Main Street.

Directions Combine each pair of sentences into a compound sentence. Use a comma and the conjunction in ( ).

1. Some murals show famous people. Our mural shows ordinary people. (but)

_____

_____

2. I will show you the mural. You can find it yourself. (or)

_____

_____

Directions Combine the sentences. Use the underlined words only once in the new sentence.

3. Diego Rivera came from Mexico. Diego Rivera painted murals in America.

_____

_____

Home Activity Your child learned about combining sentences. Point out two short related sentences in a book you are reading with your child. Have your child combine the sentences.

3.22.A.1.vii Use and understand coordinating conjunctions in the context of reading, writing, and speaking. **3.22.C.2** Use complete compound sentences with correct subject-verb agreement.

Conventions Combining Sentences **411**

Name _____

Final Syllables

Spelling Words

question	creature	furniture	division	collision
action	direction	culture	vacation	mansion
fiction	feature	sculpture	vision	celebration

Opposites Write the missing list word. It will be the opposite of the underlined word.

1. The hero in this book lives in a <u>shack</u>.

1. _____

2. At first, I had trouble with <u>multiplication</u>.

2. _____

3. Let me interrupt with a <u>statement</u> about wind power.

3. _____

4. Jed left for his <u>usual job</u>.

4. _____

5. This story is <u>true</u>.

5. _____

Context Clues Write the last word of the sentence.

6. The situation called for quick _____ .

7. The school nurse tested everyone's _____ .

8. Her cheery smile is her best _____ .

9. In art class, Tami made a plaster _____ .

10. Please come to my birthday _____ .

11. We bought some used _____ .

12. An armadillo is an odd _____ .

13. We walked in the wrong _____ .

14. The toy robots had a _____ .

15. Nature was important in the Aztec _____ .

Home Activity Your child wrote words that end with *-tion*, *-sion*, and *-ture*. Have your child underline these endings in the list words.

3.24.A.2 Use knowledge of word parts to spell. **3.24.A.3** Use knowledge of word segmentation to spell. **3.24.A.4** Use knowledge of syllabication to spell.

© Pearson Education, Inc., 3

Main Idea

Main Idea

Supporting Details

Vocabulary • Unknown Words

You can use a glossary or a dictionary to find the meaning, syllabication, and pronunciation of **unknown words.** When two words have the same first and second letter, alphabetize by the third letter.

---

en • cour • age (en kẻr' ij), *VERB.* to give someone courage or confidence; urge on **en • cour •ag • es,**
en • cour • aged, en • cour • ag • ing

lo•cal (lō' kǝl), *ADJECTIVE.* about a certain place, especially nearby, not far away

so•cial (sō' shǝl), *ADJECTIVE.* concerned with human beings as a group

sup•port (sǝ port'), *VERB.* to help; aid
sup • ports, sup • port • ed,
sup • port • ing

---

1. Write the following words in alphabetical order—*something, social, soap.*

_____

2. How did you determine the order of the words above?

_____

_____

_____

3. How many syllables does the word *encourages* have? _____

4. What does the word *support* mean? _____

5. How should you pronounce the letter *c* in local?

_____

© Pearson Education, Inc., 3

 Home Activity Your child alphabetized words to the third letter and used sample glossary entries to determine meanings, syllabication, and pronunciation of words. Have your child choose one of the sample glossary entries and explain what information readers can learn from each part of the entry.

3.4.E.1 Alphabetize a series of words to the third letter. **3.4.E.3** Use a dictionary or glossary to determine syllabication of unknown words.

Alphabetical Order

Entries or subjects in encyclopedias, dictionaries, and indexes are listed in **alphabetical order,** so you can find information quickly and easily. When two entries have the same first letter, alphabetize by the second letter. If the second letters are also the same, alphabetize by the third letter, and so on.

Directions Circle each list of words that is in alphabetical order.

1. care   drag
   family   dance
   mail   finger
   master   water
   plow   work

2. must   astronaut
   really   driver
   treat   drop
   table   event
   under   sleepy

Directions Look at the spines on this set of encyclopedias. Then look at the article topics listed below. Write the letter(s) of the volume in which you would find an article on that topic.

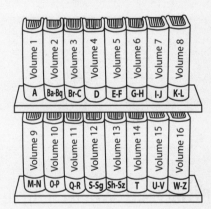

3. Architecture   _____

4. Russia   _____

5. Snow and Snowflakes   _____

6. Seashells   _____

7. Xylophones   _____

8. Dance   _____

9. Giraffes   _____

10. Boats   _____

Home Activity Your child recognized words that were in alphabetical order and used alphabetical order to find articles on topics for research. Use the illustration of the encyclopedias on this page. Name other topics of interest such as dogs, computers, and games and have your child tell in which volume he or she would find an article on that topic.

★ Arrange words in alphabetical order.

Final Syllables

Spelling Words				
question	creature	furniture	division	collision
action	direction	culture	vacation	mansion
fiction	feature	sculpture	vision	celebration

Proofread a Description Gina's class is studying local history. Circle four spelling errors. Write the words correctly. Then write the two incomplete sentences as one sentence.

> Mr. and Mrs. Hill we're very important in the history of our town. They built the Hill manshun in 1880. It still has the original furnichure. Many people tour the house when they are on vacasion. My favorite feature. Is the dolphin sculpture.

Frequently Misspelled Words

we're
were

1. _____   2. _____

3. _____   4. _____

5. _____

Proofread Words Circle the word that is spelled correctly. Write it.

6. I have a   question   quesion.   6. _____

7. It's fun to learn about a new   calture   culture.   7. _____

8. An eagle has excellent   vishun   vision.   8. _____

9. We had a big   celebration   celebrasion.   9. _____

10. Which   direction   direcsion   is the library?   10. _____

© Pearson Education, Inc., 3

Home Activity Your child identified misspelled words that end with *-tion*, *-sion*, and *-ture*. Give clues about a list word. Ask your child to guess and spell the word.

3.24.A.2 Use knowledge of word parts to spell. **3.24.A.3** Use knowledge of word segmentation to spell. **3.24.A.4** Use knowledge of syllabication to spell. **3.24.C.1** Spell high-frequency words from a commonly used list.

Combining Sentences

Directions Read the selection. Then read each question that follows the selection. Decide which is the best answer to each question. Mark the space for the answer you have chosen.

Diego Rivera: Muralist

(1) Diego Rivera is a famous Mexican painter. (2) He painted murals. (3) He used bold colors. (4) He used bright colors. (5) Rivera's colors reflected a style. (6) Aztec art had a similar style. (7) The murals often showed Mexico's history. (8) They also showed politics. (9) Sometimes Rivera's murals would upset people. (10) Many people loved them.

1 Which answer best combines sentence 1 and sentence 2?

- ⬭ Diego Rivera is a famous Mexican painter, he painted murals.
- ⬭ Diego Rivera is a famous Mexican painter of murals.
- ⬭ Diego River is a famous Mexican painter, and he painted murals.
- ⬭ Diego Rivera is a famous Mexican painter and, he painted murals.

2 Which answer best combines sentence 3 and sentence 4?

- ⬭ He used bold, bright colors.
- ⬭ He used bold, or bright colors.
- ⬭ He used bold colors, bright colors.
- ⬭ He used bold colors, but he used bright colors.

3 Read this combination of sentence 5 and sentence 6: *Rivera's colors reflected a style similar _____ Aztec art.* Which word completes the sentence?

- ⬭ in
- ⬭ for
- ⬭ of
- ⬭ to

4 Which answer best combines sentence 7 and sentence 8?

- ⬭ The murals often showed Mexico's history, politics.
- ⬭ The murals often showed Mexico's history, or showed politics.
- ⬭ The murals often showed Mexico's history and politics.
- ⬭ The murals often showed Mexico's historical politics.

5 Read this combination of sentence 9 and sentence 10: *Sometimes Rivera's murals would upset people _____ many people loved them.* Which answer completes the sentence?

- ⬭ , but
- ⬭ but,
- ⬭ , and
- ⬭ or

School + Home **Home Activity** Your child learned about combining sentences. Point out two short related sentences in a book you are reading with your child. Have your child combine the sentences.

3.22.A.1.vii Use and understand coordinating conjunctions in the context of reading, writing, and speaking. **3.22.C.2** Use complete compound sentences with correct subject-verb agreement.

Prefixes *im-*, *in-*

Directions For each definition, write a word on the line that beings with **im-** or **in-**.

1. not mature   _____

2. not efficient   _____

3. not sincere   _____

4. not polite   _____

5. not perfect   _____

6. not mortal   _____

7. not adequate   _____

8. not capable   _____

9. not partial   _____

10. not possible   _____

11. not correct   _____

12. not direct   _____

13. not practical   _____

14. not probable   _____

15. not pure   _____

Directions Now write three sentences of your own. In each sentence include at least one of the **im-** or **in-** words from above.

16. _____

17. _____

18. _____

© Pearson Education, Inc., 3

Home Activity Your child used words with the prefixes *im-* and *in-*, which mean "not." Read a newspaper or magazine article with your child. Point out words with the prefixes *im-* and *in-* and have your child explain what they mean.

⊕ **3.1.A.2.iv.1.** Decode multisyllabic words independent of context by applying common spelling patterns including using knowledge of common prefixes.

Literary Elements • Plot and Theme

- The important events in a story make up the **plot** with a beginning, middle, and end.
- The "big idea" of the story is called the **theme**. It can be stated in a single sentence.

Directions Read the following story. Then fill in the chart below.

The ants felt sorry for the grasshopper. He'd saved no food and was starving. So they shared what they had. The grasshopper swore he'd remember their kindness and repay them someday. When summer came, the ants were playing outside and accidentally hurt themselves.

How would they gather their food? Just then the grasshopper stopped by. When he heard what happened, he told the ants to climb on his back. The ants told the grasshopper where to go and what to gather. Soon the trio had all the food they needed for the winter ahead.

What happened at the beginning of the story?

1. _____

What happened in the middle of the story?

2. _____

What happened at the end of the story?

3. _____

4. What is the "big idea" of this story?

_____

© Pearson Education, Inc., 3

Home Activity Your child identified the plot and theme of a story. Read a favorite story together. Ask your child to retell the beginning, middle, and end of the story and to say one sentence that tells the "big idea."

3.8.A.1 Sequence the plot's main events. **3.8.A.2** Summarize the plot's main events.

Comprehension 419

Name _____

Writing • Comic Book

Key Features of a Comic Book

- tells a story using a series of drawings
- characters' dialogue is part of the drawing
- sometimes uses narration

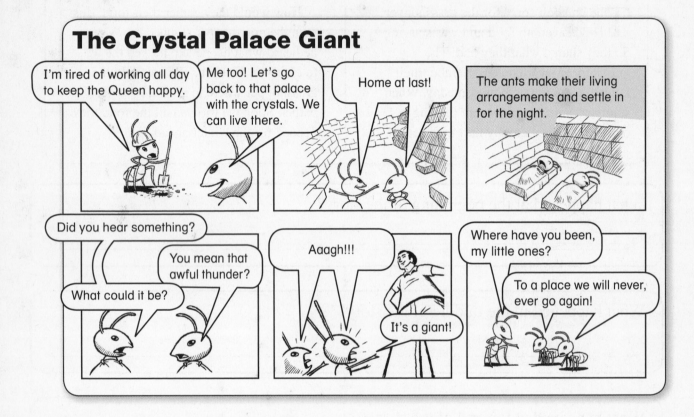

The Crystal Palace Giant

I'm tired of working all day to keep the Queen happy.

Me too! Let's go back to that palace with the crystals. We can live there.

Home at last!

The ants make their living arrangements and settle in for the night.

Did you hear something?

You mean that awful thunder?

What could it be?

Aaagh!!!

It's a giant!

Where have you been, my little ones?

To a place we will never, ever go again!

1. How many panels are used to tell the story?

_____

2. Draw a circle around the same dialogue that is spoken by more than one character

3. Draw a box around any narration.

Tell how you knew this line was narration and not dialogue.

_____

Vocabulary

Directions Read each sentence. Write the meaning of the underlined word.

> ### Check the Words You Know
> ___goal   ___discovery
> ___scoop   ___crystal
> ___journey   ___joyful
> ___disappeared   ___unaware

1. They used a <u>scoop</u> to pour the birdseed into the feeder. _____

2. The hikers were on a <u>journey</u> over the mountain. _____

3. My <u>goal</u> this summer is to learn how to swim. _____

4. I saw the ant carry a <u>crystal</u> of salt. _____

5. The chipmunk <u>disappeared</u> among the rocks. _____

Directions Match each word on the left with its meaning. Draw a line from the word to its definition.

6. discovery   not noticing

7. joyful   something new you find

8. unaware   full of happiness

9. disappeared   was no longer seen

Write a Narrative

On a separate sheet of paper, write a narrative about visiting another planet. Write about being very small compared with other things on the planet. Use as many vocabulary words as possible.

Home Activity Your child identified and used vocabulary from *Two Bad Ants*. Read a story about insects to your child. Then discuss the story using this week's vocabulary words.

3.4.B.1 Use context to determine the relevant meaning of unfamiliar words.

Name _____

Commas

Use a **comma** and a conjunction to join two sentences.

There was a crumb on the table, and the ant crawled toward it.

Use **commas** to separate words in a series.

We had sandwiches, cookies, and fruit at the picnic.

Use a **comma** after the greeting and the closing of a friendly letter.

Dear Jake,

Your friend,

Use a **comma** between the name of a city and a state in an address.

Chico, CA 95926　　Berea, Kentucky

Use a **comma** to separate the month and day from the year.

July 21, 2006

Directions Write *C* if commas are used correctly in the sentence. Write *NC* if commas are not used correctly.

1. Some kinds of ants are army ants, honey ants, and dairying ants. _____

2. Army ants travel in lines and they hunt other insects. _____

3. Dear Amy _____

Directions Write each sentence. Add commas where they are needed.

4. Some ants eat other insects but many do not.

_____

_____

5. The newspaper had an article about ants on November 14 2005.

_____

_____

Home Activity Your child learned about commas. Have your child point out five commas in a book that you are reading together.

3.23.C.1.ii.1 Recognize punctuation marks including commas in a series. **3.23.C.1.ii.2** Recognize punctuation marks including commas in dates. **3.23.C.1.ii.3** Use punctuation marks including commas in a series. **3.23.C.1.ii.4** Use punctuation marks including commas in dates.

Multisyllabic Words

Spelling Words				
leadership	gracefully	refreshment	uncomfortable	overdoing
remarkable	carefully	unbearably	ownership	unacceptable
impossibly	reappeared	unprepared	oncoming	misbehaving

Missing Syllables Add the missing syllables and write the list words.

1. The deer moved <u>grace   </u>.

2. He was <u> bear </u> rude.

3. Watch out for <u> com </u> cars.

4. That is a <u> mark </u> carving!

5. Juice is my favorite <u> fresh </u>.

6. Sam is <u> fort </u> in crowds.

7. Do the addition <u>care   </u>.

8. He took a <u>lead   </u> position.

9. She gets tired from <u> do </u>.

10. Sue was <u> pos </u> stubborn.

1. _____

2. _____

3. _____

4. _____

5. _____

6. _____

7. _____

8. _____

9. _____

10. _____

Definitions Write the list word with the same meaning as the underlined words.

11. He was <u>not prepared</u> for the test.

12. The sun <u>appeared again</u> from behind the clouds.

13. The puppy kept <u>behaving badly</u>.

14. My score on the test was <u>not acceptable</u>.

15. He claimed <u>to be the owner</u> of the stray cat.

11. _____

12. _____

13. _____

14. _____

15. _____

Home Activity Your child spelled words with many syllables. Have your child draw lines to divide the list words into syllables.

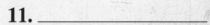 **3.24.A.2** Use knowledge of word parts to spell. **3.24.D.1** Spell words with common syllable constructions.

Story Sequence B

Title	
Characters	**Setting**

Events
1. First

2. Next

3. Then

4. Last

Vocabulary • Prefixes and Suffixes

- A **prefix** is a word part added to the beginning of a word. A **suffix** is added to the end of a word. **Prefixes** and **suffixes** can help you figure out the meaning of a word you don't know.

- The **prefixes** *un-* and *dis-* mean "not" or "the opposite of." The **suffix** *-ful* means "full of."

Directions Read each pair of sentences. Circle the word that has the same meaning as the underlined words.

1. The girl pushed ahead of me in line. That is <u>not fair</u>.

   unfair   unhappy

2. Climbing this mountain is too hard. I am <u>not able</u> to do it.

   disease   unable

3. My father did not climb the ladder. He is <u>full of fear</u> high above the ground.

   under   fearful

4. He does not keep his word. That's why I <u>do not trust</u> him.

   distrust   untrue

5. That dog is mean. I <u>do not like</u> her.

   hateful   dislike

Directions Read each sentence. Circle the underlined word that best fits the sentence.

6. My room is in such <u>disorder/unclear</u>, I can't find anything.

7. A hammer is a very <u>unused/useful</u> tool for nailing things together.

8. My mother <u>disapproves/unlike</u> of my staying up late.

9. The strong man had a very <u>unfair/powerful</u> handshake.

10. Please <u>unzip/disappear</u> your jacket and hang it in the closet.

Home Activity Your child identified and used prefixes and suffixes to understand new words. Read a story or magazine article together and encourage looking for words with prefixes and suffixes. Help your child use prefixes and suffixes to understand the meaning of unfamiliar words.

3.4.A.1 Identify the meaning of common prefixes. **3.4.A.2** Know how prefixes change the meaning of roots. **3.4.A.3** Identify the meaning of common suffixes.

Electronic Text

Directions Read the passage and answer the questions that follow.

You can find facts and opinions in books, in periodicals, and online. When you make a presentation or write a report, you restate facts and details you found in the reference sources.

There are two ways to restate information from a source. You can **quote** it, or you can **paraphrase** it. When you quote something, you copy exact words from a source. When you paraphrase, you explain the same idea in your own words.

Remember to **cite** your sources correctly. A writer often includes a **bibliography**—an alphabetical list of sources—at the end of a report. Sometimes a writer includes **footnotes.** A footnote is a citation that appears at the bottom of the page where the information is quoted or paraphrased.

This table shows you how to cite a source properly.

Type of Source	How To Cite	Example
Book	List the author, title, city where published, publisher's name, and copyright date.	Sachs, Hans. *A History of Carpenter Ants.* New York: Van Horn & Co., 2006.
Periodical	List the author, article title, periodical title, volume number, date and page numbers.	Klotz, J.H. "Trailing the Carpenter Ant." *American Entomologist,* vol. 42 (1996), pp. 33–39.
Web Site	Give the name of the Web site and the page, and copy the URL exactly as it is shown in the bar at the top of the screen.	Encyclopedia www.url.here

1. What does **quote** mean?

_____

2. What is the difference between a bibliography and a footnote?

_____

_____

3. What do you include in the citation of a Web site?

_____

_____

Home Activity Your child learned how to cite reference sources. Read an article together. Have your child quote something from the article. Then have your child paraphrase information from the article.

3.26.E.1 Differentiate between paraphrasing and plagiarism.
3.26.E.2 Identify the importance of citing valid sources.

Multisyllabic Words

Spelling Words				
leadership	gracefully	refreshment	uncomfortable	overdoing
remarkable	carefully	unbearably	ownership	unacceptable
impossibly	reappeared	unprepared	oncoming	misbehaving

Proofread an Explanation Olivia wrote about how to bowl. Circle four spelling errors. Write the words correctly. Then add the missing comma.

> Bowling is a remarkable sport. Almost every body likes it.
>
> You should start with good equipment. Don't use a ball that is unbareably heavy and don't settle for unconfortable shoes.
>
> When it's your turn, swing the ball back gracefully as you walk toward the pins. Let go when you reach the line. Always aim carefuly at the pins.

Frequently Misspelled Words

everybody
everything

1. _____   2. _____

3. _____   4. _____

Correct the Words Write the correct spelling of each misspelled word.

5. unaceptable   5. _____

6. oncomeing   6. _____

7. missbehaving   7. _____

8. inpossibly   8. _____

9. reapeared   9. _____

10. leedership   10. _____

Home Activity Your child is learning to spell words with many syllables. Have your child write a sentence using two or more of the list words.

© Pearson Education, Inc., 3

3.24.A.2 Use knowledge of word parts to spell. **3.24.C.1** Spell high-frequency words from a commonly used list. **3.24.D.1** Spell words with common syllable constructions. **Also 3.1.A.2.iv.1.**

Spelling Multisyllabic Words   **427**

Commas

Directions Read the selection. Then read each question that follows the selection. Decide which is the best answer to each question. Mark the space for the answer you have chosen.

Insect Communities

(1) Bees, wasps, termites and ants live in communities. (2) These insects work together to feed the community. (3) Other jobs in the community include builder soldier or, queen. (4) Communities are also called colonies. (5) They live in hives or nests. (6) Scientists study termite nests at the University of Kentucky in Lexington Kentucky.

1 What change, if any, should be made in sentence 1?

- ⬭ Place a comma after **termites**
- ⬭ Change **Bees, wasps** to **Bees and wasps**
- ⬭ Place a comma after **and**
- ⬭ Make no change

2 Which change, if any, should be made in sentence 2?

- ⬭ Place a comma after **insects**
- ⬭ Place a comma after **work**
- ⬭ Place a comma after **together**
- ⬭ Make no change

3 Which change, if any, should be made in sentence 3?

- ⬭ Change **builder soldier or, queen** to **builder, soldier or queen.**
- ⬭ Change **builder soldier or, queen** to **builder soldier, or queen.**
- ⬭ Change **builder soldier or, queen** to **builder, soldier, or queen.**
- ⬭ Make no change

4 Which answer correctly uses commas to combine sentence 4 and sentence 5?

- ⬭ Communities are also called colonies, they live in hives or nests.
- ⬭ Communities are also called colonies and live in hives or, nests.
- ⬭ Communities, also called colonies, live in hives, or nests.
- ⬭ Communities are also called colonies, and they live in hives or nests.

5 What change, if any, should be made in sentence 6?

- ⬭ Place a comma after **University of Kentucky**
- ⬭ Place a comma after **Lexington**
- ⬭ Place a comma after **nests**
- ⬭ Make no change

© Pearson Education, Inc., 3

 Home Activity Your child prepared for taking tests on commas. Have your child show you some sentences from a school paper or ad and explain why they need commas or not.

✪ **3.23.C.1.ii.1** Recognize punctuation marks including commas in a series. **3.23.C.1.ii.2** Recognize punctuation marks including commas in dates.

Related Words

Directions Choose the word that best matches each clue. Write the word on the line.

1. coverings for the body   (cloth   clothes)   _____

2. a person who plays sports   (athlete   athletics)   _____

3. a person's handwritten name   (sign   signature)   _____

4. a tub for washing   (bath   bathe)   _____

5. the world of living things and the outdoors   (natural   nature)   _____

Directions Read each pair of related words. Underline the parts that are spelled the same but pronounced differently. Write a sentence using one of the words in each pair.

6. feel   felt   _____

7. keep   kept   _____

8. decide   decision   _____

9. mean   meant   _____

10. define   definition   _____

11. volcano   volcanic   _____

12. please   pleasant   _____

13. relate   relative   _____

14. sign   signal   _____

15. repeat   repetition   _____

© Pearson Education, Inc., 3

Home Activity Your child read and wrote related words that have parts that are spelled the same but pronounced differently, as in *cloth* and *clothes*. Discuss the meanings of the related words on the page above. Then work together to write a story that uses some of the words.

3.4.B.1 Use context to determine the relevant meaning of unfamiliar words.

Phonics Related Words   **429**

Generalize

- When you make a general statement, you **generalize,** or tell how some things are mostly alike or all alike.
- You can use what you already know to help you make a generalization.
- When you generalize, support your generalization with facts and logic.

Directions Read the following passage. Think about generalizations you can make from what you have read.

Some cities, like New York, started small and grew larger. As more people and businesses moved in, New York became an important world center. Other cities did not do as well. Some cities in the West thrived during the Gold Rush years. But when the Gold Rush ended, people abandoned those cities. They are now ghost towns. Then there are cities that suffer tragedy and remake themselves. San Francisco and Chicago both had terrible fires years ago. But the people in those cities decided to rebuild. Today, these two cities are bigger and better than ever.

Directions: Fill in the graphic organizer with ideas from the passage that lead to the generalization. Then answer the questions.

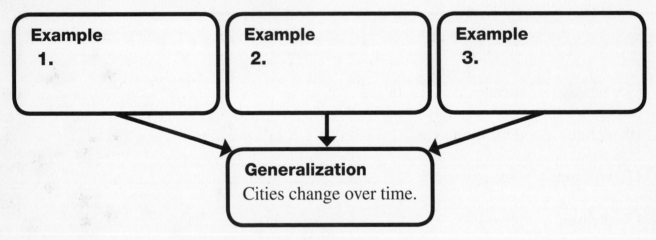

Example 1.

Example 2.

Example 3.

Generalization
Cities change over time.

4. How did you use ideas from the passage?

_____

5. What things that you already knew helped you connect to the generalization?

_____

Home Activity Your child read a passage and identified ideas that led to a provided generalization. Read an article about a city with your child and work together to use what you read to make a generalization about all or most cities.

✪ **RC–3.D.1** Make inferences about text.

Writing • Historical Fiction

Key Features of Historical Fiction

- set in the past
- events of the plot make sense
- characters, setting, or events may be based on historical fact

A Wonderful Flight

My name is Jean. I'm a servant in the castle of Chambord, France. The greatest person I've ever served was a man named Leonardo da Vinci (you may have heard of him) during the exciting days of the Renaissance period.

Da Vinci brought a flying machine he designed to the castle! Some of the servants got together and decided they wanted to take a ride. We sneaked up to the tower where da Vinci kept the flying machine. All the other servants were too scared to go flying, but I wasn't. I hopped into the machine, hung on tight, and jumped off the tower.

I flew down and soared over the castle wall. I flew round and round in a circle. Then the wind blew me right into the castle wall! Luckily I fell just a few feet. I crashed in the courtyard . . . right at the feet of Leonardo da Vinci himself! I looked up at him in fear. I was sure I'd be kicked out of the castle.

But Mr. da Vinci just grinned and said, "Isn't flying wonderful?"

1. Who is the main character? What type of job does he have?

_____

2. What is the climax of the story? Why is this moment exciting?

_____

_____

_____

Name _____

Vocabulary

Directions: Match each word on the left with its meaning on the right. Draw a line from the word to its meaning.

1. aqueducts

2. thermal

3. pillar

4. guidance

5. crouched

squatted with bent knees

advice or counseling

channels for moving water

a vertical column

relating to heat or warmth

Check the Words You Know

___aqueducts
___content
___crouched
___guidance
___honor
___pillar
___thermal

Directions: Fill in the blank with the word from the box that fits the meaning of the sentence.

6. The people were _____ to live on their island.

7. The _____ currents in the ocean kept the weather fair and warm.

8. Stone _____ carried fresh water to all parts of the island.

9. The people looked to their kind queen for _____.

10. Once a year they held a huge feast to thank and _____ her.

Write a Description Write about your ideal place to live. Use as many vocabulary words from this week as you can.

Home Activity Your child identified and used new vocabulary words from *Atlantis: The Legend of a Lost City*. Read another myth or legend with your child. Then ask your child to talk about myths and legends using the vocabulary words on this page.

3.4.B.1 Use context to determine the relevant meaning of unfamiliar words.

Quotations and Parentheses

Quotation marks (" ") show the exact words of a speaker in a conversation.

- Use a comma to separate the speaker's exact words from the rest of the sentence.
- Use a capital letter to begin the first words inside the quotation marks.
- Put the punctuation mark that ends the quotation inside the quotation marks.

"I swim very well," said Penny.

She asked, "Would you like to learn to swim?"

Quotation marks also indicate many kinds of titles, such as song, poem, story, and document titles.

We read "Atlantis."

Parentheses show explanations or examples that are extra information.

That song (written in 1996) is my favorite.

Some singers (for example, Elton John) play the piano, too.

Directions Underline the part of each sentence that is a quotation.

1. "I want to learn about Atlantis," said Jeremy.

2. "I will teach you," replied Ms. Foster.

3. Ms. Foster said, "It is a very old story."

Directions Write the sentences. Add quotation marks and commas where they are needed.

4. I like to read about many things said Jeremy.

_____

5. Jeremy read a story called The Legend of Kala.

_____

Home Activity Your child learned about quotations. Have your child read aloud a quotation in a book you are reading together and then point out each punctuation mark and explain the reason for it.

Related Words

Spelling Words				
cloth	clothes	nature	natural	able
ability	mean	meant	deal	dealt
please	pleasant	sign	signal	signature

Replacing Words Write list words to take the place of the underlined words.

1. I jumped out of the tub and put on my
   <u>shirt and shorts</u>.

1. _____

2. It has been a <u>nice</u> day.

2. _____

3. Did you <u>write your name on</u> the card?

3. _____

4. Dogs have the <u>skill</u> to hear high-pitched sounds.

4. _____

5. Mom made a kerchief from a scrap of blue
   <u>fabric</u>.

5. _____

6. Tom is never <u>cruel</u> to animals.

6. _____

7. We went to the mountains to enjoy
   <u>the environment</u>.

7. _____

8. Sara <u>gave</u> six cards to each player.

8. _____

Missing Words Write the missing word.

9. She has a _____ talent for music.

10. His hand _____ warned me to stop.

11. A bat is the only mammal that is _____ to fly.

12. That's not what I _____ .

13. I can do what I _____ on Saturday morning.

14. Her _____ is on the credit card.

15. My big sister knows how to _____ with most
    emergencies.

Home Activity Your child spelled related words. Have your child pronounce each list word and
use the word in a sentence.

3.24.A.2 Use knowledge of word parts to spell. **3.24.A.3** Use
knowledge of word segmentation to spell. **3.24.A.4** Use knowledge of
syllabication to spell.

© Pearson Education, Inc., 3

Scoring Rubric: Writing for Tests: Historical Fiction

	4	**3**	**2**	**1**
Focus/Ideas	Exciting story with interesting characters; historical time period and figures	Good story with developed characters; somewhat based on historical time period and figures	Story has some focus on characters; setting and characters are only loosely historical	Story has no focus on characters; not set in historical time period
Organization	Clear order of events	Can follow order of events	Unclear order of events	No order of events
Voice	Writer shows interest in the story and the characters	Writer shows some interest in the story and the characters	Writer shows little interest in the story or characters	Writer makes no effort to show interest in the story or characters
Word Choice	Strong use of specific adjectives to bring the story to life	Good try at using specific adjectives	Poor use of specific adjectives; descriptions are dull	No effort made to use specific adjectives
Sentences	Strong concluding statement	Adequate concluding statement	Weak concluding statement	No concluding statement
Conventions	Few, if any, errors; correct use of quotation marks and parentheses	Several small errors; use of quotation marks and parentheses	Many errors; weak use of quotation marks and parentheses	Many serious errors; incorrect or no use of quotation marks and parentheses

Vocabulary • Homographs

- **Homographs** are words that are spelled the same way but have different pronunciations and meanings.
- Use context clues, or the words around a homograph, to figure out which meaning and pronunciation to use.

Directions: Read the following passage. Then answer the questions below. Look for context clues that show the meanings and pronunciations of homographs as you read.

> There are many myths and legends about ancient Greek gods. The stories are interesting because they are full of conflict. Many of the gods were not content with their lives. They caused trouble or fought with each other. When problems arose on Earth, the gods tried to solve them. But different gods offered alternate solutions, and they usually did not agree. Each god wanted to lead the others.

1. If you read this passage aloud, would you pronounce *conflict* with the accent on the first or second syllable?

_____

2. In this passage, does *content* mean "pleased with" or "what a speech or article is about"?

_____

3. Is *lives* a noun or a verb? How do you know?

_____

4. Does *alternate* mean "take turns" or "different"?

_____

5. Does the word *lead* have a *long e* or a *short e* sound?

_____

Home Activity Your child used context clues to understand homographs. Write sentences with homographs such as *close* (to shut/near) or *dove* (a kind of bird/jumped into the water). Ask your child to use context clues to determine the meaning of each homograph and then read the sentence aloud.

3.4.C.3 Identify homographs. **3.4.C.7** Use homographs.

Quote Sources/Paraphrase Sources

- There are two ways to repeat information from a reference source. You can **quote** it or you can **paraphrase** it.

- To quote means to copy exact words from a source. When you do this, enclose the words in quotation marks.

- To paraphrase means to explain the same idea in your own words. When you paraphrase, you do not use quotation marks. When you quote or paraphrase information, you must **cite** it correctly. This table shows you how.

Type of Source	How to Cite	Example
Book	List the author, title, city where published, publisher's name, and copyright date.	Breward, Christopher. *Oxford History of Fashion.* Oxford: Oxford University Press, 2003.
Periodical	List the author, article title, periodical title, volume number, date and page numbers.	Mack, Alexandra. "Hidden Gems." *Vogue,* Oct. 2007, pp. 258–272.
Web Site	Give the name of the page on the Web site, and copy the URL exactly as it is shown in the bar at the top of the screen.	Online Directory www.url.here

Directions Take this page to the library. Use its resources and the table above. Answer the questions on a separate sheet of paper.

1. Look up a fact about glass in a book about glassmaking. Write a sentence quoting the information. Cite the source correctly.

2. The Italian island of Murano is famous for its glassblowers. Look up Murano online and write a sentence paraphrasing information you find about it. Cite the source correctly.

3. Find a magazine article about glass and write three or four sentences about glass. Quote and paraphrase information from the article. Cite the article correctly.

Home Activity Your child quoted and paraphrased information from reference sources, and cited the sources correctly. Give your child a simple research project. Have him or her write a very short paper (no more than one page) summing up the information. Make sure your child quotes, paraphrases, and cites sources correctly.

3.26.D.1 Identify the author of sources. **3.26.D.2** Identify the title of sources. **3.26.D.3** Identify the publisher of sources. **3.26.D.4** Identify the publication year of sources.

Research Quote Sources/Paraphrase Sources   **437**

Related Words

Proofread a Paragraph Circle four spelling errors and cross out the sentence that does not belong in the paragraph. Write the words correctly.

When I grow up, I whant to design clothes. I think I would be good at this. I have the abilty to draw, and I like to deal with people. I like to sketch outfits that pleese my friends. My best friend is Rosa. I am learning about cotton, wool, and other kinds of kloth.

1. _____   2. _____

3. _____   4. _____

Proofread Words Circle the word that is spelled correctly. Write it.

5. My bus driver is a **pleasant   plesant** person.

_____

6. Wave to **signel   signal** if you need help.

_____

7. Will you be **abel   able** to come to the party?

_____

8. Simon was reading a book about the wonders of **nature   natur**.

_____

Home Activity Your child spelled related words. Have your child point out a pair of related list words and explain how the spellings differ.

⭐ **3.24.A.2** Use knowledge of word parts to spell. **3.24.A.3** Use knowledge of word segmentation to spell. **3.24.A.4** Use knowledge of syllabication to spell. **3.24.C.1** Spell high-frequency words from a commonly used list.

© Pearson Education, Inc., 3

Quotations and Parentheses

Directions Read the selection. Then read each question that follows the selection. Decide which is the best answer to each question. Mark the space for the answer you have chosen.

A Conversation at the Beach

(1) The seashore is great, Tim said.
(2) Look at the ocean, I responded.
(3) Tim said, There are cliffs, too!
(4) The water goes on forever, I replied.
(5) Do sharks live here? Tim asked.

1 In sentence 1, what words and punctuation marks should go inside quotation marks?

⬭ Tim said
⬭ The seashore
⬭ The seashore is great, Tim
⬭ The seashore is great,

2 In sentence 2, what words and punctuation marks should go inside quotation marks?

⬭ Look
⬭ Look at the ocean,
⬭ Look at the ocean, I
⬭ I responded

3 In sentence 3, what words and punctuation marks should go inside quotation marks?

⬭ Tim said,
⬭ Tim said, there
⬭ There are cliffs, too!
⬭ There are cliffs,

4 In sentence 4, what words and punctuation marks should go inside quotation marks?

⬭ The water goes on forever,
⬭ The water goes on forever
⬭ The water goes on
⬭ I replied

5 In sentence 5, what words and punctuation marks should go inside quotation marks?

⬭ Do sharks
⬭ Do sharks live here?
⬭ Tim asked.
⬭ live here? Tim asked

Home Activity Your child prepared for taking tests on quotations. Have your child identify words in quotation marks in a newspaper article and explain why they are punctuated in that way.

★ Use correct mechanics.

Vowel Sounds in *moon* and *foot*

Spelling Words				
few	school	true	goose	fruit
cookie	cushion	noodle	bookmark	balloon
suit	chew	glue	Tuesday	bushel

Word Clues Read the two meaning clues. Write the list word that the clues tell about.

1. a group of fish
   place where students learn   1. _____

2. a pillow
   to pad   2. _____

3. a sticky paste
   to paste something   3. _____

4. a toy filled with air
   to get bigger   4. _____

5. matched pieces of clothing
   to please or satisfy   5. _____

Meaning Connections Change the underlined word or words to a list word. Write the word.

6. I ate a chocolate chip <u>sweet treat</u>.   6. _____

7. A <u>bird that honks</u> chased me.   7. _____

8. Darla put a <u>paper placeholder</u> in the book.   8. _____

9. On <u>the day after Monday</u>, it rained.   9. _____

10. We bought <u>apples, grapes, and pears</u>.   10. _____

11. I saw a <u>piece of pasta</u> in my soup.   11. _____

12. I <u>chomp</u> on raw carrots for a snack.   12. _____

13. The farmer put corn in the <u>32-quart</u> basket. 13. _____

14. What she said was <u>not false</u>.   14. _____

15. <u>Not many</u> people can be called heroes.   15. _____

School + Home **Home Activity** Your child spelled words with the vowel sound in *moon* (spelled *oo, ew, ue, ui*) and in *foot* (spelled *oo, u*). Play Tic-Tac-Toe. One person chooses a word for the other person to spell. If the person spells the word correctly, he or she marks an X or an O on the grid.

© Pearson Education, Inc., 3

3.24.A.1 Use knowledge of letter sounds to spell. **3.24.A.2** Use knowledge of word parts to spell.

Capital Letters

Directions If a sentence has capitalization mistakes, write correctly the words that should have capital letters. If a sentence has no capitalization mistakes, write *C*.

1. In may of 2005, my family flew to Paris, France.

   _____

2. On tuesday I visited the Eiffel Tower. _____

3. The Eiffel Tower was designed by Alexandre Gustave Eiffel.

   _____

4. The frame of the Statue of Liberty in new york was also designed by mr. Eiffel.

   _____

5. Next september, mrs. Austin will take us to see the Statue of Liberty.

   _____

Directions Write the sentences. Use capital letters correctly.

6. On independence day, Mom called philadelphia.

   _____

7. On martin luther king, jr., day in january, we went to the Washington Monument.

   _____

   _____

8. mr. and mrs. pines drove to plymouth, massachusetts, for thanksgiving.

   _____

   _____

9. Dad stopped at Mount Rushmore last memorial day.

   _____

   _____

10. On presidents' day in february, Sam visited the Lincoln Memorial.

   _____

   _____

3.23.B.1.i Use capitalization for geographical names and places.
3.23.B.1.ii Use capitalization for historical periods. **3.23.B.1.iii** Use capitalization for official titles of people.

Schwa

Spelling Words				
above	another	upon	animal	paper
open	family	travel	afraid	nickel
sugar	circus	item	gallon	melon

Classifying Write the list word that belongs with each pair of words.

1. penny, dime, ___

2. pint, quart, ___

3. go, journey, ___

4. movie, play, ___

5. thing, object, ___

6. below, beside, ___

7. group, tribe, ___

1. _____

2. _____

3. _____

4. _____

5. _____

6. _____

7. _____

Complete the Phrase Write the list word that completes each phrase.

8. not a plant but an ___

9. a pencil and some ___

10. not a berry but a ___

11. not closed but ___

12. not under but ___

13. as sweet as ___

14. ___ of the dark

15. one thing and ___

Riddle Write the letters from the boxes above to find the answer to the riddle.

What do you get when you ask a lemon for help?

___ ___ ___ ___ ___ ___ ___ ___

Home Activity Your child learned to spell words with the schwa sound (an unstressed vowel sound such as the *a* in *about*). Take turns choosing and spelling a word. Then each of you say a word you associate with the chosen word: *family—Mom, Dad*.

⊕ **3.24.A.1** Use knowledge of letter sounds to spell. **3.24.A.2** Use knowledge of word parts to spell. **3.24.B.1.vi** Spell words with abstract vowels.

© Pearson Education, Inc., 3

Abbreviations

Directions Write each sentence correctly. Use correct capitalization and periods for abbreviations.

1. On nice days, dr Chin and mr Lee meet at the park.

_____

_____

2. On Monday, dr Chin brought his son c j and his dog.

_____

_____

3. Mr and mrs. Lau were at the park also.

_____

_____

4. They had seen ms Parks and d w Cho there on Saturday.

_____

_____

5. People brought their birds and cages to l. k. Williams Park.

_____

_____

Directions Write each telephone message. Correct mistakes in initials and abbreviations.

6. j b Logan called: got your order _____

7. mr Logan, 6 parakeets, jan 10 _____

8. Pick up fri, jan 12 _____

9. ms Ryan's parakeet, p j _____

10. Got bird wed, dec 10 _____

© Pearson Education, Inc., 3

★ Recognize and use abbreviations

Conventions 443

Final Syllables

Spelling Words

question	creature	furniture	division	collision
action	direction	culture	vacation	mansion
fiction	feature	sculpture	vision	celebration

Crossword Puzzle Write the list word that each clue describes.

Across

1. north

5. a make-believe story

6. a statue

8. Aztec or Native American

9. a special trip

10. sight

Down

1. repeated subtraction

2. a big, big house

3. a party

4. a movement

5. chairs and sofas

7. an important part

Alphabetizing Read the two guide words. Write the list word that would come between them in a dictionary.

13. pride _____ rate

14. cave _____ comet

15. cracker _____ crop

collision

question

creature

School + Home

Home Activity Your child spelled words that end with *-tion*, *-sion*, and *-ture*. Use newspapers or junk mail to look for words with the lesson endings. Circle the words and spell them together. Check to see if any circled words are on the spelling list.

(★) **3.24.A.1** Use knowledge of letter sounds to spell. **3.24.A.2** Use knowledge of word parts to spell. **3.24.B.1.vi** Spell words with abstract vowels.

© Pearson Education, Inc., 3

Combining Sentences

Directions Combine each pair of sentences into a compound sentence. Use a comma and the conjunction in ( ).

1. Our class painted a mural. We worked very hard on it. (and)

   _____

   _____

2. We had never painted a mural. It looks great. (but)

   _____

   _____

3. Shall I tell you about the mural? Would you like to see it? (or)

   _____

   _____

Directions Combine each pair of sentences. Use the underlined words or a form of the underlined words only once in your new sentence.

4. Lewis and Clark sailed up the Missouri River. Lewis and Clark crossed the Rocky Mountains.

   _____

   _____

5. The land was a wilderness. The land had not been carefully explored.

   _____

   _____

6. Lewis kept a journal of the trip. Clark kept a journal of the trip.

   _____

3.22.A.1.vii Use and understand coordinating conjunctions in the context of reading, writing, and speaking. **3.22.C.2** Use complete compound sentences with correct subject-verb agreement.

Conventions 445

Prefixes, Suffixes, and Endings

Spelling Words

leadership	gracefully	refreshment	uncomfortable	overdoing
remarkable	carefully	unbearably	ownership	unacceptable
impossibly	reappeared	unprepared	oncoming	misbehaving

Word Building Read the word in dark type. Add the part or parts to the given word. Write the list word you make.

1. **grace** + suffix + suffix _____

2. prefix + **appear** + ending _____

3. **remark** + suffix _____

4. prefix + **comfort** + suffix _____

5. prefix + **accept** + suffix _____

6. **care** + suffix + suffix _____

7. prefix + **prepare** + ending _____

8. prefix + **fresh** + suffix _____

9. **lead** + suffix + suffix _____

10. **own** + suffix + suffix _____

Finish the Phrase Circle the list word that completes each phrase. Write it. Say the word. Write in the box the number of syllables you hear in the word.

11. (unprepared   unbearably) hot _____ ☐

12. (overdoing   reappeared) it a bit _____ ☐

13. (oncoming   unprepared) traffic _____ ☐

14. (leadership   misbehaving) puppy _____ ☐

15. (impossibly   carefully) difficult problem _____ ☐

Total ☐

Syllable Addition Add the numbers in the boxes. If you get 19, you did a great job!

Home Activity Your child is learning to spell words with many syllables. Together, say each word and clap the syllables. Let your child pick the three words he or she finds most difficult. Have your child write them and spell them to you.

🌎 **3.24.A.2** Use knowledge of word parts to spell.
3.24.D.1 Spell words with common syllable constructions.

© Pearson Education, Inc., 3

Commas

Directions Fix the comma errors in the sentences in the letter. If a sentence does not have a comma error, write *C*.

1. Dear Thomas,

_____

2. I saw something wonderful and I had to tell you.

_____

3. I saw millions of yellow blue and orange butterflies.

_____

4. The palm, pine, and fruit trees were full of butterflies.

_____

5. Your friend
Justin

_____

Directions Write each sentence. Add commas where they are needed.

6. We took a trip to the rain forest on June 23 2005.

_____

7. We hiked climbed and rested in the forest.

_____

8. We saw incredible plants birds and insects.

_____

9. On the ground were fire ants harvester ants and army ants.

_____

10. The ants looked dangerous but they left us alone.

_____

3.23.C.1.ii.3 Use punctuation marks including commas in a series.
3.23.C.1.ii.4 Use punctuation marks including commas in dates.

Conventions 447

Related Words

Spelling Words				
cloth	clothes	nature	natural	able
ability	mean	meant	deal	dealt
please	pleasant	sign	signal	signature

Word Pairs Write the list words that complete each sentence.

1.–2.   Here is a STOP _____, and there is a traffic _____.

3.–4.   My new _____ are made from colorful _____.

5.–6.   Plants in _____ are _____ things.

7.–8.   After you _____ the cards, they have been _____.

9.–10. If you _____ your name, you are using your _____.

Little Crosswords Read the word clue. Write a synonym for the word in the boxes going across. Write a related word in the boxes going down.

11.–12. skill

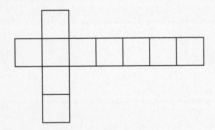

13.–14. intended

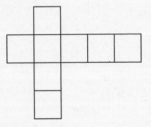

15.–16. nice

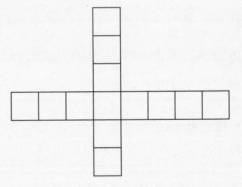

School + Home   **Home Activity** Your child is learning to spell related words. Choose two related words from the list. Say one word. Have your child say and spell the related word.

✪ **3.24.A.2** Use knowledge of word parts to spell. **3.24.A.3** Use knowledge of word segmentation to spell. **3.24.A.4** Use knowledge of syllabication to spell.

Quotations and Parentheses

Directions Write *C* if a sentence is correct. If it is not correct, make the corrections that are needed.

1. Maria said, "I can have an adventure. _____

2. I will find the lost city of Atlantis! she exclaimed. _____

3. "I will become a famous explorer," Maria said. _____

4. "Can you drive a big boat? Chris asked. _____

5. "No, but I would love to learn," Maria answered. _____

Directions Write each sentence. Add a comma and quotation marks where they are needed.

6. Maria's mother asked What will you take on your journey?

_____

_____

7. I will take maps, food, and books about Atlantis Maria answered.

_____

_____

8. Maria's mother asked How long will you be gone?

_____

_____

9. Maria replied It will take a long time to find the island.

_____

_____

10. I wish I could go with you! Maria's mother exclaimed.

_____

_____

★ Use correct mechanics.

Conventions 449

KWL Chart

Directions Fill out this KWL chart to help you organize your ideas.

Topic _____

What I <u>K</u>now	What I <u>W</u>ant to Know	What I <u>L</u>earned

Controlling Question _____

_____

3.17.A.1 Plan a first draft by selecting a genre appropriate for conveying the intended meaning to an audience. **3.17.B.1** Develop drafts by categorizing ideas.

© Pearson Education, Inc., 3

Topic and Detail Sentences

A topic sentence tells the main idea of a paragraph. Detail sentences give supporting facts, descriptions, and examples about the main idea.

Directions Decide how you will organize your paragraphs. Then write a topic sentence and supporting details for each paragraph.

Paragraph 1

Topic Sentence _____

Detail Sentences _____

_____

_____

Paragraph 2

Topic Sentence _____

Detail Sentences _____

_____

_____

Paragraph 3

Topic Sentence _____

Detail Sentences _____

_____

_____

Paragraph 4

Topic Sentence _____

Detail Sentences _____

_____

_____

3.17.B.2 Develop drafts by organizing ideas into paragraphs.

Combining Sentences

When you revise, you can combine two short simple sentences to make a compound or complex sentence. The two simple sentences must be related in some way.
- To make a compound sentence, join the sentences with a comma and a conjunction such as *and, but,* or *or.*
- To make a complex sentence, join the sentences with a word such as *when, because,* or *if.*

Directions Use the word in ( ) to combine each pair of sentences. Use a comma with exercises 1 and 2.

1. Washington, D.C., has many monuments. People like to visit them. (and)

_____

_____

2. Many of the monuments honor presidents. Some monuments honor soldiers or

other heroes. (but) _____

_____

_____

3. People visit the Lincoln Memorial. They see a huge statue of Abraham Lincoln.
(when)

_____

_____

4. The Washington Monument is easy to see. It is the tallest monument. (because)

_____

_____

⊕ **3.17.C.2** Revise drafts for use of organization. **3.17.C.3** Revise drafts for use of simple sentences. **3.17.C.4** Revise drafts for use of compound sentences.

Peer and Teacher Conferencing
Research Report

Directions Read your partner's report. Refer to the Revising Checklist as you write your comments or questions. Offer compliments as well as revision suggestions. Then take turns talking about each other's draft. Give your partner your notes. After you and your teacher talk about your report, add your teacher's comments to the notes.

Revising Checklist

Focus/Ideas

☐ Is the research report focused?

☐ Are there enough facts, details, and explanations?

Organization

☐ Are the paragraphs organized?

☐ Does each paragraph have a central idea stated in a topic sentence?

☐ Does each paragraph have supporting sentences that tell facts, details, or explanations?

Voice

☐ Does the writer sound interested in the topic?

Word Choice

☐ Has the writer paraphrased the material?

Sentences

☐ Have some short, simple sentences been combined to make compound or complex sentences?

Things I Thought Were Good _____

_____

Things I Thought Could Be Improved _____

_____

Teacher's Comments _____

_____

© Pearson Education, Inc., 3

★ Revise final draft in response to feedback from peers. ★ Revise
final draft in response to feedback from teacher.